Elementary Concepts
of
Modern Mathematics

The Appleton-Century Mathematics Series

Edited by Raymond W. Brink

A First Year of College Mathematics, 2nd ed., by Raymond W. Brink
Algebra—College Course, 2nd ed., by Raymond W. Brink
Analytic Geometry, rev. ed., by Raymond W. Brink
College Algebra, 2nd ed., by Raymond W. Brink
Essentials of Analytic Geometry, by Raymond W. Brink
Intermediate Algebra, 2nd ed., by Raymond W. Brink
Plane Trigonometry, 3rd ed., by Raymond W. Brink
Spherical Trigonometry, by Raymond W. Brink
Modern Basic Mathematics, by Hobart C. Carter
Elementary Concepts of Modern Mathematics, by Flora Dinkines
    Parts also available individually under the following titles:
    Part I, *Elementary Theory of Sets*
    Part II, *Introduction to Mathematical Logic*
    Part III, *Abstract Mathematical Systems*
Introduction to the Laplace Transform, by Dio L. Holl, Clair G. Maple, and
    Bernard Vinograde
Introductory Analysis, by V. O. McBrien
College Geometry, by Leslie H. Miller
Advanced Calculus, by John M. H. Olmsted
Intermediate Analysis, by John M. H. Olmsted
Real Variables, by John M. H. Olmsted
Solid Analytic Geometry, by John M. H. Olmsted
Analytic Geometry, by Edwin J. Purcell
Analytic Geometry and Calculus, by Lloyd L. Smail
Calculus, by Lloyd L. Smail
The Mathematics of Finance, by Franklin C. Smith

Elementary Concepts of
Modern Mathematics

PART I   **ELEMENTARY THEORY OF SETS**

PART II   **INTRODUCTION TO MATHEMATICAL LOGIC**

PART III   **ABSTRACT MATHEMATICAL SYSTEMS**

Flora Dinkines

UNIVERSITY OF ILLINOIS, CHICAGO

New York

APPLETON · CENTURY · CROFTS
DIVISION OF MEREDITH PUBLISHING COMPANY

Preface

During the last century, mathematics has made many remarkable advances which have influenced the scientific world. These advances are due to a tremendous development of profound mathematical research, the automation revolution, and the introduction of the high-speed, automatic digital computer. Many new branches of mathematics have been developed and many old branches have found new applications. Large scale efforts are being made to produce mathematics courses which reflect these remarkable advances.

This book provides basic material for many of these courses in its three main parts on sets, mathematical logic, and abstract mathematical systems. Each of these parts is relatively independent of the others and assumes only that the reader has had one year of high school algebra and one year of plane geometry. Each is a comprehensive elementary treatment, carefully and accurately presented, with numerous examples, illustrations, and exercises.

The part on sets covers mixed set operations, power sets, Cartesian product sets, one-to-one correspondences, and cardinal numbers. In addition to the applications of sets given in the main body of the text, there are other important applications in the supplements. Supplements I and II, Relations and Functions, are closely related and can be introduced as soon as the concept of Cartesian Product has been covered. Supplements III and IV, Solution Sets and Graphs of Solution Sets, can best be used following Supplements I and II. Supplement V, Application of Boolean Algebra to Switching Networks, by L. R. Sjoblom, is a self-contained unit which can be readily understood by readers who have covered the section on Boolean Algebra or have had some other training in elementary abstract reasoning.

The part on logic covers both the statement calculus and the restricted predicate calculus with emphasis on negation and logically valid arguments.

The part on abstract mathematical systems introduces the reader to groups, rings, and fields and the related topics of subgroups, cyclic groups, and isomorphisms. The axiomatic approach and the power of abstract proofs are emphasized.

This book was written as a text for a course in introduction to modern mathematics at the Chicago Undergraduate Division of the University of Illinois, and a preliminary version of it has been successfully used in this course by the author and other members of the mathematics staff. Parts of it have also been used successfully by the author at two National Science Foundation Summer Institutes for Junior High School Teachers of Mathematics at Washburn University, and also as introductory material for a course in modern higher algebra at Argonne National Laboratory.

The material presented here is also available in three individual volumes under the titles *Elementary Theory of Sets, Introduction to Mathematical Logic,* and *Abstract Mathematical Systems*.

It is hoped that this book will be valuable and inspirational to all who are interested in the technological and scientific advances of our times, many of which are dependent upon the spirit and content of modern mathematics, thus serving to emphasize the need for modern topics and the modern approach to classical topics.

I want to thank the University of Illinois for a sabbatical leave during which most of the material on logic was written.

Special thanks are due Professor R. W. Brink, the Appleton-Century Mathematics Series Editor, for thoroughly editing the manuscript and giving many helpful suggestions. I also appreciate very much the interest and encouragement of my colleagues who taught this material in regular courses or used some parts of it in mathematics clubs. Thanks are also due to Mrs. Adelaide Riedl who typed the section on logic for the mimeographed edition.

F. D.

Chicago, Illinois

Contents

vii

Supplements

Part II. INTRODUCTION TO MATHEMATICAL LOGIC

The Statement Calculus   235

Part III. ABSTRACT MATHEMATICAL SYSTEMS

Part I

Elementary
Theory of Sets

Theory of Sets

Set concepts provide the best means of understanding many phases of mathematics and its applications to other branches of learning. For this reason the theory of sets is receiving attention today at many levels of mathematical instruction. Though many of the elementary concepts of sets are simple and can be readily grasped, a complete study of sets involves deep concepts and reveals that there is a close relationship between sets and logic, as well as the fact that all of mathematics can be built up with set theory as its basic structure. Set paradoxes exist that puzzle the reader and challenge his ability to think clearly.

It is not surprising then that those who train for modern science and technology, those who apply mathematics to scientific and non-scientific fields of knowledge, and those who desire a broad general education feel a need for some information on set theory.

The following exposition attempts to introduce as quickly and as simply as possible some of the basic set concepts and their applications.

1. EXAMPLES OF SETS

Though we shall not define the word "set" we shall think of a *set* as a well-defined collection of objects.

1

Examples of sets

1. The peaches in farmer Smith's bushel basket.
2. This book, the letter A, and Thomas Jefferson.
3. The numbers 2, 4, 6, 8, and 10.
4. The leaves on a given tree.
5. The cars in Chicago at 8 A.M. today.
6. The baseball teams in the National League.
7. The children of Carl Friedrich Gauss, the great mathematician. (Four sons and two daughters)
8. All two-legged animals.
9. The ancestors of George Washington.
10. The grains of sand on the beaches of Lake Michigan.
11. The twelve months of the year.
12. The numbers 5, 13, and 19, New York City, a specified piece of chalk, a particular coat, and the planet Venus.

Each object in a set is an **element** *of the set or a* **member** *of the set.*

Observe that the members of a set need not have any common property other than the property of being considered as members of the same collection. Examples 2 and 12 are given to emphasize this fact.*

2. SET DESIGNATION

A set can be designated in various ways. Since it is important that a set be well-defined, any type of set designation must indicate whether a given object is, or is not, a member of the set. This means that only two possibilities can exist; namely, the object (a) **is a member,** or (b) **is not a member** of the given set. It is then impossible for an object to be simultaneously *in* and *out* of the given set. If a set designation indicates unambiguously all possible objects having certain specified properties we say that the designation **determines** or **defines** a set consisting of these objects.

---

* We assume here that the words set, class, totality, aggregate, and collection have the same meaning though there may be occasions where it will be convenient to assign different meanings to some of these words.

Usually small letters such as a, b, x, or y will be used to indicate the elements of a set, and capital letters such as A and B, or numbers, letters, or names enclosed in brackets, such as $\{a, y\}$, will be used to indicate the sets. The symbol ϵ, which is the Greek letter epsilon, will mean "is an element of" and $\notin$ will mean "is not an element of". The following examples illustrate this notation.

$x \in A$ is read "x is an element of A", or
  "x, an element of A".
$x \notin A$ is read "x is not an element of A", or
  "x, not an element of A".
$A = \{c, d\}$ is read "A is the set with elements c and d".

We shall determine or define sets in three ways, two of which have already been used in the preceding examples. Frequently the elements will be listed as in examples 2, 3, and 12, or they will be described as in the remaining examples. In addition to these two ways we shall sometimes employ the rule method.

Two examples are given to illustrate these three ways of indicating sets.

1. A set may be indicated by a *statement*.
   C is the set of Lincoln's sons.
   D is the set of all whole numbers between 1 and 10.
2. A set may be indicated by the *listing method*.
   $C = \{$Robert Lincoln, Edward Lincoln, William Lincoln, Thomas Lincoln$\}$
   $D = \{2, 3, 4, 5, 6, 7, 8, 9\}$
3. A set may be indicated by the *rule method*.
   $C = \{x \mid x$ is a son of Abraham Lincoln$\}$
   $D = \{x \mid x$ is a whole number between 1 and 10$\}$

The vertical bar is read "such that". The first example under the rule method is read "C is the set of all x such that x is a son of Abraham Lincoln". Similarly, the second is read "D is the set of all x such that x is a whole number between 1 and 10".

In a specific discussion one of these methods of indicating a set may be preferred because of certain advantages such as clarity, conciseness, or simplicity.

3. NULL SETS AND UNIT SETS

The number of objects in a set may be large or small. If there are no objects having certain specified properties we call the set so designated a *null set*, an *empty set*, a *void set*, or a *vacuous set*.

Definition. *A null set is a set which has no elements.*

Examples of null sets
1. All human beings born with wings.
2. Space ships that reached the moon before 1855.
3. All distances which are greater than a foot and also less than an inch.

Definition. *A unit set is a set which has only one element.*

Examples of unit sets
1. The President of the United States in 1959.
2. The set which has the number 5 as its only element.
3. The planet on which we live.

4. SPECIAL SETS OF NUMBERS

Throughout this book the following sets of numbers will frequently be considered. For the sake of clarity we state specifically what is included in each set.

Definition. *The **positive integers** are the positive whole numbers:* 1, 2, 3, 4, 5, $\cdots$. *We shall frequently denote the set of positive integers by I.*

Remark: Three dots at the *end* of a list of numbers indicate that the set continues without end, following the same rule of formation as indicated by the first few terms. Thus {1, 2, 3, 4, $\cdots$} represents the set of *all* positive whole numbers, and {2, 4, 6, $\cdots$} represents the set of *all* positive whole numbers which can be obtained by multiplying whole numbers by the number two. In general, three dots denote the omission of terms of the kind indicated by the terms given. Thus 3, 6, 9, $\cdots$, 123 means all integral multiples of 3 beginning with 3 and stopping with 123.

Definition. *The **integers** are the numbers* 0, 1, -1, 2, -2, 3, -3, 4, -4, $\cdots$. *We shall frequently denote the set of all integers by* **J**.

Definition. *The **even integers** are the numbers of the form* 2n, *where* n *is an integer; that is,* 0, 2, -2, 4, -4, 6, -6, $\cdots$.

Definition. *The **odd integers** are the numbers of the form* 2n + 1 *(or* 2n $-$ 1*) where* n *is an integer; that is,* 1, -1, 3, -3, 5, -5, $\cdots$. Observe that when $n = 0$, then $2n + 1 = 1$; when $n = -1$, then $2n + 1 = -1$; when $n = 1$, then $2n + 1 = 3$, and so on.

Definition. *The **rational numbers** are the numbers that can be expressed in the form* p/q, *where* p *and* q *are integers and* q $\neq$ 0. (Here we *assume* that these quotients are added and multiplied according to the rules for fractions, with which the reader is familiar, and that two such quotients p/q and c/d are equal if and only if pd = cq.) *We shall frequently denote the set of all rational numbers by* $\bar{R}$.

5. INTEGRAL DIVISORS AND INTEGRAL MULTIPLES

In order to define the set of prime numbers we first define an integral divisor.

Definition. *The integer* a *is an **integral divisor** of the integer* b *if there is one and only one integer* c *such that* ac = b. *If* a *is an integral divisor of* b *then* b *is **integrally divisible** by* a, *and* b *is an **integral multiple** of* a.

Since the word "unique" means "one and only one" the words "a unique" can replace the words "one and only one" in the definition. The integer b is the *dividend* and the unique integer c is the *quotient*.

Definition. *Those integral divisors of the integer n which are different from* ±1 *and* ±n *are* **proper integral divisors** *of n.*

Examples

1. The integer 4 is a proper integral divisor of the integer 20 since
there is one and only one integer, 5, which when multiplied by 4,
produces 20, and 5 ≠ ±1, and 5 ≠ ±20. The integer 20 is an integral
multiple of both 4 and 5. We frequently write 20/4 = 5. The integer
20 is the dividend and 5 is the quotient in this division process.

2. The integer 7 is an integral divisor of 0 since there is one and
only one integer, namely 0, which multiplied by 7 produces 0. Thus
0/7 = 0.

3. The fact that 0 is *not* an integral divisor* of any integer follows
from the following two cases: A nonzero integer, such as 7, cannot
have 0 as an integral divisor because there is no integer which multiplied by 0 produces a nonzero number, such as 7. The integer 0 cannot
have 0 as an integral divisor because there are *too many integers*
which when multiplied by 0 produce 0. In fact, 0 multiplied by any
integer produces 0; therefore the unique part of the definition cannot
be satisfied, for it is not true that there is *only one* number c such that
c multiplied by 0 produces 0.

6. PRIME NUMBERS

Now we are able to state specifically which integers are prime
numbers.

Definition. *A* **prime number** *is a positive integer n, different from* 1,
such that the only positive integral divisors of n are the number 1 *and the
integer n itself.*

This definition shows that 2 is a prime number because the only
positive integral divisors of 2 are the number 1 and the number 2 itself.
Similarly, the only positive integral divisors of 3 are 1 and 3. The

---

* "Division by zero" presents certain logical problems. See Suppes, *Introduction to Logic* (Princeton, N. J., Van Nostrand, 1957), pp. 163–164, and
pp. 166–169.

number 4 is not a prime because its positive integral divisors are 1, 2, and 4. The first ten elements of the set of prime numbers are 2, 3, 5, 7, 11, 13, 17, 19, 23, and 29. Can you find other prime numbers?

7. UNIVERSAL SET

In order to avoid certain paradoxes that might arise we shall assume that for a given discussion a *universal set* is given and that the sets considered are collections of objects from the universal set.

Examples

1. The set of integers could be used as a universal set from which the objects for the set $S = \{5, -2, 7, 3\}$ are chosen.

2. The set of all living men could serve as a universal set for the set of men in Denver who are seven feet tall, or the set of all French lawyers, or the set consisting of all baseball players who belong to teams in the American League.

The universal set is frequently denoted by U, and is sometimes referred to as *the universe,* or *the universe of discourse.*

EXERCISES

1. Indicate at least five elements of each of the following sets, or indicate all elements if there are less than five.

(a) All integers between 0 and 50, each of which has 3 as its last digit.

(b) The presidents of the United States.

(c) All square roots of the number 9.

(d) The playing positions in baseball; such as catcher or first baseman.

(e) All integers which are integrally divisible by 5.

(f) All positive integers between -3 and 2, not including these numbers.

(g) Shakespeare's plays.

(h) All square roots of 25 that are even numbers.

(i) The rational numbers.

(j) All numbers which when added to a rational number r, produce the sum r.

(k) The even integers between -5 and 7.

(l) The prime integers between 30 and 50.

2. For each of the preceding examples give a universal set from which its members could be chosen.

3. Let n represent an integer. Find the numbers in each of the following sets which correspond to the values of n from -4 to 4, inclusive.

(a) $\{x \mid x = 5n - 6\}$.   (c) $\{x \mid x = \dfrac{2n}{3} - 1\}$.

(b) $\{x \mid x = 2n - 1\}$.   (d) $\{x \mid x = 6 - 2n\}$.

4. Which of the following are examples of empty sets?

(a) All states in the United States which are larger than Texas.

(b) All integers ending in 2 which are perfect squares.

(c) All television sets more than 200 years old.

(d) All living people who were born before 1950.

(e) All even integers ending in 7.

(f) All living signers of the Declaration of Independence.

5. Express each of the following sets in a different way.

(a) $\{1, 2, 3, 4, 5, \cdots\}$.

(b) $\{x \mid x$ is a number such that $2x = 12\}$.

(c) $\{$George Washington$\}$.

(d) $\{y \mid y$ is the name of a state in the United States starting with the letter $z\}$.

(e) $\{x \mid x$ is the name of a state in the United States starting with the letter $k\}$.

6. Express each of the following sets in two other ways.

(a) $\{x \mid x = 2n$ where n is an integer$\}$.

(b) The set of all integral multiples of three.

(c) $\{-5, -4, -3, -2, -1, 0, 1, 2\}$.

(d) $\{x \mid x$ is a positive integral divisor of 60$\}$.

7. Give all proper positive integral divisors of (a) 12; (b) 30; (c) 128; (d) 190; (e) 180.

8. Restate the definition of a prime integer using the concept of a proper integral divisor.

9. Explain why the following definition of a rational number is equivalent to the one given in the text.

A rational number is a number which can be expressed as the quotient of two integers.

8. INCLUSION, PROPER INCLUSION, AND IDENTITY

When two sets from the same universe are considered we may find that some of the objects in one set are also objects in the second set. Since this is specific information to which we may need to refer, we have specific terminology which indicates how much overlapping there is in the sets.

Definition. (*Inclusion*) *A set A is a **subset** of the set B if every element of A is an element of B. In this case B is a **superset** of A.*

The fact that A is a subset of B is also expressed by saying that "*A is included in B*" and this relation is indicated symbolically by $A \subseteq B$, which is read "*A is a subset of B*" or "*A is included in B*".

The fact that B is a superset of A is also expressed by saying that "*B includes A*" and this relation is indicated symbolically by $B \supseteq A$, which is read "*B is a superset of A*" or "*B includes A*". If A is not a subset of B we write $A \nsubseteq B$ or $B \nsupseteq A$.

The set {John, William} is a subset of the set {John, Harry, William, Frank}; and the set of odd integers is a subset of the set of all integers. Can you find other subsets of these sets?

We observe that the statement "every element of A is an element of B" means the same as "there are no elements of A which are not elements of B". In certain applications such as those involving a null set it may be more convincing to apply the second statement.

Let S be a set with elements in a universal set U. Applying the definition of a subset to the sets S and U shows that S is a subset of U. Applying the definition to S and S shows that S is a subset of itself.

Application of the definition also shows that a null set N—that is, a set containing none of the elements of this universe—is a subset of S, for there are no objects in N, and therefore there are no objects in N which are not in S. By the same type of reasoning this null set N is shown to be a subset of itself and also a subset of every other set drawn from this universal set. In particular, if N and M represent two null sets, each is a subset of the other.

Let the set B be all peaches in farmer Smith's bushel basket, and the set A be the set of all green peaches in the same basket. Then set B includes set A even though there may be no green peaches in the basket and A may be the null set.

Definition. (*Proper inclusion*) *The set A is a **proper subset** of the set B if A is a subset of B but there is at least one element in B which is not in A.*

Proper inclusion is denoted by the symbol $A \subset B$ which is read "A is a proper subset of B" or "A is properly included in B"; and also by the symbol $B \supset A$ which is read "B is a proper superset of A" or "B includes A properly". The fact that A is not a proper subset of B can be indicated by $A \not\subset B$ or $B \not\supset A$.

Examples of proper inclusion

1. If at least one peach in farmer Smith's basket is not green, then the set of green peaches is a proper subset of the set of all peaches in the basket.

2. The set of all children is a proper subset of the set of all human beings, for some human beings are adults.

Definition. (*Identity*) *Two sets are **identical** if they have exactly the same objects in them.*

If two sets A and B are identical we shall frequently refer to them as the same set, as equal sets, or as identical sets and shall write $A = B$. If they are not equal sets we shall write $A \neq B$. In order to show that $A = B$ we must show that every element of A is an element of B, and that every element of B is an element of A; therefore we shall agree that $A = B$ if and only if $A \subseteq B$ and $B \subseteq A$.

Examples

1. If all the peaches in farmer Smith's basket are green, then the set of all peaches in the basket is the same as the set of all green peaches in the basket.

2. If $A = \{$needle, Halloween$\}$ and $B = \{$Halloween, needle$\}$ then $A = B$.

3. If C is the set having the first three positive integers as its only elements, and D is the set consisting of the three distinct roots obtained by solving the equations $5x = 15$, $x + x = 2$, and $x + 2 = 4$, then $C = D$.

We showed earlier in this section that each of two null sets N and M is a subset of the other. By our definition of equality we now have $N = M$. This means that all null sets are equal, and that we can consider all null sets as the same set. We shall therefore speak of *the* null set and henceforth shall use the symbol $\varnothing$ to denote the null set.

EXERCISES

1. State symbolically as many proper inclusion relations as possible among the following sets. Count repeated letters as the same letter.

A = set of all letters of the alphabet.

B = set of vowels a, e, i, o, u.

C = set of all letters except the vowels a, e, i, o, u.

D = set of all different letters in the word "uncomplimentary."

E = set of all different letters in the sentence "The quick brown fox jumps over the lazy dog."

2. A bag contains four black balls and one white one. One ball is drawn at random from the bag. Let

B = set of 4 black balls, and

L = set of black balls left in the bag after the drawing.

Make a symbolic statement about the relation between the sets B and L.

3. Let A = set of all of the types of fruit in a salad, and

B = set of all of the types of citrus fruit in a salad.

Put into words the following statements where each statement refers to a different salad and A is not the null set.

   (a) $B \subset A$.   (b) $B = A$.

  4. Let A = set of all equilateral triangles,
        B = set of all isosceles triangles,
        C = set of all triangles, and
        D = set of all equiangular triangles.

(a) State symbolically that all equilateral triangles are equiangular.

(b) Make the correct symbolic statement about the set of all equilateral triangles and the set of all isosceles triangles.

(c) Make the correct symbolic statement about sets C and B.

9. SET OPERATIONS

Intersection

When elements belong to two or more sets we often refer to them as the "elements common to the sets". These common elements form the intersection of the sets.

Definition. *The **intersection** of two sets A and B is the set of elements which are in the set A and also in the set B.*

For example, if A is the set of points in the xy-plane indicated in Figure 1 by the triangle and its interior, and B is the set of points on the circle and in its interior, then the intersection is the shaded area.

Symbolically, we write $A \cap B$ for "the intersection of A and B". (For brevity this is sometimes read "A cap B" or "A intersect B".) Symbolic notation enables us to produce a more compact but equivalent form of this definition of intersection.

Definition. $A \cap B = \{x \mid x \in A \quad and \quad x \in B\}$.

This symbolic definition shows clearly what conditions an object must satisfy in order to be an element of the intersection of two sets.

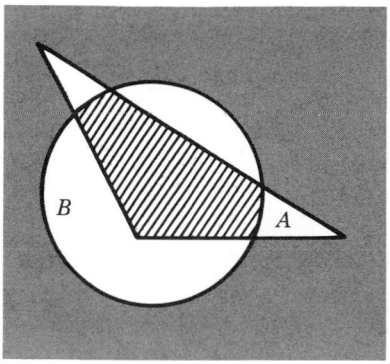

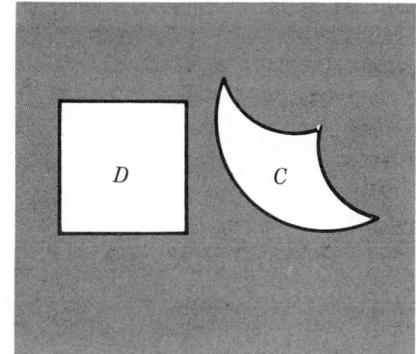

FIG. 1   FIG. 2

An element can be in the set $A \cap B$ only when it belongs to A and also belongs to B.

As a second example of set intersection let M be the set of all musicians who live in Los Angeles, and let C be the set of all chemists who live in the same city. Then a person is in the set $M \cap C$ if and only if he lives in Los Angeles and is both a musician and a chemist.

Definition. *Two sets are **disjoint** if their intersection is the empty set.*

Observe that disjoint sets have no common elements. The sets of points C and D in Figure 2 are disjoint.

Union

A set of elements can be formed by using all of the elements in two given sets. Such a collection is the union of the given sets.

Definition. *The **union** of two sets A and B is the set of all elements which are in the set A, or in the set B, or in both sets A and B.*

The union of the sets A and B indicated in Figure 1 is shown by the shaded area in Figure 3. Some points of the union are in A only, some are in B only, and some are in both A and B. Can you indicate the set, or sets, from which each of the five parts of this figure is obtained?

The shaded area in Figure 4 shows the union of the two disjoint sets in Figure 2.

Symbolically, we write $A \cup B$ for "the union of A and B". (For brevity this is sometimes read "A cup B" or "A union B".) The following statement is a more concise form of the definition of set union.

Definition. $A \cup B = \{x \mid x \in A \quad or \quad x \in B\}.$

If, as before, M denotes the set of all musicians in Los Angeles and C denotes the set of all chemists in the same city, then $C \cup M$ denotes a set containing all of the musicians and the chemists. It should be observed that an individual in Los Angeles qualifies for membership in $C \cup M$ if he is a chemist, or if he is a musician, or if he is both a chemist and a musician.

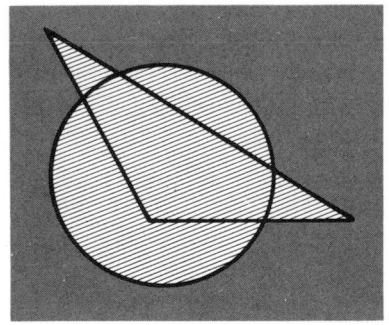   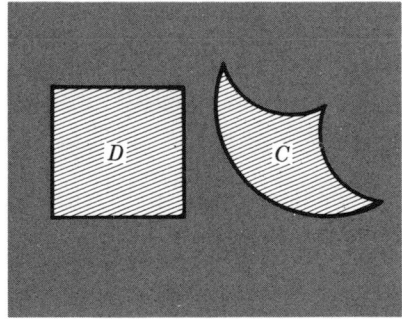

FIG. 3   FIG. 4

Remarks on "or."   In order to understand the preceding definition the reader needs to understand the general usage of "or" as well as the mathematical usage. In general, the word "or" is used in two different ways. The *exclusive* use of the word is frequently employed in everyday speech. "Satisfaction or your money back" is interpreted to mean that the purchaser gets satisfaction from a product or he gets his money back, but it does not indicate that the purchaser is entitled to satisfaction and a refund. Thus the exclusive "or" means either satisfaction or a refund, *but not both.*

On the other hand, when a student is told that he will be given a free ticket to a particular game if he is a class officer or a patrol boy, he does not expect to be refused a ticket because he is both an officer and a patrol boy. This type of "or" is the *inclusive* "or" which means either a class officer or a patrol boy, *or both*. It is the inclusive use that occurs most frequently in mathematics. Unless there are instructions to the contrary, "or" in mathematics should be interpreted in the inclusive sense. This is the interpretation that should be used on "$x \in A$ or $x \in B$" in the preceding definition. Thus x is in A, or x is in B, or x is in both sets.

In summary, we say that the *exclusive* "or" means "this or that *but not both*" and the *inclusive* "or" means "this or that *or both*".*

When the mathematician needs to use "or" in the exclusive sense, he must indicate that both possibilities may not occur simultaneously. This was done for set membership. When we say, as in §2, that "x is a member of a set A, or x is not a member of set A" for a specific element x and a specific set A we are using the exclusive "or"; for we do not consider a set well-defined if both conditions are simultaneously true.

Complementation

Let A be a subset of a given universal set U. Then, since A is well-defined, each element of U either is in A, or is not in A. Thus the elements of U fall into two sets; namely, those which are in A and those which are not in A. The collection of all elements of U

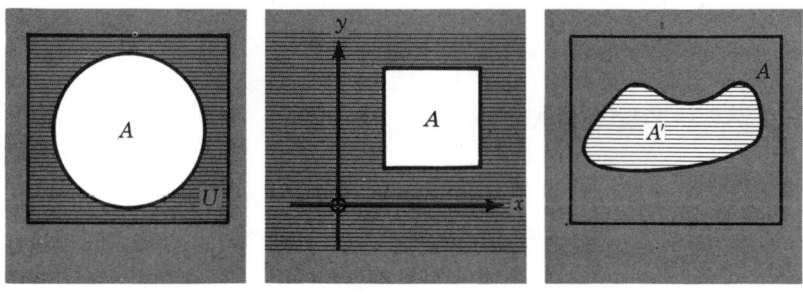

| FIG. 5 | FIG. 6 | FIG. 7 |

* See Exner and Rosskopf, *Logic in Elementary Mathematics* (New York, McGraw-Hill, 1959), pp. 23–24; Tarski, *Introduction to Logic* (New York, Oxford, 1946), pp. 21–22.

that are not in A is the *complement of A with respect to U*, and, for brevity, we shall usually refer to it as "the complement of A".

Definition. *If A is a subset of the universal set U, then the **complement of A with respect to** U is the set of all elements of U which are not in A.*

The complement of A in Figure 5 is the shaded region.

If we denote the complement of A by A', the symbolic form of the definition can be given.

Definition. $A' = \{x \mid x \in U \quad and \quad x \notin A\}$.

In Figure 6, U is the entire xy-plane and A is a square plus its interior. The complement A' is the set of all points in the plane which are outside the square.

If A is the unshaded part of Figure 7, then A' is the shaded region.

Since no elements are simultaneously in A and in A', the sets A and A' are always disjoint.

For an example involving intersection, union, and complementation let $U = \{\text{James, sleeping bag, canteen, knife, cook kit, flashlight}\}$, $S = \{\text{canteen, knife, flashlight}\}$ and $T = \{\text{James, knife, canteen}\}$.

Then $S \cap T = \{\text{knife, canteen}\}$,

$\qquad\qquad\ S \cup T = \{\text{James, canteen, knife, flashlight}\}$,

and $T' = \{\text{sleeping bag, cook kit, flashlight}\}$.

10. SET DIAGRAMS

Set operations can be illustrated by *Venn diagrams*.* In a Venn diagram the universal set is usually represented by the points of a

---

* John Venn used this type of representation in a paper concerning some of George Boole's theories of logical systems. Boole (1815–1846) was an English mathematician and logician whose works are of great importance to pure mathematics. It should be emphasized that diagrams are not acceptable proofs of set properties.

rectangle plus its interior; and subsets of U, such as P and Q, are represented by the points of circles plus their interiors; though other figures besides rectangles and circles can be used to give graphic representations.

If U is the set of all Freshmen in a given high school, P is the set of all Freshmen taking general science, and Q is the set of all Freshmen who weigh less than 110 pounds, then $P \cap Q$ is the set of all Freshmen in this high school who weigh less than 110 pounds and take general science. The shaded area in Figure 8 indicates $P \cap Q$ in this Venn diagram. If $P \cap Q = \varnothing$ a Venn diagram can be drawn using non-overlapping circles to represent P and Q. Frequently we do not know whether the intersection is the empty set or a non-empty set but are content to use the accompanying figure as a graphic representation of either case.

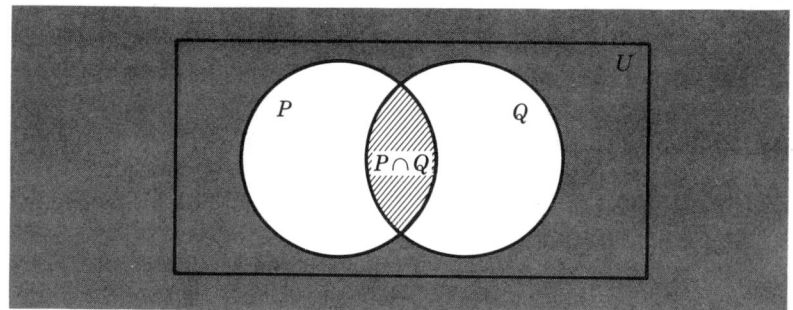

FIG. 8

$P \cup Q$ and P' can be represented in a similar manner. In some cases the universal set is not indicated in the diagram but is merely understood.

For the set E of all even integers, the set D of all odd integers, and the set J of all integers we observe that $E \cup D = J$, $E' = D$, and $D' = E$. The statement $E \cup D = J$ indicates that every integer is even or odd; the statement $E' = D$ indicates that those integers which are not even are odd; and the statement $D' = E$ indicates that those integers which are not odd are even. These relationships can be illustrated in several ways, among which are the following graphical representations. The third representation is called an Euler diagram in honor of the great Swiss mathematician Leonhard Euler (1707–1783).

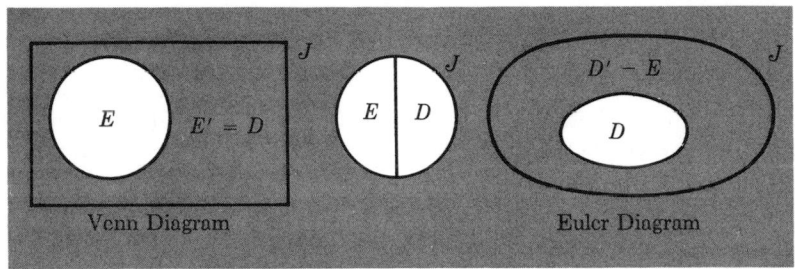

FIG. 9

11. RELATIVE COMPLEMENT

Closely related to the concept of the complement of A in U is the relative complement of A in B. This is the set of elements in B which are not in A. This generalization of complementation exists even when A is not a subset of B.

The shaded areas in the accompanying Venn diagrams show three cases of the relative complement of A in B. The case where B is a subset of A is not shown. What is the relative complement of A in B for this case?

Definition. *If A and B are subsets of the universal set U, then the* **relative complement of A in** B *is the set of all elements in B which are not in A.*

The symbol $B–A$ denotes "the relative complement of A in B", or "the complement of A with respect to B". For brevity it is sometimes read "B minus A".

For the example involving James and his camping equipment

$$T–S = \{\text{James}\} \quad \text{and} \quad S–T = \{\text{flashlight}\}.$$

It should be observed that the relative complement of A in B can be expressed as an intersection. Since an element of this relative

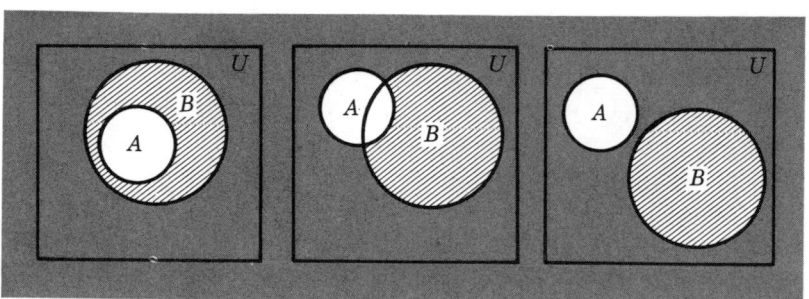

FIG. 10

complement is not in A it must be in A'. If this element is also in B then it must be in the intersection of B and A'. Therefore $B-A = B \cap A'$.

EXERCISES

1. Let $A = \{1, 2, 3, \cdots, 10\}$, $B = \{2, 4, 6, \cdots, 10\}$, and $C = \{1, 3, 5, \cdots, 9\}$. Find the following sets:

(a) $A \cap B$; (c) $A \cap C$; (e) $B \cap C$; (g) $A - B$;
(b) $A \cup B$; (d) $A \cup C$; (f) $B \cup C$; (h) $A - C$.
(i) If A is the universe what notation can be used for $A - B$?

2. Find the set obtained by the following set operations where U is the universal set and A is a subset of U.

(a) $A \cap A'$; (c) $A \cup A'$; (e) $A \cap \varnothing$; (g) $U \cap \varnothing$;
(b) $A \cap U$; (d) $A \cup U$; (f) $A \cup \varnothing$; (h) $U \cup \varnothing$.

3. Using U and A as given in Exercise 2, find a set equal to each of the following:

(a) $A \cap A$; (b) $A \cup A$; (c) U'; (d) $\varnothing'$.

4. Let U be the set of all members of the U.S. Congress,
     B be the set of all men who are members of Congress, and
     C be the set of all women who are members of Congress.
Find the following sets.

(a) $B \cap C$; (b) $B \cup C$; (c) B'; (d) C'.

5. In Figures 11 and 12 each of the letters X, Y, Z, and U denotes a circle plus its interior. The complements X', Y', and Z' are taken with respect to U. Draw a similar figure and shade

(a) $(X \cup Y') \cup (X' \cap Z)$;   (b) $(X' \cup Y)' \cap Z$.

Write a symbolic expression for the section with

(c) horizontal shading in Figure 11;

(d) vertical shading in Figure 11;

(e) horizontal shading in Figure 12.

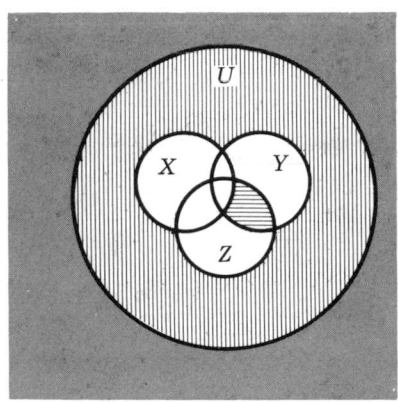

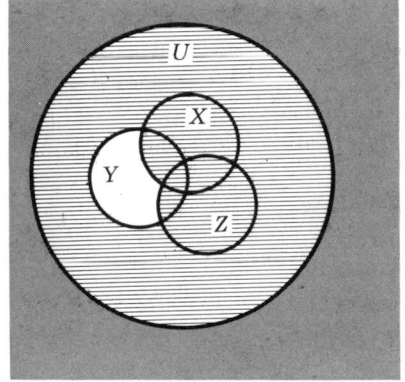

FIG. 11   FIG. 12

6. Use circles to represent the set of all automobiles, and the sub-sets of all green cars, all convertibles, and all two-toned models. On separate diagrams shade the areas to represent the following sets, and write symbolic expressions for each.

(a) two-toned green convertibles;

(b) two-toned but not convertible;

(c) two-toned but not green nor convertible.

7. Let A = set of all even integers,

B = set of all integers which are integral multiples of 3,

C = set of all integers which are integral multiples of 4, and

J = set of all integers.

Describe the following sets.

(a) $A \cap B$;   (b) $A \cup B$;   (c) $B \cap C$;

(d) $A \cup J$;   (e) $A \cup C$.

(*f*) The complement of C with respect to A. (Notice that $C \subset A$.)

(*g*) The complement of C with respect to J.

8. Let R be the set of points of the rectangle $ABCD$ and its interior. Let T be the set of points of the triangle ABE and its interior. Let Z be the set of points of the trapezoid $AECD$ and its interior. Find the following sets:

(*a*) $R \cap T$;   (*d*) $T \cup Z$.

(*b*) $R \cup T$;   (*e*) Are T and Z disjoint?

(*c*) $T \cap Z$;   (*f*) Is $T' = Z$?

FIG. 13

9. Let A, B, and C be subsets of the universal set U.

(*a*) What set is equal to $(A')'$? (This set is usually denoted by A''.)

(*b*) If $B \cap C = \varnothing$ and $B \cup C = U$, what can be said about B'? About C'?

10. Let A be a subset of the universal set U. Find a set equal to each of the following:

(*a*) $U - A$;   (*b*) $A - U$;   (*c*) $A - \varnothing$;

(*d*) $\varnothing - A$;   (*e*) $A - A$.

11. Sketch two rectangles for which the set of the points of intersection of the perimeters is

(*a*) a null set;   (*b*) one point;   (*c*) two points;

(*d*) three points;   (*e*) four points.

12. Sketch two plane "curves" for which the set of points of intersection is

(*a*) a null set;   (*b*) four elements;   (*c*) seven elements.

13. The following intersections correspond to the eight parts of Figure 11: $X \cap Y \cap Z$; $X \cap Y \cap Z'$; $Y \cap Z \cap X'$; $X \cap Z \cap Y'$;

$X' \cap Z' \cap Y$; $Y' \cap Z' \cap X$; $X' \cap Y' \cap Z$; $X' \cap Y' \cap Z'$. Draw a similar figure and label the corresponding parts with the numbers from 1 to 8, respectively. The part which represents $X \cap Y \cap Z$ should be labeled 1; the part which represents $X \cap Y \cap Z'$ should be labeled 2, etc.

14. Let the universe of discourse be the set of all integers; S be the subset of all integral multiples of 3; T be all integral multiples of 2; and W be all integral multiples of 5. Express each of the following as the result of operations on the given sets by using symbols such as $T \cup S$, $T \cap W$ and $(T \cup S \cup W)'$.

(a) The set of all integral multiples of 6.

(b) The set of all integral multiples of 10.

(c) The set of all integral multiples of 15.

(d) The set of integers which are not even and are not multiples of 3.

(e) The set of integers which are not even, are not multiples of 3, and are not multiples of 5.

(f) The set of integral multiples of five which are odd.

(g) The set of all integral multiples of 30.

(h) The set of integers which are divisible by 5 but not divisible by 6.

12. POWER SETS

Frequently it is useful to consider all sets that can be formed by choosing objects from a given set. For example, let

$$A = \{1, 2, 3, 4, 5\}.$$

We shall list first the subsets having only one element. These we have agreed to call unit sets. They are $\{1\}$, $\{2\}$, $\{3\}$, $\{4\}$, and $\{5\}$. Those of two elements are $\{1, 2\}$, $\{1, 3\}$, $\{1, 4\}$, $\{1, 5\}$, $\{2, 3\}$, $\{2, 4\}$, $\{2, 5\}$, $\{3, 4\}$, $\{3, 5\}$, and $\{4, 5\}$. These can be quickly obtained by pairing the element 1 with each element that follows it, then pairing the element 2 with each element that follows it, then pairing the element 3 with each element that follows it, and finally pairing 4 with 5. To list quickly the subsets of three elements we list those left when the sets of two elements are chosen. For example, when the set $\{1, 2\}$ is chosen the set $\{3, 4, 5\}$ is left. It consists of the elements that were not chosen, and is the complement of $\{1, 2\}$ in A. We observe that since there were ten sets of two elements there should be ten sets of three elements, and we quickly write them down. They are $\{3, 4, 5\}$, $\{2, 4, 5\}$, $\{2, 3, 5\}$, $\{2, 3, 4\}$, $\{1, 4, 5\}$, $\{1, 3, 5\}$, $\{1, 3, 4\}$, $\{1, 2, 5\}$, $\{1, 2, 4\}$, and $\{1, 2, 3\}$. To obtain the sets having four elements we observe that one element will remain when four are chosen, therefore an easy way out is to decide which element to omit. This amounts to saying that we are choosing the complements of the unit sets. They are $\{2, 3, 4, 5\}$, $\{1, 3, 4, 5\}$, $\{1, 2, 4, 5\}$, $\{1, 2, 3, 5\}$, and $\{1, 2, 3, 4\}$. There is only one subset of five elements and that is the set itself. If we choose no objects from the given set we obtain the empty set which completes the set of all subsets. In this case the total number is $5 + 10 + 10 + 5 + 1 + 1 = 32$, or 2^5.

In finding all of the subsets of a finite set it is frequently helpful to use a systematic procedure whereby we list first the subset having no elements, then the subsets having one element, then those having two elements, and so on until we reach the one having all elements in it. This example, stripped of all the discussion, could be indicated in the following manner.

$$A = \{1, 2, 3, 4, 5\}$$

Subsets of A

$\varnothing$

$\{1\}$, $\{2\}$, $\{3\}$, $\{4\}$, $\{5\}$,

$\{1, 2\}$, $\{1, 3\}$, $\{1, 4\}$, $\{1, 5\}$, $\{2, 3\}$, $\{2, 4\}$, $\{2, 5\}$, $\{3, 4\}$, $\{3, 5\}$, $\{4, 5\}$,

$\{3, 4, 5\}$, $\{2, 4, 5\}$, $\{2, 3, 5\}$, $\{2, 3, 4\}$, $\{1, 4, 5\}$, $\{1, 3, 5\}$, $\{1, 3, 4\}$, $\{1, 2, 5\}$, $\{1, 2, 4\}$, $\{1, 2, 3\}$,

$\{2, 3, 4, 5\}$, $\{1, 3, 4, 5\}$, $\{1, 2, 4, 5\}$, $\{1, 2, 3, 5\}$, $\{1, 2, 3, 4\}$,

A.

Definition. *The **power set** of a set S is the set of all subsets of S.*

For simplicity, we shall frequently denote the power set of a set S by P, though the power set of S is usually denoted by 2^S in mathematical literature. The reason for this notation should become apparent after the student has considered carefully how the number of elements in the power set P is related to the number of objects in the set S.

We observe for the set $A = \{1, 2, 3, 4, 5\}$ that if $P = 2^A$, then

$$P = \{\varnothing, \{1\}, \{2\}, \{3\}, \cdots, \{1, 2, 3, 5\}, \{1, 2, 3, 4\}, A\}$$

where the dots indicate that the reader should mentally fill in the remaining sets listed under "Subsets of A".

The knowledge that there are 32 subsets of a set of 5 elements is useful if we are considering the *total number of committees* that can be formed from a set of five people, where a committee can be any number of people from one to five, inclusive. The only subset that will not represent a satisfactory committee is the null set; therefore there are 31 possible committees, or one less than the total number of subsets.*

Notice that each element of a power set is itself a *set*, and that two such elements of the power set do not necessarily contain the same number of objects. Another example of a set whose elements are themselves sets is the set of baseball teams in the National League. Each of its elements is a baseball team and each baseball team is a set of players. It is not true, however, that the elements of the National League are players, for no individual player can become a member of the National League. Only teams can become members.

Number of Elements in the Power Set. As a second example, let the set B be a set of two colors, red and green. Thus $B = \{\text{red, green}\}$. As we form the power set P we shall try to decide how to predict the number of objects in the power set. We must decide for each object in B whether to use it or not to use it in forming a subset. As far as the color red is concerned there are two possibilities; namely, take it or leave it.

If we decide to take red, there are still two possibilities for the color green. After red has been chosen shall we take green or leave green? If we take green also, we have a set of two elements which is

---

* Readers familiar with the theory of combinations may recognize $2^n - 1$ as the *total number of combinations of n objects*, frequently denoted by $C(n, 1) + C(n, 2) + \cdots + C(n, n-1) + C(n, n) = 2^n - 1$. If S denotes a set of n elements, then since $C(n, r)$ is the number of combinations of n objects taken r at a time, where $0 < r \leq n$, it is also the number of subsets of S which contain exactly r elements. Since S has $2^n - 1$ nonempty subsets this is also the total number of combinations.

the set B itself. Thus {red, green} $= B$. If we leave green we have the unit set {red}.

If, on the other hand, we decide to leave red, there are again two possibilities for green. If we take green we have the unit set {green}. If we leave green also we have $\varnothing$, the null set, since neither red nor green has been chosen. This exhausts all of the possibilities and we conclude that the power set of the set B is

$$P = \{\varnothing, \{red\}, \{green\}, B\},$$

a set of four elements.

We can emphasize these choices by the following tree diagram, accompanied by the resulting sets, where a blank indicates that the color was not chosen.

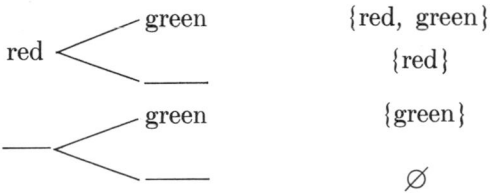

Observe that there were two decisions to make for the color red and for each decision made for red there remained two decisions to be made for green. Therefore there were $2 \cdot 2 = 4$ possibilities. The reader should now be able to make a tree diagram for a set of three objects; or for a set of more than three objects. After doing this can you explain why there were 32 subsets of the set of five elements which was discussed at the beginning of this section?

EXERCISES

1. Let the elements of a set D be the letters a, b, and c. List all of the elements in the power set of D. Make a tree diagram to indicate the number of choices.

2. How many elements are there in the power set of a set having the following number of objects?

(a) none; (c) two; (e) four;
(b) one; (d) three; (f) five;
(g) n, where n is zero or a positive integer.

3. Find the total number of committees that can be obtained from a set containing the following number of persons.

(*a*) one;　　　　　　(*c*) three;　　　　　　(*e*) five;
(*b*) two;　　　　　　(*d*) four;　　　　　　(*f*) six;
(*g*) *n*, where *n* is a positive integer.

13. SET RELATIONS AND MIXED SET OPERATIONS

We are now able to discover certain simple statements concerning given sets A, B, and C in a universe U. After discovering a statement that we believe expresses a worthwhile relationship we shall attempt to present a discussion which will support our belief that the statement is true. The accompanying diagrams are not necessary to the discussion of these statements, but they demonstrate their plausibility.*

We consider first the statement that each set is a subset of itself. This result was obtained merely by using the definition of a subset, which states that "The set A is a subset of the set B if every element of A is an element of B" and substituting A for B to obtain "The set A is a subset of the set A if every element of A is an element of A".

This statement and the discussion supporting it can be written in more concise and systematic form as follows:

Statement 1. $A \subseteq A$.

Discussion	Reasons
(1) If $x \in A$, then $x \in A$.	(1) Same statement repeated.
(2) Therefore, $A \subseteq A$.	(2) Definition of inclusion.　　■†

---

* The nature of mathematical reasoning is discussed in a later section. In the sections which precede Section 28 our approach to the theory of sets is an intuitive one which aims to encourage the reader to discover the facts for himself and to relate new concepts to his previously acquired knowledge. If the reader is familiar with the axiomatic approach he can substitute the words "theorem" and "proof" for the words "statement" and "discussion", respectively; for the discussions given are proofs when preceded by the proper undefined terms, definitions, and assumptions.

† The symbol ■ will be used to mark the end of a discussion or argument.

We now ask what is true if A is a subset of B, and B is a subset of C. A sketch shows us that A should then be a subset of C. We therefore write Statement 2 and follow it by a discussion which shows that under these conditions every element of A is an element of C. This is done by naming an element of A, showing that since it is in A then it must be in B, and since it is an element of B it must also be an element of C. Thus every element of A is an element of C, hence $A \subseteq C$.

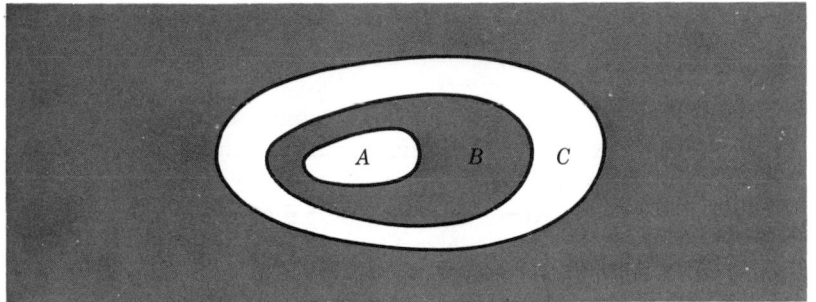

FIG. 14

Statement 2.   *If $A \subseteq B$, and $B \subseteq C$, then $A \subseteq C$.*

Discussion	Reasons*
(1) If $x \in A$, then $x \in B$.	(1) Definition of $A \subseteq B$.
(2) Since $x \in B$, then $x \in C$.	(2) Def. of $B \subseteq C$.
(3) If $x \in A$, then $x \in C$.	(3) By statements (1) and (2).
(4) Therefore, $A \subseteq C$.	(4) Def. of $A \subseteq C$.

How is the intersection of two sets related to the sets? The definition of intersection and a sketch both indicate that either set should contain the intersection. In Statement 3 we show that the intersection of A and B is contained in A. The same type of argument will show that the intersection is contained in B.

Statement 3. $A \cap B \subseteq A$.

Discussion	Reasons
(1) If $x \in A \cap B$, then $x \in B$ and $x \in A$.	(1) Def. of $A \cap B$.

---

* "Definition" will be abbreviated as "Def." in the reasons.

(2) Therefore, if $x \in A \cap B$, then   (2) By statement (1).
    $x \in A$.

(3) Therefore $A \cap B \subseteq A$.   (3) Def. of inclusion.   ∎

How are the complements of two sets related if one is a subset of the other? A simple approach to this problem might be to think of the complement of a set B in a universal set U as the part of U which is left after B is "removed" from the universe. If A is a subset of B there are two possibilities: (1) $A = B$, in which case A and B have exactly the same elements, and (2) $A \subset B$, where B has at least one element not in A. We readily conclude that if the same objects were taken away from the universal set, the remaining sets would be equal. Therefore, we try to show in Statement 4, that if $A = B$, then $A' = B'$. If A is a proper subset of B, taking A away from the universal set should leave at least one more object than taking B away from the universal set; for if we take away fewer objects there should be more remaining. Therefore, in Statement 5, we show that if $A \subset B$, then $B' \subset A'$.

In order to show that two sets are equal in Statement 4 we must show that they contain exactly the same elements. This is usually done in two parts; by first proving that every element of the first set is an element of the second set, and then proving that every element of the second set is an element of the first set. By keeping Statement 4 free of symbols, and, in the proof, letting A represent either of the given equal sets, we can establish both parts of the proof simultaneously. That is, we can show that an element in either complementary set is an element of the other complementary set. This establishes the desired equality.

Statement 4.   *If two sets are equal, their complements are equal.*

Discussion   Reasons

(1) Since the sets are equal let   (1) Given.
    A represent *either one* of the
    sets and B represent the other.

(2) If $x \in A'$, then $x \notin A$.   (2) By the definition of the com-
                                                  plement, a set and its com-
                                                  plementary set have no ele-
                                                  ments in common.

(3) Since $x \notin A$, then $x \notin B$.

(3) $A = B$ was given; th[...] and B have exactly the same elements.

(4) Since $x \notin B$, then $x \in B'$.

(4) By the definition of the complement, an element of the universe must lie in a subset of the universe or in its complement.*

(5) Therefore every element in one of the complementary sets must also be an element of the other complementary set.

(5) Def. of inclusion.

(6) Therefore the complementary sets are equal.

(6) Def. of equal sets.   ∎

Statement 5. *If $A \subseteq B$, then $B' \subseteq A'$.*

In order to show that B' is a subset of A' we must show that every element in B' is in A'.

Discussion	Reasons
(1) Let $x \in B'$, then $x \notin B$.	(1) Def. of complement.
(2) Since $x \notin B$, then $x \notin A$.	(2) A is a subset of B.
(3) Since $x \notin A$, then $x \in A'$.	(3) Def. of complement.
(4) Therefore $B' \subseteq A'$.	(4) Def. of inclusion. ∎

We now show that if A is a proper subset of B then B' is a proper subset of A'. From Statement 5 we know that $B' \subseteq A'$, for this is true whether B includes A properly or improperly. In order to show that A' includes B' properly we must show that there is at least one element in A' which is not in B'. Since the proper inclusion of the complementary sets is a result of the proper inclusion of the given sets we accomplish this by using an element y in B which is not in A. Proper inclusion indicates that there is at least one such element.

---

* In the discussions that follow, this reason will be shortened to "Def. of complement".

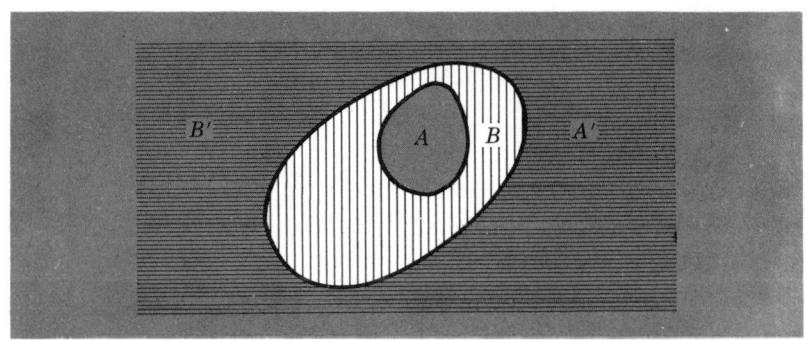

FIG. 15

Statement 6. *If $A \subset B$ then $B' \subset A'$.*

Discussion	Reasons
(1) $B' \subseteq A'$.	(1) By Statement 5, if B includes A, properly or improperly, then $B' \subseteq A'$.
(2) Since $A \subset B$, there is an element $y \in B$ such that $y \notin A$.	(2) Def. of $A \subset B$.
(3) Therefore $y \in A'$.	(3) If $y \notin A$, then $y \in A'$.
(4) Then $y \in A'$ and $y \notin B'$.	(4) (2) and (3).
(5) $B' \subset A'$.	(5) Def. of proper inclusion. ∎

Statements involving sets frequently involve more than one operation. For this reason it is advisable to learn methods of quickly identifying the set resulting from such operations, and of finding its relationship to other sets obtained from combined set operations.

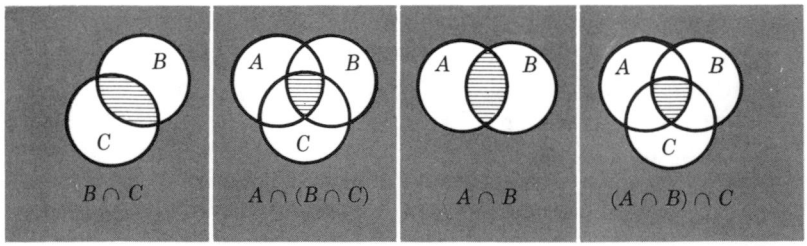

FIG. 16

How does the set $A \cap (B \cap C)$ compare with the set $(A \cap B) \cap C$? We shall use the Venn diagrams to help us find the answer. In the first diagram of Figure 16 we show $B \cap C$. Since the parentheses in $A \cap (B \cap C)$ indicate that we must find the intersection of A and $B \cap C$, the second diagram shows this intersection. Now let us consider the second set $(A \cap B) \cap C$. The third diagram in this set shows $A \cap B$ and the fourth shows the intersection of $A \cap B$ and C. Finally we compare the second and fourth diagrams. These figures indicate that $A \cap (B \cap C)$ and $(A \cap B) \cap C$ represent the same set of elements; namely, those elements that are in all three sets. We now need to present an argument independent of the diagrams which will show that $A \cap (B \cap C) = (A \cap B) \cap C$.

We have observed that to prove two sets X and Y equal we must show that they contain exactly the same elements. This means that we must show that every element of X is an element of Y and that every element of Y is an element of X. This amounts to proving that $X \subseteq Y$ and $Y \subseteq X$.

Statement 7. $A \cap (B \cap C) = (A \cap B) \cap C$.

The two sets that we are trying to prove equal are $A \cap (B \cap C)$ and $(A \cap B) \cap C$. In order to emphasize the fact that each of these expressions represents a single set we shall refer to these two sets as the right and left sides of the given statement. We must then prove that every element of the left side is an element of the right side and that every element of the right side is an element of the left side.

Discussion	Reasons

First we show that every element of the left side is an element of the right side.

(1) Let $x \epsilon A \cap (B \cap C)$, then $x \epsilon A$ and $x \epsilon B \cap C$.	(1) Def. of intersection.
(2) Since $x \epsilon B \cap C$, then $x \epsilon B$ and $x \epsilon C$.	(2) Same as (1).
(3) Therefore $x \epsilon A$, $x \epsilon B$ and $x \epsilon C$.	(3) By (1) and (2).
(4) Since $x \epsilon A$ and $x \epsilon B$, then $x \epsilon A \cap B$.	(4) Def. of intersection.

(5) Since $x \in A \cap B$ and $x \in C$,   (5) Def. of intersection.
then $x \in (A \cap B) \cap C$.

(6) Therefore every element of   (6) Def. of inclusion.
the left side is an element of
the right side. Symbolically,
$A \cap (B \cap C) \subseteq (A \cap B) \cap C$.

Now we show that every element of the right side is an element of
the left side.

(7) If $y \in (A \cap B) \cap C$, then   (7) Def. of intersection.
$y \in C$ and $y \in A \cap B$.

(8) Since $y \in A \cap B$, $y \in A$ and   (8) Same as (7).
$y \in B$.

(9) Therefore $y \in A$, $y \in B$ and   (9) By (7) and (8).
$y \in C$.

(10) Since $y \in B$ and $y \in C$, then   (10) Def. of intersection.
$y \in B \cap C$.

(11) Since $y \in A$ and $y \in B \cap C$,   (11) Def. of intersection.
then $y \in A \cap (B \cap C)$.

(12) Therefore every element of   (12) Def. of inclusion.
the right side is an element
of the left side. Symbolically,
$A \cap (B \cap C) \supseteq (A \cap B) \cap C$.

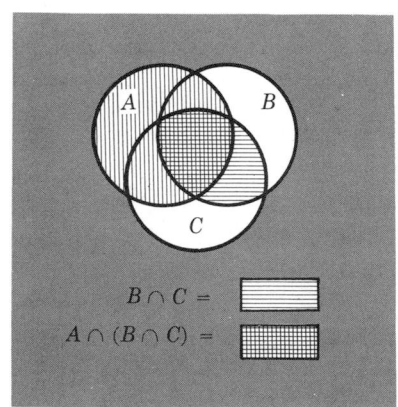
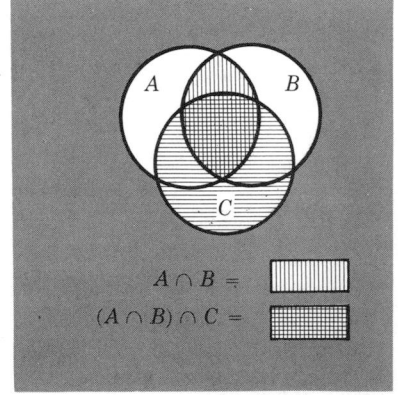

FIG. 17

(13) Finally, since each element   (13) Def. of equal sets.
of either set is an element of
the other, the two sets are
equal.
$A \cap (B \cap C) = (A \cap B) \cap C.$ ∎

The Venn diagrams in Figure 17 also illustrate Statement 7.

Let us now define the intersection of the three sets A, B, and C as the set of elements common to these sets, and denote this intersection by $A \cap B \cap C$.

Definition. $A \cap B \cap C = \{x \mid x \, \epsilon \, A, x \, \epsilon \, B, and \, x \, \epsilon \, C\}.$

Using a discussion similar to the one used for Statement 7 the reader can easily show that $(A \cap B) \cap C = A \cap B \cap C$. It is also easy to show, for every pair of sets X and Y, that $X \cap Y = Y \cap X$. Using these facts and Statement 7, we can obtain

$$A \cap B \cap C = A \cap (B \cap C) = A \cap (C \cap B) = B \cap (A \cap C)$$
$$= B \cap (C \cap A) = C \cap (A \cap B) = C \cap (B \cap A),$$

and also

$$A \cap B \cap C = (B \cap C) \cap A = (C \cap B) \cap A = (A \cap C) \cap B$$
$$= (C \cap A) \cap B = (A \cap B) \cap C = (B \cap A) \cap C.$$

Thus three sets connected by intersection signs indicate the same set regardless of how they are arranged or grouped.

A similar definition can be given for the intersection of four sets A, B, C, and D, or for the intersection of any collection of subsets of a given universal set. However, it is somewhat more difficult to show that these intersections are independent of the way in which the sets are arranged or grouped.‡

Can we find a set equal to $A \cap (B \cup C)$? We sketch $B \cup C$ and then the intersection of A and $B \cup C$, and observe that if $X = A \cap (B \cup C)$ then part of X is in $A \cap B$ and part is in $A \cap C$. Therefore, we can obtain a set equal to X by uniting $A \cap B$ and $A \cap C$. We therefore sketch $A \cap B$, then $A \cap C$ and finally

‡ For a similar proof concerning the arrangement and grouping of sums and products see J. M. H. Olmsted, *Intermediate Analysis* (New York, Appleton-Century-Crofts, 1956) or *Real Variables* (New York, Appleton-Century-Crofts, 1959), p. 8.

$(A \cap B) \cup (A \cap C)$. We conclude that the second and fifth diagrams represent equal sets. We therefore attempt to give a discussion independent of the diagrams which will show this equality.

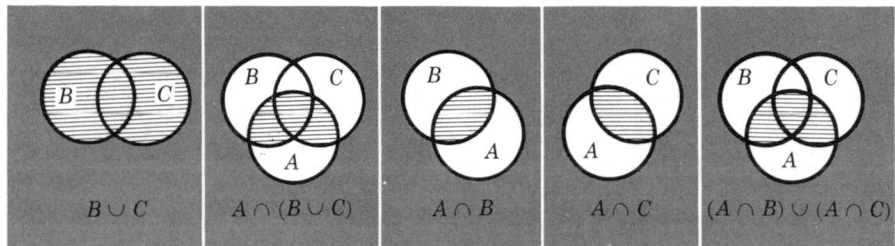

FIG. 18

Statement 8. $A \cap (B \cup C) = (A \cap B) \cup (A \cap C)$.

As in the previous statement we must show that every member of the left set is a member of the right set, and that every member of the right set is a member of the left set.

Discussion	Reasons
(1) Let $x \,\epsilon\, A \cap (B \cup C)$, then $x \,\epsilon\, A$ and $x \,\epsilon\, B \cup C$.	(1) Def. of intersection.
(2) Since $x \,\epsilon\, B \cup C$, then $x \,\epsilon\, B$ or $x \,\epsilon\, C$.	(2) Def. of union.
(3) Therefore $x \,\epsilon\, A$ and $x \,\epsilon\, B$, *or $x \,\epsilon\, A$ and $x \,\epsilon\, C$.*	(3) By (1) and (2).
(4) Hence $x \,\epsilon\, A \cap B$ *or* $x \,\epsilon\, A \cap C$.	(4) Def. of intersection.
(5) $x \,\epsilon\, (A \cap B) \cup (A \cap C)$.	(5) Def. of union.
(6) Therefore every member of the left set is a member of the right set and $A \cap (B \cup C) \subseteq (A \cap B) \cup (A \cap C)$.	(6) Def. of inclusion.

We now prove the inclusion in the opposite direction.

| (7) If $y \,\epsilon\, (A \cap B) \cup (A \cap C)$, then $y \,\epsilon\, A \cap B$ or $y \,\epsilon\, A \cap C$. | (7) Def. of union. |

(8) If $y \in A \cap B$, then $y \in A$ and $y \in B$.

(8) Def. of intersection.

(9) If $y \in A \cap C$, then $y \in A$ and $y \in C$.

(9) Same as (8).

(10) In either case, $y \in A$ and y is an element of one of the sets B or C.

(10) Statements (8) and (9).

(11) Therefore $y \in A$ and $y \in B \cup C$.

(11) Since y is in A or B it is in the union.

(12) Therefore $y \in A \cap (B \cup C)$.

(12) Def. of intersection.

(13) Therefore every member of the right set is a member of the left set and $A \cap (B \cup C) \supseteq (A \cap B) \cup (A \cap C)$.

(13) Def. of inclusion.

(14) Therefore, $A \cap (B \cup C) = (A \cap B) \cup (A \cap C)$.

(14) Def. of equal sets.   ∎

The diagrams in Figure 19 also illustrate Statement 8.

It should be observed that since $X \cap Y = Y \cap X$, then $(B \cup C) \cap A = A \cap (B \cup C) = (A \cap B) \cup (A \cap C) = (B \cap A) \cup (C \cap A)$, and finally by leaving out the middle steps $(B \cup C) \cap A = (B \cap A) \cup (C \cap A)$. If the set $(H \cap K) \cup (H \cap J)$ is given,

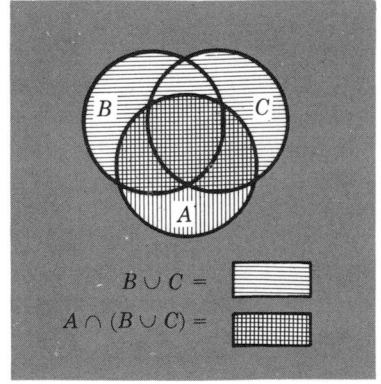
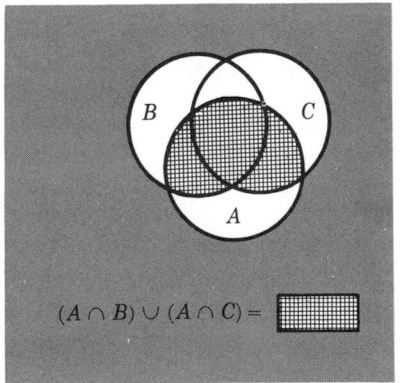

FIG. 19

it is equal to the set $H \cap (K \cup J)$; also $(E \cap F) \cup (G \cap F) = (E \cup G) \cap F$. In simplifying set expressions we shall frequently substitute one of two equal sets for the other; therefore a knowledge of various ways of expressing the same set is useful.

We now consider the complement of a union which we shall represent by $(A \cup B)'$. We sketch $A \cup B$ and $(A \cup B)'$ and observe that the shaded portion lies outside of A and outside of B. It should then lie in A' and in B'. Therefore it should be equal to $A' \cap B'$. We sketch A', B', and $A' \cap B'$ and conclude that we should try to show that $(A \cup B)' = A' \cap B'$.

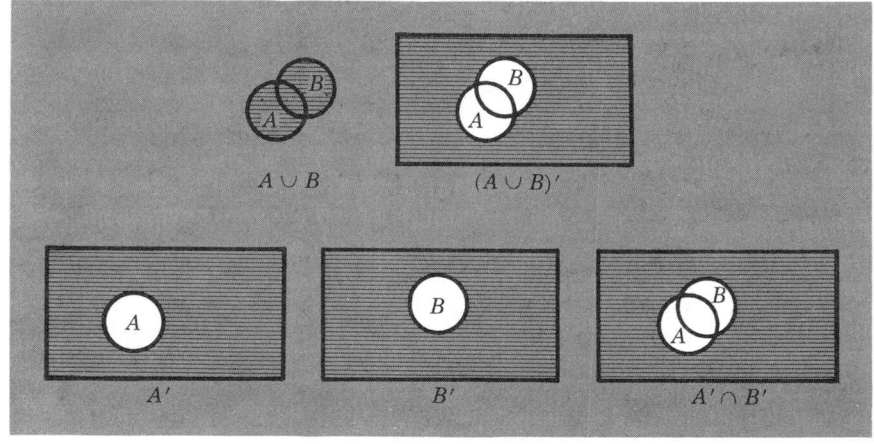

$A \cup B$ $(A \cup B)'$

A' B' $A' \cap B'$

FIG. 20

Statement 9. $(A \cup B)' = A' \cap B'$.

Discussion	Reasons
(1) Let $x \in (A \cup B)'$, then $x \notin A \cup B$.	(1) Def. of complement.
(2) Therefore $x \notin A$ and $x \notin B$.	(2) If $x \in A$ or $x \in B$ then $x \in A \cup B$.
(3) Hence $x \in A'$ and $x \in B'$.	(3) Def. of complement.
(4) Therefore $x \in A' \cap B'$.	(4) Def. of intersection.
(5) $(A \cup B)' \subseteq A' \cap B'$.	(5) Def. of inclusion.

(6) Let $y \in A' \cap B'$, then   (6) Def. of intersection.
   $y \in A'$ and $y \in B'$.

(7) Therefore $y \notin A$ and $y \notin B$.   (7) Same as (1).

(8) Hence $y \notin A \cup B$.   (8) Def. of union.

(9) Therefore $y \in (A \cup B)'$.   (9) Same as (3).

(10) Hence $(A \cup B)' \supseteq A' \cap B'$.   (10) Def. of inclusion.

(11) $(A \cup B)' = A' \cap B'$.   (11) Def. of equality.   ∎

The diagrams in Figure 21 also illustrate Statement 9.

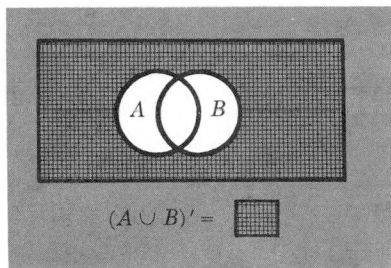 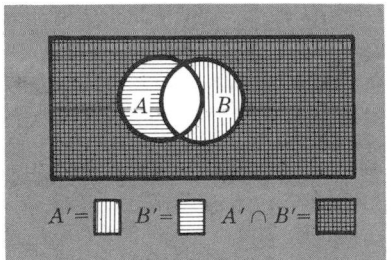

FIG. 21

Simplification of Set Expressions. Established statements concerning sets can be used to simplify set expressions. A few examples are given here. The reader who cannot follow the steps in these examples should read the explanations given below.

1. Simplify $C \cap B \cap C'$.
   $$C \cap B \cap C' = B \cap C \cap C' = B \cap \varnothing = \varnothing$$

2. Simplify $(C' \cup \varnothing) \cup C$.
   $$(C' \cup \varnothing) \cup C = C' \cup C = U.$$

3. Simplify $(H \cup K) \cap K'$.
   $$(H \cup K) \cap K' = (H \cap K') \cup (K \cap K')$$
   $$= (H \cap K') \cup \varnothing = H \cap K'.$$

4. Simplify $(C \cap B) \cup (C' \cap B)$.
   $$(C \cap B) \cup (C' \cap B) = (C \cup C') \cap B = U \cap B = B.$$

5. Simplify $(A \cup B)' \cup (A' \cap B)$.
   $$(A \cup B)' \cup (A' \cap B) = (A' \cap B') \cup (A' \cap B)$$
   $$= A' \cap (B' \cup B) = A' \cap U = A'$$

6. Simplify $[(C \cap D) \cup (C \cap D')] \cap (C' \cup D)$.

$[(C \cap D) \cup (C \cap D')] \cap (C' \cup D)$

$= [C \cap (D \cup D')] \cap (C' \cup D) = [C \cap U] \cap (C' \cup D)$

$= C \cap (C' \cup D) = (C \cap C') \cup (C \cap D)$

$= \varnothing \cup (C \cap D) = C \cap D.$

Explanations

1. The intersection of three sets does not depend upon the order in which the sets are arranged. We therefore say that $C \cap B \cap C' = B \cap C \cap C'$. Since $C \cap C' = \varnothing$, substitute $\varnothing$ for this intersection. Since $B \cap \varnothing = \varnothing$, the null set is the final answer.

2. Observe that $C' \cup \varnothing = C'$ and $C' \cup C = U$.

3. Using the fact that $(B \cup C) \cap A = (B \cap A) \cup (C \cap A)$, from the discussion following Statement 8, we obtain $(H \cup K) \cap K' = (H \cap K') \cup (K \cap K')$. But $K \cap K' = \varnothing$ and the union of the null set and any given set is merely the given set.

4. Set B is "factored" out of the expression by using $(X \cup Y) \cap Z = (X \cap Z) \cup (Y \cap Z)$. That is, the right side is given and it is replaced by the left side. Also $C \cup C' = U$, and $U \cap B = B$ are used.

5. First use Statement 9 to substitute $A' \cap B'$ for $(A \cup B)'$, then factor out A'.

6. No new concepts are involved here.

14. GENERAL REMARKS

At this point it is wise to emphasize some concepts and clarify others. First of all, care should be taken not to confuse the use of the symbol ϵ with the inclusion symbols. The symbol ϵ expresses a relationship that exists between a set and one of its elements, while each of the symbols $\subseteq$, $\subset$, $\supseteq$, and $\supset$ expresses a relationship between two sets.

Further consideration will point out more clearly the difference between ϵ and each of the inclusion relations. Let us consider the following questions.

(1) If $A \subseteq B$ and $B \subseteq C$, is $A \subseteq C$?

(2) Does the answer remain the same when each occurrence of the symbol $\subseteq$ in this question is replaced by the symbol $\subset$? By $\supseteq$? By $\supset$?

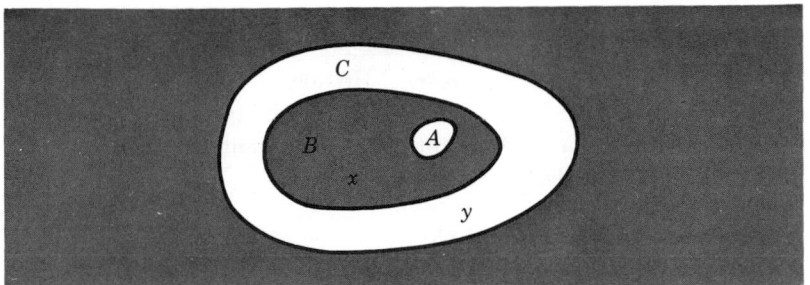

FIG. 22

The answer to the first question is given by Statement 2, which says that if $A \subseteq B$ and $B \subseteq C$, then $A \subseteq C$. Mathematicians usually indicate this property by saying that the relationship expressed by the inclusion symbol is a *transitive relation*. The reader may be familiar with other transitive relations. Equality is a transitive relation, for if $a = b$ and $b = c$, then $a = c$. Similarity of triangles is also a transitive relation. That the use of this terminology facilitates our discussion of relations can be seen by rephrasing the original question. We are really asking whether or not each type of set inclusion has the transitive property. Therefore, the questions could be stated as follows:

Which of the following relations are transitive?

(a) $\subseteq$ (b) $\subset$ (c) $\supseteq$ (d) $\supset$.

Consider part (b). If $A \subset B$ and $B \subset C$, is $A \subset C$? That is, if B contains all of the elements of A and at least one element x not in A, and C contains all of the elements of B and at least one element y not in B, does C contain all of the elements of A and at least one element not in A? A simple argument would show that proper inclusion is also a transitive property of sets. Similarly, it can be shown that if $A \supseteq B$ and $B \supseteq C$, then $A \supseteq C$; and also that if $A \supset B$ and $B \supset C$, then $A \supset C$. Therefore, each inclusion symbol expresses a transitive property.

We now ask whether the relationship expressed by the symbol ϵ is transitive. That is, if $t \, \epsilon \, B$ and $B \, \epsilon \, C$, is it then necessarily true that $t \, \epsilon \, C$? If we can find an example where this is not true we will show that this statement is not *always* true, or in mathematical terminology "is not true in the general case". It should be observed here that when the mathematician asks whether a statement is true, he is really asking whether the statement is *always true*. He does not accept a statement as true, nor state it as a fact, unless it is true in *all* cases. Frequently an example can be found where the given statement is not true. Such a specific example is called a counterexample.

Definition. *A counterexample of a given mathematical statement is an example which shows that the statement is not always true.*

If, then, we can give an example where $t \in B$ and $B \in C$ but $t \notin C$ this example will show that the set relationship expressed by the symbol ϵ is not a transitive property, for this set relationship is transitive if and only if $t \in C$ *every* time that $t \in B$ and $B \in C$.

Given the sets $B = \{3, 7\}$ and $C = \{\{3, 7\}, \{a, b\}, \{R, T\}\}$, we observe that $3 \in B$ and that C is a collection of three sets each containing two objects. One of the elements of C is B, thus $B \in C$. Therefore $3 \in B$ and $B \in C$, but $3 \notin C$, for 3 is not a set containing two objects. This counterexample shows that the relationship indicated by ϵ is *not transitive*, and in this respect it differs from each of the inclusion relations.

Secondly, one should not confuse the elements of a set with the set itself. In general the properties of the elements are different from the properties of the set. For example, if the set under consideration is the set of cars within the city limits of Chicago at 8 A.M. today, one can say that each car has four wheels, but one cannot say that the set of cars has four wheels. If 450 of these cars are red this does not make the set red. Similarly, the set can be large without making the individual elements of the set large. The size of the set need not have any relation to the size of its objects. There are large sets made up of small objects and small sets made up of large objects.

One usually finds it easy to distinguish between a set and its objects when the set contains more than one object, or even when it contains no objects. Though no elements exist in the empty set, the set itself exists.

In the case where the set consists of only one object more difficulty is encountered. Here it is necessary to be on guard against thinking that the element and the set containing the single element are identical. An example may help to clarify this point. Let $\varnothing$ denote the null set, as usual, and recall that it is a set that has no objects in it. However, the set having the null set as its only element is denoted by $\{\varnothing\}$, and it is a unit set.

As another example assume that the town of Briarpatch has only one dogcatcher, and that the city statutes do not allow him to be fired. What can be done about this situation? One cannot act against the dogcatcher, the *member* of the set. Can one act against the *set*? Yes, one can pass a law abolishing the job of dogcatcher. Thus one destroys the set without firing its only member. The dogcatcher no longer has a job because no such job exists, yet he was not fired. The set of all dogcatchers in Briarpatch no longer exists. Its former member still exists but probably is now the member of the set described as the saddest person in Briarpatch.*

Observe further that if the universe U is the set of all integers, then 5 is an element of the set U and we write $5 \, \epsilon \, U$. However, 5 is not a subset of U. The unit set $\{5\}$ is a proper subset of U, therefore $\{5\} \subset U$, but $\{5\} \not\subset U$. On the other hand, the power set 2^U of U, which has all of the subsets of U as its elements does contain $\{5\}$ as an element, therefore $\{5\} \, \epsilon \, 2^U$.

If the reader has difficulty at this point it will probably help to think of a set as a "mental bundle". The number 5 is the element that goes into the "bundle", or set, and $\{5\}$ indicates that 5 has been "bundled" into a set of one object, the putting on of the braces $\{\quad\}$ being the "bundling" process. Similarly the two numbers 3 and 7 can be chosen from the set of all integers to form a subset $\{3, 7\}$. Let $A = \{5\}$ and $B = \{3, 7\}$. Sets can be formed having sets such as A and B as elements. Let us consider the unit set D which has B as its only element. Then $D = \{B\} = \{\{3, 7\}\}$. Though D is a unit set, B is a set of two elements. The elements of B are numbers, but the element of D is a set. Furthermore, $7 \, \epsilon \, B$ and $B \, \epsilon \, D$, but $7 \not\epsilon D$. Also $E = \{A\}$ has the set A as its only element, and $E = \{A\} = \{\{5\}\}$, where $5 \, \epsilon \, A$, $A \, \epsilon \, E$, but $5 \not\epsilon E$. Observe that starting with the number 5 two operations of forming sets were necessary to produce E. The number 5 was first "bundled" to form the unit set $\{5\}$, which has a *number* as its only element, then this set was "bundled" to form the

---

* For further discussion of the distinction between an element and the set consisting of this element see *Fundamental Mathematics*, 3rd ed., Vol. I (Chicago, The University of Chicago Press, 1948), p. 7.

unit set E which has a *set* as its only element. If one set of brackets were omitted from $E = \{\{5\}\}$ this would indicate that $5 \,\epsilon\, E$, which is not true. Another set that can be considered is $F = \{A, B\} = \{\{5\}, \{3, 7\}\}$, a set of two elements. Also $7 \,\epsilon\, B$, $B \,\epsilon\, F$, but $7 \notin F$.

Care must be taken in listing the elements of the power set of a given finite set. Let $B = \{g, n\}$. If we denote the power set of B by P, then

$$P = \{\varnothing, \{g\}, \{n\}, B\},$$

and the power set of P, denoted by Q is a set containing 16 elements. In order to list the sets with ease we shall let $G = \{g\}$ and $N = \{n\}$ and then substitute. Then

$$P = \{\varnothing, G, N, B\}$$

and

$$Q = \{\varnothing, \{\varnothing\}, \{G\}, \{N\}, \{B\}, \{\varnothing, G\}, \{\varnothing, N\}, \{\varnothing, B\}, \{G, N\},$$
$$\{G, B\}, \{N, B\}, \{\varnothing, G, N\}, \{\varnothing, G, B\}, \{\varnothing, N, B\}, \{G, N, B\}, P\}.$$

Substitution produces

$$Q = \{\varnothing, \{\varnothing\}, \{\{g\}\}, \{\{n\}\}, \{B\}, \{\varnothing, \{g\}\}, \{\varnothing, \{n\}\}, \{\varnothing, B\},$$
$$\{\{g\}, \{n\}\}, \{\{g\}, B\}, \{\{n\}, B\}, \{\varnothing, \{g\}, \{n\}\}, \{\varnothing, \{g\}, B\},$$
$$\{\varnothing, \{n\}, B\}, \{\{g\}, \{n\}, B\}, P\}.$$

Observe also that $P = 2^B$ and $Q = 2^P = 2^{2^B}$.

EXERCISES

1. Show that

(a) $A \cap (B \cap C) = A \cap B \cap C$.

(b) $A \cup (B \cup C) = (A \cup B) \cup C$.

(c) $A \cup (B \cap C) = (A \cup B) \cap (A \cup C)$.

(d) $(A \cap B)' = A' \cup B'$.

(e) If $A \subset B$ and $B \subset C$, then $A \subset C$.

2. Show that

(a) If $A \cap B = B$, then $A \cup B = A$ and $A \supseteq B$.

(b) If $A \supseteq B$, then $A \cap B = B$ and $A \cup B = A$.

(c) If $A \cup B = A$, then $A \cap B = B$ and $A \supseteq B$.

These three statements are summarized by the *consistency principle* which states that if one of the three statements $A \cap B = B$, $A \supseteq B$, and $A \cup B = A$ is true then the remaining two statements must also be true.

3. The *Law of Absorption* for sets states that

$$X \cap (X \cup Y) = X \cup (X \cap Y) = X.$$

Show that this law is true by using Statement 8 to show that $X \cap (X \cup Y) = X \cup (X \cap Y)$, and then using Statement 3 and the consistency principle to prove that $X \cup (X \cap Y) = X$.

4. Let a, b, and c be numbers used in arithmetic. Then the *Five Fundamental Laws of Arithmetic* hold:

I.	$a + b = b + a$	(Commutative Law of Addition)
II.	$ab = ba$	(Commutative Law of Multiplication)
III.	$(a + b) + c = a + (b + c)$	(Associative Law of Addition)
IV.	$(ab)c = a(bc)$	(Associative Law of Multiplication)
V.	$a(b + c) = ab + ac$	(Distributive Law of Multiplication with Respect to Addition)

By replacing the numbers a, b, and c by sets A, B, and C, replacing addition by set union, and multiplication by set intersection obtain five statements about sets. Are these statements true?

5. In the set statements obtained from Exercises 1, 2, and 3 interchange the symbols $\cup$ and $\cap$ and determine which of the resulting statements are true.

6. The set statements $A \cap (B \cup C) = (A \cap B) \cup (A \cap C)$
$$A \cup (B \cap C) = (A \cup B) \cap (A \cup C)$$

are distributive laws for sets. The first is the *distributive law of set intersection with respect to set union*, and the second is the *distributive law of set union with respect to set intersection*. Are the statements obtained from these distributive laws by replacing the sets by numbers, replacing $\cup$ by $+$, and $\cap$ by juxtaposition (for multiplication), true statements of arithmetic? Give numerical examples to illustrate your answers.

7. Use the distributive laws to find a set equal to each of the following.

(a) $R \cap (S \cup T)$

(b) $S \cup (R \cap T)$

(c) $(Z \cup Y) \cap X$

(d) $(M \cap N) \cup P$

(e) $(B \cap A) \cup (B \cap C)$

(f) $(T \cup R) \cap (T \cup S)$

(g) $(W \cap P) \cup (H \cap P)$

(h) $(B \cup D) \cap (C \cup D)$

8. Simplify the following set expressions by using statements that have been established in the text or in the preceding exercises.

(a) $C \cup B \cup C'$

(b) $(C \cap U) \cup C'$

(c) $(C \cup B') \cap (C' \cup B')$

(d) $(C \cup U) \cap C'$

(e) $(A \cap U)' \cup A'$

(f) $[(C \cup \varnothing)' \cup C]'$

(g) $(X \cap W') \cup W'$

(h) $(A \cap B) \cup (A \cup B')$

(i) $[(H \cap K) \cup (H \cap K') \cup (H' \cap K)] \cap K$

9. Simplify the following set expressions.

(a) $A \cup T \cup A'$

(b) $A \cup (T \cup A)$

(c) $(\varnothing \cap Z) \cup W$

(d) $A \cap R \cap A'$

(e) $(U \cup R) \cap S$

(f) $(A \cap \varnothing) \cap U$

(g) $(A \cap \varnothing) \cup U$

(h) $[A \cap (B \cup A')] \cup B$

(i) $(A \cap \varnothing)' \cup U$

(j) $(A \cup B)' \cup B'$

(k) $[(D \cup T) \cap (D \cup T')] \cap (D \cup T)$

(l) $(X \cap U) \cup X'$

(m) $[(C \cap \varnothing)' \cap C]'$

(n) $(A \cap B) \cup (A' \cup B)$

(o) $(C \cup D) \cap (C' \cap D)$

(p) $[(A \cap B) \cup (A' \cup B)] \cup [(B \cap A) \cup (B' \cup A)]$

(q) $[(B \cup U)' \cup B'] \cap B$

(r) $(A \cup B \cup C) \cap [Z \cup (A \cup B \cup C)]$

(s) $[(K' \cup T) \cap (K' \cup T')] \cup (R \cap K')$

(t) $(T \cup R) \cup [(W \cup Z) \cap (T \cup R)]$

(u) $[(X \cap Y) \cap (P \cup Q)] \cup (X \cap Y) \cup Y$

(v) $[(A \cup B) \cap (C \cup D)] \cup (A \cup B) \cup A$

10. By using the methods of this section, work $5(a)$ and (b) in the exercises following Section 11.

11. Show that if $A \subseteq B$, then $A \cap B' = \varnothing$.

12. Let P be the power set of a given set $B \neq \varnothing$. Which of the following statements are correct?

    $(a)\ B \in P$ $(b)\ B \subset P$ $(c)\ B \subseteq P$ $(d)\ B \notin P$

13. Let $X = \{n\}$, a unit set.

    (a) Find the power set P of the set X.
    (b) Find the power set Q of the set P.

14. A set T has as its elements the points of intersection of the lines L_1, L_2, L_3, and L_4 as shown in the accompanying figure. Describe the power set of T and tell how many elements it contains.

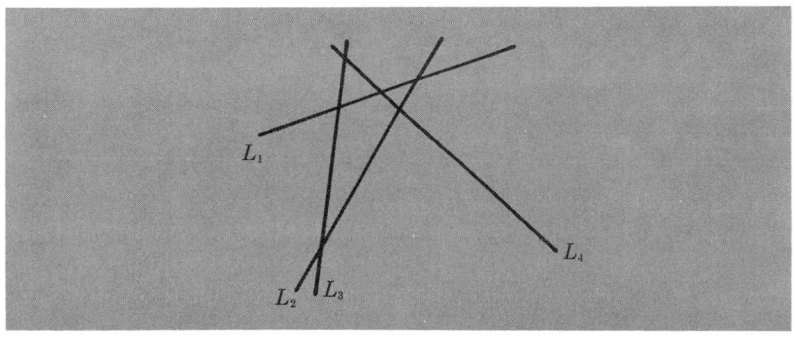

FIG. 23

15. Let $A = \{1, 2, 3, \cdots, 50\}$,
          $B = \{2, 4, 6, \cdots, 50\}$,
          $C = \{1, 3, 5, \cdots, 49\}$,
and $D = \{3, 6, 9, \cdots, 48\}$.

Using A as the universal set find the following sets:

    (a) A';
    (b) B';
    (c) C';
    (d) D';

    (e) $B' \cap D$;
    (f) $B \cap (D \cup C)$;
    (g) $(B \cap D) \cup (A \cap C)$;
    (h) $(D \cup C)'$;

    (i) $D' \cap C'$;
    (j) $(D \cap C)'$;
    (k) $D' \cup C'$.

16. Give an example where $t \,\epsilon\, B$, $B \,\epsilon\, C$, and $t \,\epsilon\, C$. Does this mean that the relationship expressed by ϵ is a transitive relationship?

17. (a) Define $A \cap B \cap C \cap D$ and show that this set is equal to $(A \cap B) \cap (C \cap D)$.

(b) List at least ten sets equal to the set $A \cap B \cap C \cap D$ which can be denoted by inserting parentheses in the notation $A \cap B \cap C \cap D$ and rearranging terms. Some such examples are $A \cap (B \cap C) \cap D$; $(A \cap D) \cap (B \cap C)$; and $A \cap (B \cap C \cap D)$.

18. Show that

(a) $(A - B) - C = A - (B \cup C)$.

(b) $A - (B - C) = (A - B) \cup (A \cap C)$.

(c) $A \cup (B - C) = (A \cup B) - (C - A)$.

(d) $A \cap (B - C) = (A \cap B) - (A \cap C)$.

19. The *symmetric difference* of two sets A and B is the relative complement of $A \cap B$ in $A \cup B$. It is denoted by $A \bigtriangleup B$.

(a) Make two statements of equality which express $A \bigtriangleup B$ in terms of the sets $A \cap B$ and $A \cup B$.

(b) Draw Venn diagrams and indicate the symmetric difference for each of the following cases: A and B overlap but neither is a subset of the other; $A = B$; $A \subset B$; $A \supset B$; A and B are disjoint.

(c) Prove that $(A \bigtriangleup B) \bigtriangleup C = A \bigtriangleup (B \bigtriangleup C)$.

15. CARTESIAN PRODUCTS

Given two sets $A = \{1, 2, 3\}$ and $B = \{5, 7\}$ we form from them the set of all pairs such that each pair contains an element of A and an element of B arranged in a specified order. If the elements of A are first in the pairs we denote this set by $A \times B$, read "the Cartesian Product of A and B" or simply "A cross B".

The pairs which are the elements of this set are $(1, 5)$, $(1, 7)$, $(2, 5)$, $(2, 7)$, $(3, 5)$, and $(3, 7)$. Thus

$$A \times B = \{(1, 5), (1, 7), (2, 5), (2, 7), (3, 5), (3, 7)\}.$$

Observe that A contains 3 elements, B contains 2 elements, and $A \times B$ contains 6 elements.

If the elements of B are first in the pairs we denote the set by $B \times A$. Thus

$$B \times A = \{(5, 1), (5, 2), (5, 3), (7, 1), (7, 2), (7, 3)\}$$

and it also contains 6 elements. Observe also that merely interchanging the order of the pairs in $A \times B$ produces $B \times A$.

A graphical representation of the Cartesian Products under consideration will emphasize their difference. $A \times B$ is the set of six points denoted by crosses on the accompanying graph, and $B \times A$ is the set of six points denoted by circles on the graph.

In many places in mathematics we need to distinguish between the pair (a, b) and the pair (b, a). The usual two-dimensional graph represents these pairs by distinct points unless, of course, $a = b$. When the order of a pair is of importance the pair is referred to as an ordered pair.

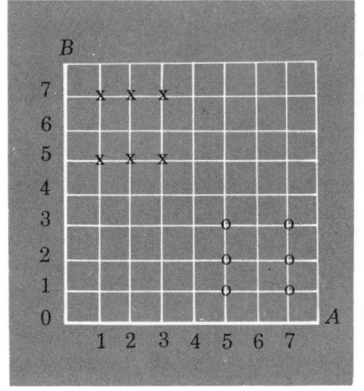
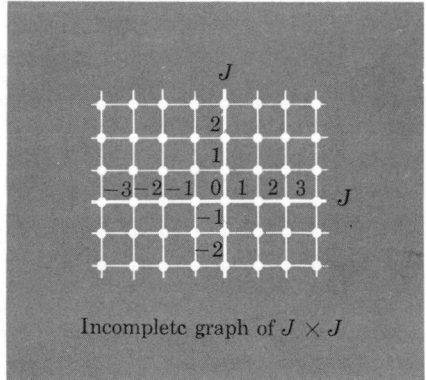

Incomplete graph of $J \times J$

FIG. 24

Definition. *An **ordered pair** of objects is a set of two objects for which it has been decided which is first in the pair and which is second.*

Cartesian Products exist for any two sets, finite or infinite, distinct or not distinct. For example, if J represents the set of integers, then $J \times J$ is the set of all pairs of integers. The accompanying graph indicates some of the elements in this Cartesian Product set. Since it is impossible to represent all of the pairs which are in the plane and belong to $J \times J$ we say that the graph is incomplete. The reader should understand that these points extend throughout the plane.

Definition.   *The **Cartesian Product** $A \times B$ of two sets A and B is the set of all ordered pairs (a, b), where $a \in A$ and $b \in B$.*

Using set notation we can write this definition in more compact form.

Definition. $A \times B = \{(a, b) \mid a \in A \quad and \quad b \in B\}$.

If $A = \{\text{red, blue}\}$ and $B = \{*, /\}$, then

$$B \times A = \{(*, \text{red}), (*, \text{blue}), (/, \text{red}), (/, \text{blue})\}.$$

Even though the elements involved here are not numbers it is still possible to obtain a graphical representation of the Cartesian Product, sometimes referred to as a lattice representation, which provides a systematic method of finding all pairs.

*	(*, red)	(*, blue)
/	(/, red)	(/, blue)
	red	blue

Cartesian Products can also be represented by tree diagrams.

For example, if $A = \{r, s, t\}$ then $A \times A$ can readily be found by using the accompanying tree diagram. Tree diagrams may be especially helpful when we are interested in some proper subset of $A \times A$, such as those elements that pair distinct elements of the original set. In this case the elements (r, r), (s, s) and (t, t) are not needed, and the tree diagram reduces to the one indicated on the right. The *number* of distinct pairs, can be found without any type of graphical representation. We merely observe that there are three ways to choose the first entry, but after it is chosen there are only two ways to choose a different element to pair with it. That is, with each of the first three elements we may pair the two remaining elements, therefore, there are 3 choices for the first entry, 2 choices for the second entry, and $3 \cdot 2 = 6$ pairs with distinct elements.

16. THE NUMBER OF ELEMENTS IN A∪B

Throughout this section we shall restrict the discussion to sets whose elements can be counted. For each set considered there will be a nonnegative integer which indicates the number of elements in the set.

We shall use $n(A)$ to represent the number of objects in the set A. If A and B are disjoint sets then the number of objects in their set union $A \cup B$ is equal to the sum of the numbers in the separate sets. Examples are easy to find. If set A contains 5 apples and set B contains 7 pears, then set $A \cup B$ contains 12 pieces of fruit. If A and B are not disjoint, the number of objects in $A \cup B$ is not equal to the sum of the numbers in the separate sets, for this sum counts the objects in $A \cap B$ twice, once as elements of A and once as elements of B.

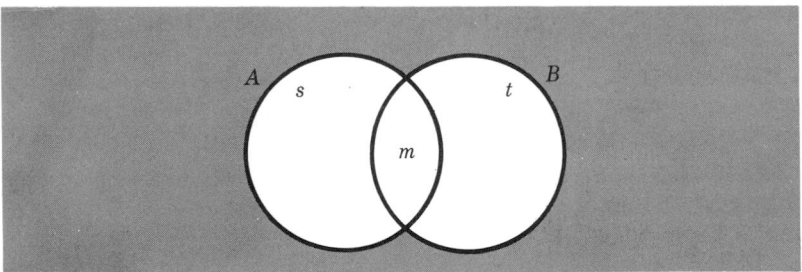

FIG. 25

For example, if A contains $s + m$ objects, m of which are in B, and B contains $t + m$ objects, m of which are in A, then $n(A \cap B) = m$ and $n(A) + n(B) = s + m + t + m = s + t + 2m$, while $n(A \cup B) = s + m + t$. Therefore

$$n(A \cup B) = n(A) + n(B) - n(A \cap B).$$

This formula indicates that we must subtract the number of elements in the intersection from $n(A) + n(B)$ because these objects have been counted twice.

The formula for the number of objects in the union of two sets can be used to find a formula for the number of objects in the union of three sets as follows:

$$
\begin{aligned}
n(A \cup B \cup C) &= n[(A \cup B) \cup C] \\
&= n(A \cup B) + n(C) - n[(A \cup B) \cap C] \\
&= n(A) + n(B) - n(A \cap B) + n(C) \\
&\quad - n[(A \cap C) \cup (B \cap C)] \\
&= n(A) + n(B) + n(C) - n(A \cap B) - n(A \cap C) \\
&\quad - n(B \cap C) + n[(A \cap C) \cap (B \cap C)] \\
n(A \cup B \cup C) &= n(A) + n(B) + n(C) - n(A \cap B) - n(A \cap C) \\
&\quad - n(B \cup C) + n(A \cap B \cap C),
\end{aligned}
$$

since $(A \cap B) \cap (B \cap C) = A \cap B \cap C$.

This formula will seem simpler if we interpret it by means of a Venn diagram. First we add the numbers representing the separate sets, then because of overlapping we subtract the numbers representing the intersections of two sets at a time; namely $n(A \cap B), n(A \cap C)$, and $n(B \cap C)$. Observe that $n(A \cap B \cap C)$ should be included just once in the desired number. It was included three times in the terms $n(A)$, $n(B)$, and $n(C)$ and then subtracted three times in the terms $n(A \cap B)$, $n(A \cap C)$, and $n(B \cap C)$; therefore, it must be included again, as it is in the final term of the formula. If we assign letters to each section of the diagram we have the following:

$$
\begin{aligned}
n(A) &= p + t + s + m, & n(A \cap B) &= s + m, \\
n(B) &= q + u + s + m, & n(A \cap C) &= t + m, \\
n(C) &= r + t + u + m, & n(B \cap C) &= u + m.
\end{aligned}
$$

Therefore, $n(A) + n(B) + n(C) = p + q + r + 2s + 2t + 2u + 3m$, and $n(A \cap B) + n(A \cap C) + n(B \cap C) = s + t + u + 3m$. Thus

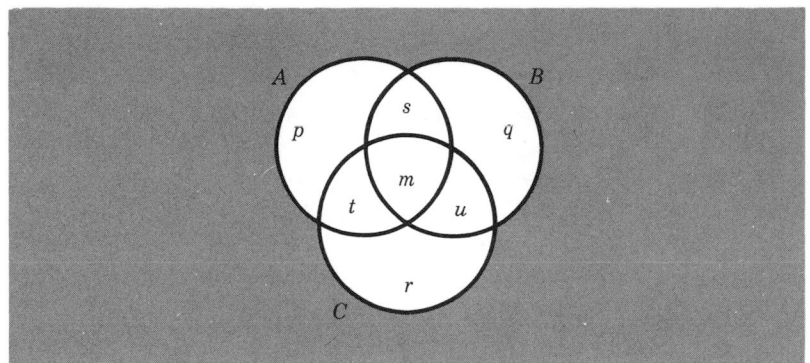

FIG. 26

the formula for the number of objects in the union of three finite sets gives

$$n(A \cup B \cup C) = (p + q + r + 2s + 2t + 2u + 3m)$$
$$- (s + t + u + 3m) + m$$
$$= p + q + r + s + t + u + m$$

as indicated in the diagram.

The formulas obtained in this section are useful in checking certain types of statistical data.

If we were told that in a certain school there are 2000 students taking mathematics, science, or history, and also that

> 1523 take mathematics,
> 1241 take history,
> 1322 take science,
> 735 take mathematics and history,
> 620 take science and history,
> 1125 take mathematics and science, and
> 250 take mathematics, science, and history,

we might ask whether these figures are consistent. We can test them by the formulas of this section.

$$n(A \cup B \cup C) = n(A) + n(B) + n(C) - n(A \cap B) - n(A \cap C)$$
$$- n(B \cap C) + n(A \cap B \cap C)$$
$$= 1523 + 1241 + 1322 - 735 - 620 - 1125 + 250$$
$$= 1856 \neq 2000$$

Since the number of objects in the union is not 2000, we conclude that these figures are inconsistent. However, this method does not tell us where the error is. On the other hand, if we are *sure* that all of the figures are correct except the one indicating how many take all three subjects, we can use the formula to find that this number should be 394 instead of 250. With a correct set of data we can then determine how many students take mathematics and history but not science, as well as other related information that may be of value.

The following example shows that there are certain problems involving statistical data that can be solved readily without using the formulas of this section.

In a survey involving 150 factories it was found that

> 72 purchased item A,
> 69 purchased item B,
> 75 purchased item C,
> 27 purchased items A and B,
> 30 purchased items A and C,
> 50 purchased items B and C, and
> 10 purchased items A, B, and C.

Find how many factories purchased

(a) at least one of these items;   (b) none of these items;
(c) exactly two of these items;   (d) exactly one of these items.

This question is readily answered by using a Venn diagram. We enter first the number of factories using all three items. Then since

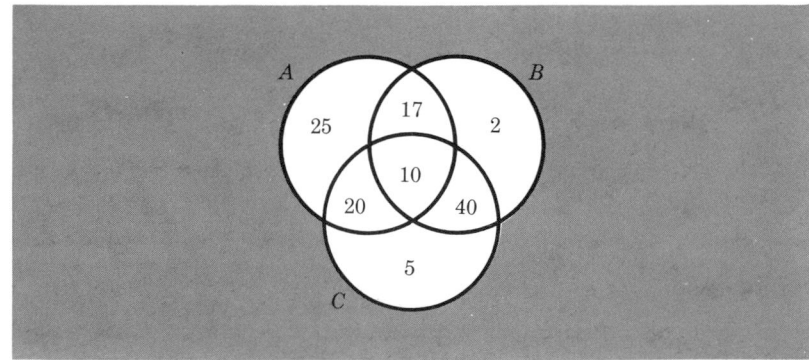

FIG. 27

27 used both A and B we enter the number 17 in the section represented by $A \cap B \cap C'$ (that is, those who purchased A and B but did not purchase C). Similarly we enter 20 in the section $A \cap C \cap B'$. Since the total number using A is 72 we enter $72 - (20 + 10 + 17) = 25$ in the section $A \cap B' \cap C'$. Continuing in this manner we obtain numbers for all spaces. The sum of all the numbers in the diagram is 119. This is the answer to (a). For (b) we have $150 - 119 = 31$. For (c) we have $20 + 17 + 40 = 77$. For (d) we have $25 + 2 + 5 = 32$.

EXERCISES

1. Find the Cartesian Product Sets $S \times T$ for the following sets.

(a) $S = \{-2, 1, 0\}$, $T = \{4\}$.

(b) $S = T = \{7\}$.

(c) $S = \{1/2, -1, 8, -3/8\}$, $T = \{a, x, z, t\}$.

2. (a) Find a formula for $n(A \times B)$.

(b) Find a formula for $n(A \times A)$.

3. (a) Give a lattice representation of $B \times A$ where

$A = \{+, 0, *, -\}$ and $B = \{m, t, p, q, r\}$.

(b) Also give a tree diagram.

4. Using $A \times B \times C = \{(a, b, c) \mid a \, \epsilon \, A, \ b \, \epsilon \, B,$ and $c \, \epsilon \, C\}$ find this type of Cartesian Product for

$A = \{1, 2, 3\}$, $B = \{4, 5\}$, and $C = \{6, 7, 8, 9\}$.

5. (a) Find a formula for $n(A \times B \times C)$.

(b) Find a formula for $n(A \times A \times A)$.

6. There are 5 roads connecting the towns of Cherryville and Newton and 6 roads connecting Newton and Flint. In how many ways can one travel by car along these roads from Cherryville to Flint by way of Newton without traveling exactly the same route more than once?

7. A room has 4 doors. In how many ways can an individual make a trip into this room and out again if he must enter and leave only by means of the doors.

8. There are three trains that run between town X and town Y. In how many ways can one make a round trip by train from Y to X?

9. Explain how exercises 6, 7, and 8 are related to Cartesian Products.

10. What are the answers to exercises 7 and 8 if the route of return must be different from the route going?

11. A college has an enrollment of 3,000 students. If 2,500 students from this college attend a certain football game and 1275 from this college attend a certain baseball game, find

(a) the smallest number that could have seen both games;
(b) the largest number that could have seen both games; .
(c) the number that saw at least one of the games if 1000 saw both games.

12. For the example involving 150 factories let L, N, T, and E represent the answers for parts (a), (b), (c), and (d), respectively. Let $Z = 10$, the number that purchased all items.

(i) Show how L could be found from Z, T, and E.
(ii) Give a formula involving L, Z, T, and E and check it using the numbers in this example.

13. A survey was made of 9,000 housewives to find what types of detergents each had used within the last three years.

> 3224 had used brand A,
> 3571 had used brand B,
> 5656 had used brand C,
> 1820 had used both A and B,
> 2376 had used both A and C,
> 2476 had used both B and C, and
> 1545 had used brands A, B, and C.

It was then reported that 8,305 housewives used at least one of these products.
(a) Is this figure correct? (b) How many housewives used exactly two of these detergents? (c) How many used exactly one?

17. ONE-TO-ONE CORRESPONDENCE

Definition. *A **one-to-one correspondence** between two sets, A and B, is a pairing of the elements of these two sets in such a way that each* *element of A is paired with one and only one element of B and each element of B is paired with one and only one element of A.*

We shall frequently write "1–1 correspondence" for "one-to-one correspondence".

When the child in kindergarten counts the fingers on his hands by calling the numbers from one to ten, he is assigning to each finger one and only one number, and to each number one and only one finger. Such a matching is a one-to-one correspondence. It is easy to see that this counting or matching can be done in several ways, hence there may be several ways of setting up a one-to-one correspondence between two sets; nevertheless, it takes only *one* such correspondence to show that the set of fingers and the set of whole numbers from 1 to 10 inclusive contain the same number of objects.

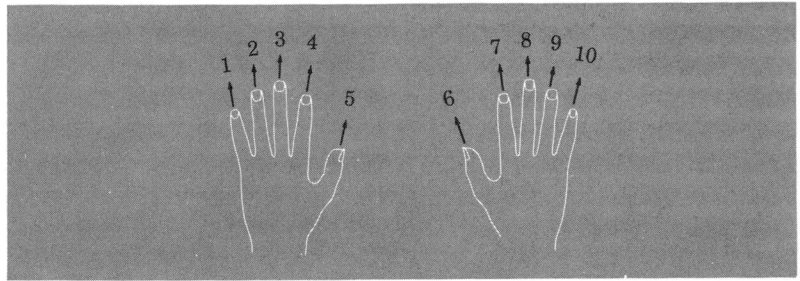

FIG. 28

One may not even know the seating capacity of a large auditorium but if he is sure that there is one and only one person in each seat, and that each person is occupying one and only one seat, he can conclude that the number of people is the same as the number of seats. Conditions which might prevent a 1–1 correspondence of people and seats are a vacant seat, two or more people occupying one seat, a person occupying two or more seats, or a person standing. (See Figure 29.)

For additional examples, let us consider some sets of points which are parts of geometric figures.

1. Considered as sets of points, two sides of a triangle, regardless of their lengths, can be put into 1–1 correspondence by drawing lines parallel to the third side. (See Figure 30).

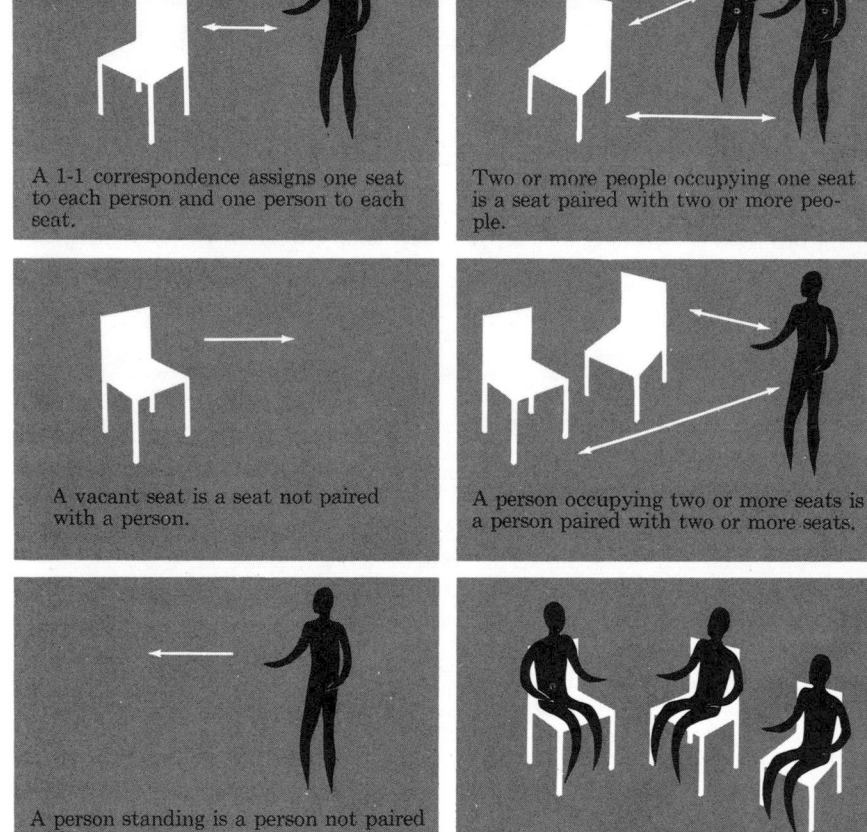

A 1-1 correspondence assigns one seat to each person and one person to each seat.

Two or more people occupying one seat is a seat paired with two or more people.

A vacant seat is a seat not paired with a person.

A person occupying two or more seats is a person paired with two or more seats.

A person standing is a person not paired with a seat.

FIG. 29

For brevity, we shall often omit the words "considered as sets of points" when speaking of 1–1 correspondences between geometric figures; nevertheless, these words are to be understood and the reader should mentally supply them.

2. A circle lying inside a square can be put into 1–1 correspondence with the square merely by extending the radii to intersect the square.

3. If a circle and a square are disjoint, let O be the center of the circle and T be a point inside the square. Parallel lines through O and T will set up a 1–1 correspondence between the two figures.

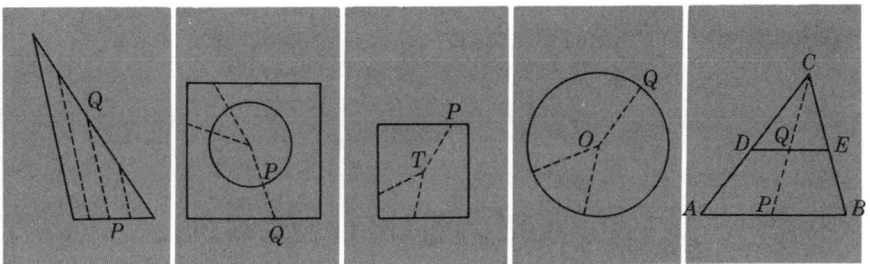

FIG. 30

4. Let ABC be a triangle and let D and E be the midpoints of the sides AC and BC, respectively. We ask whether the set of points on the short segment DE can be put into 1–1 correspondence with the set of points on the longer segment AB. If P is a point on the segment AB, how do we choose a point on DE to pair with it? The line CP cuts the line DE in a point which we shall call Q. This will pair one and only one point Q with the point P. What happens if we start with Q instead of P? The line CQ will cut AB in the point P and this will pair one and only one point P with the point Q. Therefore, lines through C that cut DE and AB set up a 1–1 correspondence between the set of points in DE and the set of points in AB, even though AB is a longer segment. Can you find a 1–1 correspondence between DE and AB that matches A with E and D with B? There are many that do.

18. FINITE AND INFINITE SETS

Definition.   *A set* **contains n elements** *if it can be put into 1–1 correspondence with the set* $\{1, 2, 3, \cdots, n\}$, *where n is a positive integer.*

Definition. *A set is a **finite set** if it contains n elements or if it is the empty set, which contains no elements.*

This essentially means that a set is finite if its elements can be counted. Thus there are no objects in the set or there is a positive integer which indicates the number of objects in the set.

Definition. *If a set is not finite, it is an **infinite set**.*

If one applies the definition of a finite set to the examples at the beginning of Section 1 he will find that each of them is a finite set, even the set of the grains of sand on the beaches of Lake Michigan. Though the number of objects in this set is very large, the set is nevertheless finite.

A set that occurs frequently in mathematical discussions is the set of positive whole numbers $I = \{1, 2, 3, 4, 5, \cdots\}$, also called the set of positive integers. If we could set up a 1–1 correspondence between the set of numbers from 1 to 5 and the set I we could prove that the set I contains exactly five elements. Let $B = \{1, 2, 3, 4, 5\}$ and let us pair the numbers in B with the following numbers in I

$$
\begin{array}{ccccc}
1 & 2 & 3 & 4 & 5 \\
\updownarrow & \updownarrow & \updownarrow & \updownarrow & \updownarrow \\
5 & 17 & 29 & 1000 & 2{,}875{,}632
\end{array}
$$

This means that we have selected five numbers from the set I for the pairing. Is this a 1–1 correspondence? Obviously not, for the number 2 in I has not been paired with any number in B, neither have the numbers 1,000,000 and 2,685,732,846,921,851, as well as most of the other numbers in I. Would some other correspondence be one-to-one? The reader would probably readily agree that it is impossible to set up a one-to-one correspondence between these two sets. Even if B were the set of numbers from 1 to 1,862, or B were the set from 1 to 7,000,000,000, it would still be impossible to set up a 1–1 correspondence between I and B. Therefore, we have reason to believe that I does not contain exactly 5 elements, nor exactly 1,862 elements, nor exactly 7,000,000,000 elements. This type of reasoning leads us to believe that no whole number, however large, can indicate the exact number of elements in the set I. The following arguments present evidence that I is an infinite set.

Statement 10. If a set A contains n elements and is a proper subset of a set B which contains m elements, then $m > n$.

Discussion. Since A contains n elements there exists a 1–1 correspondence between the set $\{1, 2, 3, \cdots, n\}$ and A, and we denote the corresponding elements of A by $a_1, a_2, a_3, \cdots, a_n$, respectively. Thus 3 corresponds to a_3 and, in general, k corresponds to a_k. Since A is a proper subset of B there is at least one element in B which is not in A. Denote those elements of B which are not in A by $b_1, b_2, \cdots, b_j$. When the elements of B are arranged in the order $\{a_1, a_2, \cdots, a_n, b_1, b_2, \cdots, b_j\}$ a correspondence is set up between B and the set of integers $\{1, 2, \cdots, n, n + 1, n + 2, \cdots, n + j\}$. Therefore, by definition, B contains $n + j$ elements, and $m = n + j$, where $j \geqq 1$. Therefore $m > n$. ∎

Statement 11. The set I of positive integers is an infinite set.

Discussion. Let us assume that I is a finite set. Since $I = \{1, 2, 3, \cdots\}$, it is not the empty set. If $I \neq \varnothing$ is finite there must be a positive integer n such that I can be put into 1–1 correspondence with $N = \{1, 2, 3, \cdots, n\}$ and by definition I contains n elements. But the finite set N which contains n elements is a proper subset of the supposedly finite set I which contains n elements, because I contains the integer $n + 1$ whenever it contains the integer n. Therefore, to say that I contains n elements, contradicts Statement 10, which says that the number of elements in a finite superset must be greater than the number of elements in a proper subset. Since the assumption that I is finite leads to a contradiction we conclude that I is an infinite set. ∎

In fact, I is one of the simplest infinite sets that we can consider and we shall use it as a "measuring stick" to determine the cardinal number of other infinite sets.

EXERCISES

1. Find the number of elements in each of the following sets. If possible, set up a 1–1 correspondence between the pairs of sets listed.

(a) $\{1, 2, 3, \cdots, 10\}$ and $\{1, 4, 9, 25, \cdots, 81,100\}$.

(b) $\{-5, -4, \cdots, 0, 1, \cdots, 5\}$ and $\{1, 2, \cdots, 10\}$.

(c) $\{5, 6, 7, \cdots, 37\}$ and $\{0, 1, 2, \cdots, 32\}$

(d) $\{21, 28, 35, \cdots, 700\}$ and $\{0, 1, 2, \cdots, n\}$, where n is a positive integer.

2. Can the following pairs of sets be put into 1–1 correspondence?

(a) States in the United States and cards in a pinochle deck.

(b) Jacob's sons and the months of the year.

(c) Fingers on one hand, excluding the thumb, and the legs of a normal dog.

(d) Legs and animals in a herd of cattle.

(e) Heads and animals in a herd of cattle.

(f) Bowling pins used in one alley and the normal number of toes of a man.

3. The line segments AB and CD are parallel. Show that there are two different 1–1 correspondences between the two sets of points in AB and CD. In one correspondence pair A with C and B with D. In the other, pair A with D and B with C.

4. Let A, B, and C be three points on a straight line. Set up a 1–1 correspondence between the sets of points in the segments AB and BC.

5. In triangle ABC, let D and E be the midpoints of the sides AC and BC, respectively.

(a) Set up a correspondence between the sets of points in DC and AB.

(b) If D and E are arbitrary points on the sides AC and BC, respectively, can a 1–1 correspondence always be set up between DE and AB?

6. In *how many ways* can a 1–1 correspondence be set up between the following pairs of sets in which r, s, t, x, and y are distinct elements? Tree diagrams may be helpful.

(a) $\{1\}$, $\{r\}$

(b) $\{1, 2\}$, $\{r, s\}$

(c) $\{1, 2, 3\}$, $\{r, s, t\}$

(d) $\{1, 2, 3, 4\}$, $\{r, s, t, x\}$

(e) $\{1, 2, 3, 4, 5\}$, $\{r, s, t, x, y\}$

7. Obtain a formula which will indicate the *number of ways* that a finite set of n elements can be put into 1–1 correspondence with the first n positive integers.

8. Use the formula obtained in the preceding exercise to answer the following questions:

(*a*) In how many ways can five men be seated in a row?

(*b*) In how many ways can seven men be placed in seven administrative positions if each man is qualified for all positions?

(*c*) In how many ways can nine books be placed side by side on a given shelf?

(*d*) In how many ways can the books of exercise (*c*) be arranged on the shelf if two of them are volumes 1 and 2 of world history and must be kept together in that order?

19. COUNTABLE SETS

It is interesting to notice that the set of positive integers can be put into 1–1 correspondence with a proper subset of itself. It can be paired with the set $E = \{2, 4, 6, \cdots\}$ of even positive integers in the following way.

$$
\begin{array}{cccccc}
1 & 2 & 3 & 4 & \cdots & n & \cdots \\
\updownarrow & \updownarrow & \updownarrow & \updownarrow & & \updownarrow & \\
2 & 4 & 6 & 8 & \cdots & 2n & \cdots
\end{array}
$$

We shall later learn that *every* infinite set has the property that it can be put into 1–1 correspondence with *some* proper subset of itself. This is one of the characteristic properties of an infinite set.

We also observe that each of the sets $H = \{59, 60, 61, 62, \cdots\}$ and $K = \{-7, -6, -5, -4, -3, -2, -1, 0, 1, 2, \cdots\}$ can easily be put into 1–1 correspondence with the set of positive integers, which we shall continue to denote by I, for they are already arranged so that there is a first one to match the number 1, a second one to match the number 2, and, in general, an nth one to match the number n. The correspondence between I and H could be given by the formula $n \leftrightarrow n + 58$. Can you find a formula for a 1–1 correspondence between K and I?

Putting the set $T = \{\cdots, -10, -5, 0, 5, 10, \cdots\}$ into 1–1 correspondence with I is not much harder even though there is no first element. This can be accomplished by starting with zero and then alternating positive and negative elements.

1	2	3	4	5	6	7	$\cdots$
$\updownarrow$	$\updownarrow$	$\updownarrow$	$\updownarrow$	$\updownarrow$	$\updownarrow$	$\updownarrow$	$\cdots$
0	5	-5	10	-10	15	-15	$\cdots$

There are many other ways of setting up a correspondence between I and T. Can you find some of them?

Definition. *A set which can be put into* 1–1 *correspondence with the set of positive integers is a* **countably infinite set.**

Definition. *A set is* **countable** *if it is a finite set or a countably infinite set.*

A countable set is also called a **denumerable set** or an **enumerable set.**

We now ask whether the set union of three countable sets is a countable set. We could use the given sets H, K, and T to form $H \cup K \cup T$ and attempt to set up the correspondence for this specific case. The reader should try to devise a scheme for matching the sets in this example.

We shall give a general plan which will work for all such unions of three countable sets. We can represent the first countable set by* $\{a_1, a_2, a_3, \cdots, a_n, \cdots\}$. Then we represent those elements of the second set which are not in the first set by $\{b_1, b_2, b_3, \cdots, b_n, \cdots\}$. This means that in order to avoid repetitions we have not indicated those elements in the second set which are also in the first set. Finally we represent those elements of the third set which are not in the first set nor in the second set by $\{c_1, c_2, c_3, \cdots, c_n, \cdots\}$. Can we arrange the elements in these three sets in such a way as to establish a 1–1 correspondence between their union and the set of all positive in-

---

* The symbol a_1 is read "a sub one"; the symbol a_2 is read "a sub two"; and, in general, a_n is read "a sub n". The number that appears at the bottom of the symbol a_n is called a subscript. The fact that the indicated set is a countable set can readily be seen by observing that a_1 corresponds to 1, a_2 corresponds to 2, and, in general, a_n corresponds to n; that is, the subscript indicates the integer that the element is paired with.

tegers? We do so by first taking all of the elements with subscript 1, then all of the elements with superscript 2, and proceeding in this fashion.

$$1 \quad 2 \quad 3 \quad 4 \quad 5 \quad 6 \quad 7 \quad 8 \quad 9 \cdots$$
$$\updownarrow \quad \updownarrow \quad \updownarrow \quad \updownarrow \quad \updownarrow \quad \updownarrow \quad \updownarrow \quad \updownarrow \quad \updownarrow$$
$$a_1 \quad b_1 \quad c_1 \quad a_2 \quad b_2 \quad c_2 \quad a_3 \quad b_3 \quad c_3 \cdots$$

In the event that one or two sets are finite this process will eventually exhaust all of the elements of the finite sets and will then draw elements only from the infinite sets. If all three sets are finite, having respectively n_1, n_2, and n_3 elements then at most $n = n_1 + n_2 + n_3$ integers will be needed to set up the correspondence. The union will be a finite set and therefore a countable set.

After showing that the union of three countable sets is a countable set we ask whether the union of five countable sets is a countable set. What can be said of the union of twenty-seven countable sets, or one hundred countable sets, or any finite number of countable sets? We shall leave these questions to the reader and consider one which is a bit more difficult.

Is the union of a countably infinite number of countably infinite sets a countably infinite set?

If we have a countably infinite number of sets given, there is one set corresponding to each positive integer n. Let the set corresponding to n be denoted by the symbol S_n, which is read "S sub n". Thus the set corresponding to 1 is S_1 (read "S sub one"), that corresponding to 2 is S_2 (read "S sub two"); and so on. To indicate the elements in each of these sets we use two numbers in the subscript of each symbol that represents an element, such as a_{35} (read "a sub three five"). The first subscript denotes the set to which the element belongs and the second subscript denotes the position of the element in the set. Thus a_{13} is the third element of the first set and a_{75} is the fifth element of the seventh set.

Since we have not defined the union of an infinite number of sets we state that the union of the sets S_1, S_2, S_3, $\cdots$, S_n, $\cdots$ is the set of all x such that $x \in S_n$ for at least one n, where n is a positive integer. Let us also digress long enough to give general definitions of set union and set intersection. In what follows Y will represent a set whose elements are themselves sets, a typical one of which we shall denote by A.

Definition. *If Y is a set and each member of Y is a set A, then the* **union of all the sets in Y** *is the set of all x such that x is an element of one or more of the sets A which are members of the set Y. This union is denoted by* $\bigcup_{A \epsilon Y} A$, *and, symbolically,* $\bigcup_{A \epsilon Y} A = \{x \mid x \epsilon$ *some* A, *and* $A \epsilon Y\}$.

In our particular case $Y = \{S_1,\ S_2,\ S_3,\ \cdots\}$ and the union is denoted by $\bigcup_{S_n \epsilon Y} S_n$.

Definition. *If Y is a nonempty set and each member of Y is a set A, then the* **intersection of the sets in Y** *is the set of all x such that x is an element of every set A which is a member of the set Y. This intersection is denoted by* $\bigcap_{A \epsilon Y} A$, *and, symbolically,*

$$\bigcap_{A \epsilon Y} A = \{x \mid x \epsilon \text{ every } A, \text{ when } A \epsilon Y\}.$$

We now return to the question of whether or not the union of a countably infinite number of countably infinite sets is a countably infinite set. In the discussion which follows we shall assume that no two of the given sets have any elements in common, and shall leave the case of overlapping sets for an exercise.

We first systematically indicate some of the elements in the union and omit the set brackets of the union. The elements in the first line are those which were in the first set; the elements in the second line are those which were in the second set; and so on.

$$
\begin{array}{cccccccc}
a_{11} & a_{12} & a_{13} & a_{14} & a_{15} & a_{16} & a_{17} & \cdots \\
a_{21} & a_{22} & a_{23} & a_{24} & a_{25} & a_{26} & a_{27} & \cdots \\
a_{31} & a_{32} & a_{33} & a_{34} & a_{35} & a_{36} & a_{37} & \cdots \\
a_{41} & a_{42} & a_{43} & a_{44} & a_{45} & a_{46} & a_{47} & \cdots \\
a_{51} & a_{52} & a_{53} & a_{54} & a_{55} & a_{56} & a_{57} & \cdots \\
a_{61} & a_{62} & a_{63} & a_{64} & a_{65} & a_{66} & a_{67} & \cdots \\
a_{71} & a_{72} & a_{73} & a_{74} & a_{75} & a_{76} & a_{77} & \cdots \\
\cdot & \cdot & \cdot & \cdot & \cdot & \cdot & \cdot & \cdots \\
\cdot & \cdot & \cdot & \cdot & \cdot & \cdot & \cdot & \cdots \\
\cdot & \cdot & \cdot & \cdot & \cdot & \cdot & \cdot & \cdots \\
\end{array}
$$

The dots indicate that it is impossible to list all of the elements. (It is suggested that the reader make a similar array of elements. This will provide practice in writing elements with subscripts and will allow him to indicate the pattern of selection as it is set up. No lines have been drawn through this array lest the solution to the problem be revealed before the reader has time to discover it.) Can we now arrange all of these elements in such a way as to set up a 1–1 correspondence with the positive integers? Can we choose a first one, then a second one, and continue the process in such a way as to use all of these elements? When we were arranging three countable sets we used the first element in each set, then the second element of each set, and proceeded in that fashion. Will that method work here? We find that it will not because there are enough first elements to correspond to *all* of the positive integers and no positive integers would be left to correspond to the remaining elements of the union.

We must therefore find some other way to set up the correspondence. Since neither horizontal nor vertical choices will work we consider a diagonal approach. Diagonal "slicing" from upper left to lower right across the array of elements leads again to an infinite set in each "slice", but by "slicing" diagonally from upper right to lower left we can cut off a finite number of elements at a time. First we "slice" off the upper left tip of the array. This produces a_{11} to be matched with the positive integer 1. The next diagonal "slice" produces two elements a_{12} and a_{21} to be matched with the positive integers 2 and 3, respectively. The third "slice" produces a_{13}, a_{22}, and a_{31} to be matched with the positive integers 4, 5, and 6, respectively. A solution is now evident and a correspondence is given here.

1	2	3	4	5	6	7	8	9	10	$\cdots$
$\updownarrow$	$\updownarrow$	$\updownarrow$	$\updownarrow$	$\updownarrow$	$\updownarrow$	$\updownarrow$	$\updownarrow$	$\updownarrow$	$\updownarrow$	$\cdots$
a_{11}	a_{12}	a_{21}	a_{13}	a_{22}	a_{31}	a_{14}	a_{23}	a_{32}	a_{41}	$\cdots$

Will the element a_{53} be reached eventually? It is clear that after a sufficient number of diagonal "slices" it will be reached. Which slice will pick up a_{53}? How is the number of the slice related to the sum of the numbers in the subscript of a_{53}? What is the sum of the numbers in the subscript of each element of this particular slice?

Let us consider some questions, the answers to which will help show that every element will eventually be assigned to a positive integer. If a_{jk} is an element of the nth diagonal slice what can be said of $j + k$ for a fixed value of n? What is the relationship between n and $j + k$?

A little consideration shows that the sum of the subscripts of the element in the first slice is 2; the sum of the subscripts of each element in the second slice is 3; and, in general, $j + k = n + 1$. Therefore a_{jk} is reached by the slice whose number is $j + k - 1$, and each element of the union is assigned an integer.

The preceding discussion is enough to establish a 1–1 correspondence. If a formula can be obtained which will indicate the correspondence it is preferred because of its conciseness. Many times such a formula is hard to find, and we must be content with a discussion. In this particular case $a_{jk} \leftrightarrow \frac{1}{2}(j + k - 1)(j + k - 2) + j$. The reader should verify that this formula is correct for the corresponding elements shown above and should also observe that $a_{53} \leftrightarrow \frac{1}{2}(7)(6) + 5 = 26$.

Can you find other ways of setting up a 1–1 correspondence for this problem?

EXERCISES

1. For each set which is countably infinite indicate a 1–1 correspondence between the given set and the set of positive integers.

(a) The integers.
(b) All integral multiples of 3.
(c) The odd integers.
(d) Integers of the form $5n + 2$, where n is an integer.
(e) Integers of the form $12k - 7$, where k is an integer.
(f) The fractions $m/7$, where m is an integer.

2. Let H, K, and T be the countable sets described in the preceding section. Show that $H \cup K \cup T$ is a countable set.

3. Show that the union of a countable number of countable sets is a countable set even though the sets may overlap.

4. Write a formula which will set up a 1–1 correspondence between the positive integers and the elements of the array in the preceding section, by slicing from lower left to upper right.

5. Given the plane figure as shown in Figure 31, where PD and QC are perpendicular to CD, and BP and AQ are perpendicular to AB. Let S represent the set of all points in AB, and R represent the set of all points in CD. Set up a correspondence between $y \, \epsilon \, S$ and $x \, \epsilon \, R$ by means of the curve K and the perpendiculars L_1 and L_2 to AB and CD, respectively.

(a) Is this correspondence 1–1?

(b) Are there other curves which will give a 1–1 correspondence by following the same procedure?

(c) Is it necessary that L_1 and L_2 be perpendicular to AB and CD, respectively, in order to obtain a 1–1 correspondence? Show why.

(d) Is there a more direct method for setting up a 1–1 correspondence between AB and CD?

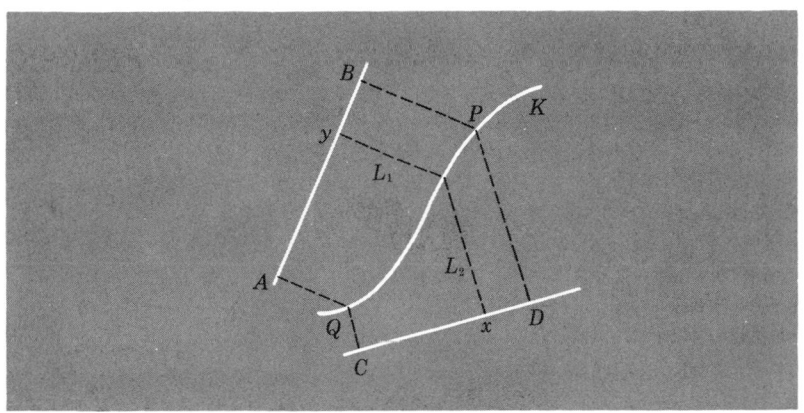

FIG. 31

6. The symbol $[x]$ denotes the greatest integer less than or equal to the number x. Evaluate each of the following.

(a) $[0]$.   (c) $[-.5]$.   (e) $[-1.7]$.   (g) $-[-2.7]$.

(b) $[2.37]$.   (d) $[1.02]$.   (f) $[3.81]$.   (h) $-[-.5]$.

7. (Roger G. Hill). On page 66 a formula was given which indicated which positive integer n was assigned to each element a_{jk}. The following formulas assign an element a_{jk} to each positive integer n.

(a) For the first fifteen values of n compute j and k and indicate the correspondence.

$$r = -\left[\frac{3 - \sqrt{1 + 8n}}{2}\right]; \quad j = n - \frac{r(r + 1)}{2};$$

$$\text{and} \quad k = \frac{r^2 + 3r + 4}{2} - n;$$

where $[x]$ is the greatest integer $\leq x$.

*(b) Show how these formulas can be derived.

20. THE SET OF REAL NUMBERS

A few definitions are needed in order to introduce the set of real numbers which will provide many additional examples of infinite sets. We shall assume that the reader is familiar with the decimal representation of certain sets of numbers by means of positional notation involving the digits 0, 1, 2, 3, 4, 5, 6, 7, 8 and 9. A finite decimal is a finite sequence of digits with a decimal point, or the negative of such a sequence. The number 253.7624 is a positive finite decimal; the number 00.000 is a finite decimal representation of the number 0, which is neither positive nor negative; and the number -48.25413 is a negative finite decimal.

Definition. *A* **finite decimal** *is a number written in the form* $\pm c_1c_2c_3 \cdots c_k.a_1a_2a_3 \cdots a_j,$ *where each c, as well as each a, is one of the digits* 0, 1, 2, 3, 4, 5, 6, 7, 8, 9.

Not all numbers can be written as finite decimals. The decimal representation of $19/7$ is $2.714285714285714285 \cdots$ which continues to repeat the block of digits 714285. There are also nonrepeating decimals which are not finite, such as $\sqrt{2} = 1.41421 \cdots$, and the number $.101001000100001000001 \cdots$, where each pair of successive 1's is separated by one more zero than the preceding pair. Regardless of whether there is repetition, if the number can be written using an infinite number of a's it can be represented as an infinite decimal. Each finite decimal can be written as an infinite decimal merely by following the finite representation by an infinite number of zeros. Thus $253.7624 = 253.7624000 \cdots; 0 = 0.000 \cdots;$ and $-48.25413 = -48.25413000 \cdots.$

Definition. *An **infinite decimal** is a number written in the form* $\pm c_1 c_2 c_3 \cdots c_k . a_1 a_2 a_3 \cdots$, *where each* c, *as well as each* a, *is one of the digits* 0, 1, 2, 3, 4, 5, 6, 7, 8, 9.

For an infinite decimal to exist, some rule must be stated or understood by means of which the digit a_j can be determined for each positive integer j.

Definition. *A **real number** is a number that is equal to an infinite decimal.*

We shall frequently denote the set of real numbers by Q.

Definition. *A real number which is not a rational number is an **irrational number**.*

Some real numbers have two decimal representations. The number 2 can be written as 2.0000 $\cdots$ or as 1.9999 $\cdots$, and .125 can be written as .1250000 $\cdots$ or as .1249999 $\cdots$. In order to have a unique decimal representation for each real number, if a number has two representations, we shall discard the representation for which every digit to the right of a certain fixed digit is a zero, and retain the representation for which every digit to the right of a certain fixed digit is a nine. Since the number 0 does not have two representations it will be the only number used for which every digit to the right of a certain fixed digit is zero. It will be convenient to speak of a *terminal part* of a decimal representation. By this we shall mean that part of the representation to the right of a certain fixed digit in the representation. Thus we can say that the number .125 has two representations, .12500 $\cdots$, which has a terminal part consisting only of zeros and .12499 $\cdots$, which has a terminal part consisting only of nines. It is even more convenient to say that one decimal representation of .125 *terminates* in zeros and the other terminates in nines.

Given a straight line and a convenient unit of measure there will be points on this line corresponding to the integers $0, 1, -1, 2, -2, \cdots$. These points divide the line into unit intervals. By dividing each interval into ten equal parts, points can be obtained which correspond to other real numbers. Continued subdivisions will produce other points corresponding to real numbers. We shall *assume* that to each point on the line there corresponds a real number, and also that to each real number there corresponds a point on the line. *We shall further assume that this correspondence between the real numbers and the points on the line is a one-to-one correspondence which preserves order.* By this we mean that if a and b are real numbers corresponding to the points A and B on a straight line, and c is a real number such that $a < c < b$, then c corresponds to a point C between A and B. Because of this 1–1 correspondence we sometimes refer to a straight line, such as the x-axis, as *the real line.*

The reader should understand that the set of real numbers and the set of points on a line are two different sets and therefore they are not equal sets. Nevertheless, for convenience, when speaking of points on the x-axis, we shall often say "the point .783" instead of "the point corresponding to the real number .783".

Every rational number is a real number, for if p and q are integers and $q \neq 0$, the ordinary process of long division produces an infinite decimal for $p \div q$, which may or may not terminate in zeros. Let us consider some of the points on the x-axis which correspond to rational numbers. Let T represent the set of points between 0 and 1, inclusive. Draw a long line segment $A_2 B_2$ to represent this interval and indicate those points in the interval corresponding to numbers which can be written in the form $n/2$, where n is an integer. There are three such points: 0, 1/2, and 1; that is, the end points and the point obtained by bisecting the interval. If the resulting intervals are bisected, two additional points can be obtained; namely, those corresponding to 1/4 and 3/4. These numbers are of the form $n/2^2$. If the four resulting intervals are bisected the points 1/8, 3/8, 5/8 and 7/8 are obtained, and these numbers are of the form $n/2^3$. Repeated bisections will produce points in the interval corresponding to numbers of the form $n/2^k$, where n and k are integers. Since there is no limit to the number of times that the resulting intervals can be bisected it is evident that there is no finite number which will indicate the number of points in the interval that correspond to rational numbers having denominators which are powers of 2. Between every two points of the interval there are many points which correspond to numbers of the form $n/2^k$. Is this all of the rational numbers in the interval? Obviously not. Even though this process of bisecting will cut the interval into pieces as short as we choose to make them, there are still other points that correspond to rational numbers. We shall consider some more of them in the exercises.

EXERCISES

1. In setting up a 1–1 correspondence between the set L of points on a straight line and the set Q of real numbers, a convenient unit of measure was used.

   (*a*) Explain the effect on the correspondence of using a unit of measure twice as long as the original one.

   (*b*) Are there 1–1 correspondences between L and Q that are not order preserving? If so, produce one.

2. (*a*) By repeatedly trisecting the interval T from 0 to 1 obtain the points of the form $n/3^k$, where n and k are integers, and draw A_3B_3, a second representation of the segment T, parallel to the representation A_2B_2 and equal to it in length. On this segment indicate some of the points of trisection. If the second representation is superimposed on the first, which points of trisection will coincide with points of bisection?

   (*b*) Draw a segment A_5B_5 similar to A_3B_3 by making 5 divisions each time instead of 3. If A_3B_3 and A_5B_5 are both superimposed on A_2B_2 which points of subdivision will coincide?

   (*c*) If the segment A_pB_p is similarly obtained by using a prime integer p and the segments A_3B_3, A_5B_5, $\cdots$, A_pB_p, $\cdots$ are superimposed on A_2B_2 which points of subdivision will coincide?

   (*d*) If A_6B_6 is similarly obtained, the points of subdivision correspond to real numbers of the form $n/6^k$, where n and k are integers. After the jth subdivision, where $j = 1$, 2, and 3, how many of the points inside the interval correspond to numbers of the form $n/2^k$, $n/3^k$, or $n/5^k$?

3. (*a*) If the real number k is added to each of the rational numbers in the unit interval T from 0 to 1, in what interval H of the x-axis will the resulting numbers lie if k is the number 1? If

k is zero, or any positive or negative integer? If k is any real number?

(b) How does the length of H compare with the length of T?

(c) For what values of k will the resulting numbers be rational?

(d) Show that the resulting numbers are dense in H; that is, show that every subinterval, regardless of length, contains one of the resulting numbers.

*4. Set up a 1–1 correspondence between the set of positive integers and each of the following sets if such a correspondence exists.

(a) The rational numbers.

(b) All numbers of the form $3r + 5$, where r is a rational number.

(c) All pairs of integers the first of which is a fixed integer a.

(d) All pairs of integers.

(e) All triples of integers.

*5. (a) Set up a 1–1 correspondence between a finite line segment, excluding the end points, and the entire x-axis, if such a correspondence exists.

(b) Set up a 1–1 correspondence between a finite line segment, including the end points, and the entire x-axis, if such a correspondence exists.

21. EQUIVALENT SETS

In order to determine the number of elements in a given finite set H we count the elements. This process of counting sets up a 1–1 correspondence between H and the set $S_n = \{1, 2, 3, \cdots, n\}$ of the first n positive integers. We then say that H and S_n have the same number of elements in them, or that they *have the same finite cardinal number*. If n is the fifth positive integer we say that H has five elements in it, or that H has cardinal number five. Even without defining a cardinal number we can decide what is meant by saying that *two given sets have the same finite cardinal number*.

In like manner, we shall say that two infinite sets *have the same infinite cardinal number*, or *transfinite cardinal number*, if they can be put into 1–1 correspondence.

Definition. *Two sets are **equivalent** if they can be put into* 1–1 *correspondence.*

If A is equivalent to B we shall write $A \approx B$.

Definition. *Two sets **have the same cardinal number** if they are equivalent sets.*

We have shown that the set I of positive integers and the set E of even positive integers can be put into 1–1 correspondence; therefore, they are equivalent sets and have the same infinite cardinal number, even though E is a proper subset of I. Since no finite set can be put into 1–1 correspondence with a proper subset of itself, no finite set can have the same cardinal number as one of its proper subsets. Nevertheless, the preceding example shows that there is at least one infinite set which can be put into 1–1 correspondence with one of its proper subsets. Observe that there are proper subsets of I which cannot be put into 1–1 correspondence with I; namely, the finite subsets.

A symbol which is used to indicate a number is usually called a *numeral* to distinguish it from the number itself. Thus we take mental note of the fact that an object is different from the symbol which represents, or names, that object. For example, a person and his name are two different things. The set X consisting of the elements John, James, Jack and Joe is a set of four people and should not be confused with the set consisting of the four names "John", "James", "Jack" and "Joe".

Different symbols, such as the Arabic numeral 5, the Roman numeral V, the word "five", the word that means five in some other language, or even an arbitrarily chosen symbol, can be used to represent the number five, which we have not defined, even though we have a rule for determining when the cardinal number of elements in a set is five.

We now ask what symbol should be used to indicate the cardinal number of I, the set of all positive integers. Though the cardinal number of every finite set is an integer, a bit of reflection will show that no integer can be the cardinal number of an infinite set, for the infinite sets were defined to be those sets which cannot be put into 1–1 correspondence with $S_n = \{1, 2, 3, \cdots, n\}$, regardless of which positive integer n represents. Cantor, the German mathematician who developed much of the theory of infinite sets, used the Hebrew letter aleph with a zero subscript, written $\aleph_0$, and read "Aleph-null", to represent the cardinal number of the set I of positive integers. Thus, if we are asked how many positive integers there are, the correct answer is $\aleph_0$. Since the set E of even integers has the same cardinal number as the set of positive integers, its cardinal number is also $\aleph_0$. What is the cardinal number of the set of odd integers?

It is advisable to refrain from using the word "more" in connection with infinite sets in order to avoid ambiguity of meaning. When asked if the set I of positive integers has more elements than the set E of even positive integers, we may be inclined to interpret "more" as meaning that there are elements in I which are not in E; that is, that E is a proper subset of I. If so, we may give an affirmative answer. On the other hand, since E and I are equivalent sets they have the same cardinal number. Since the cardinal number of a set is a measure of the "size" of the set we may argue that the two sets under consideration have the same number of elements, therefore I does not contain more elements than E. Confusion will be avoided if we refrain from using the word "more" and merely say that even though E is a proper subset of I, these two sets have the same cardinal number.

How many points are there on the x-axis in the interval from 0 to 1? Since there is a 1–1 correspondence between this set of points and a subset of the real numbers we can state this question in the following way. What is the cardinal number of the set

$$T = \{x \mid 0 \le x \le 1 \text{ and } x \text{ is a real number}\}?$$

Is T equivalent to the set I of positive integers? If so, it is countably infinite. We conjecture that T is not a countably infinite set.

Statement 12.   *The set* $T = \{x \mid x \text{ is real and } 0 \le x \le 1\}$ *is not a countably infinite set.*

Discussion.   Let us use an indirect argument. We assume that there is a one-to-one correspondence between the set I of positive integers and the set T. Each element of T, including 0 and 1, can be represented in the form $.a_1 a_2 a_3 \cdots$, and we have agreed to use the decimal representation terminating in nines if two representations exist. We shall let the element of T that corresponds to the integer 1 be represented by $.a_{11}a_{12}a_{13} \cdots$, the first subscript indicating that this number corresponds to 1. Similarly, the element of T that corresponds to 2 will be $.a_{21}a_{22}a_{23} \cdots$, and so on. This produces the following array of numbers.

$$1 \leftrightarrow .a_{11}a_{12}a_{13} \cdots$$
$$2 \leftrightarrow .a_{21}a_{22}a_{23} \cdots$$
$$3 \leftrightarrow .a_{31}a_{32}a_{33} \cdots$$
$$\cdot \qquad \cdot \cdot \cdot \cdot \cdot \cdot$$
$$\cdot \qquad \cdot \cdot \cdot \cdot \cdot \cdot$$
$$\cdot \qquad \cdot \cdot \cdot \cdot \cdot \cdot$$
$$n \leftrightarrow .a_{n1}a_{n2}a_{n3} \cdots$$
$$\cdot \qquad \cdot \cdot \cdot \cdot \cdot \cdot$$
$$\cdot \qquad \cdot \cdot \cdot \cdot \cdot \cdot$$

Now we show that there is a number $y = .b_1b_2b_3 \cdots$ in T which does not appear in this array, and therefore this number does not correspond to any positive integer. We consider the digit a_{11}. If $a_{11} \neq 3$ we choose $b_1 = 3$, and if $a_{11} = 3$ we choose $b_1 = 7$. If $a_{22} \neq 3$ we choose $b_2 = 3$, and if $a_{22} = 3$ we choose $b_2 = 7$. In general, if any diagonal element $a_{jj} \neq 3$ we choose $b_j = 3$, and if $a_{jj} = 3$ we choose $b_j = 7$. The number $y = .b_1b_2b_3 \cdots$ lies between 0 and 1; therefore it is in T. It is not the first number in the array because it does not have the same first digit. It is not the second number because it does not have the same second digit, and, in general, it is not the jth number because it does not have the same jth digit. Therefore, y is in T but it does not correspond to any positive integer. Thus the correspondence is not 1–1. What we assumed was a 1–1 correspondence between I and T is a correspondence between I and a proper subset of T. Therefore no 1–1 correspondence exists between I and T, and T is not a countably infinite set. ∎

Remarks. It is not essential that the digits 3 and 7 be used in this discussion. They can be replaced by any other pair of unequal digits, except that 0 should not be used. The digit 0 should be excluded because it may lead to a second representation of a number in the array, and thus fail to produce a number outside of the array. The fact that other pairs of digits can be used shows that many numbers are missing from this array.

Since T is not a countably infinite set its cardinal number cannot be $\aleph_0$. Some mathematicians use the symbol $\aleph_1$ to represent the cardinal number of T. We shall use a capital C to suggest the word "continuum", a word which, in nontechnical language, means that there are no holes in a straight line or in a line segment. Any two line segments, regardless of length, can be put into 1–1 correspondence, therefore the cardinal number of every line segment is C. In question 5 of the preceding exercises the reader was asked to set up a 1–1 correspondence between a finite line segment and the entire x-axis. Such a correspondence exists; therefore the cardinal number of the x-axis is C and the cardinal number of the set of real numbers is C.

It can be shown that the set of points in a plane can be put into 1–1 correspondence with the set of points on the x-axis. As a first step toward establishing this correspondence let us show that a unit square plus its interior is equivalent to a line segment. The remaining steps will be left as exercises for the reader.

First recall that when a real number has two decimal representations we have agreed to use only the representation terminating in nines. Therefore the representation of 0 is the only representation that we shall use which terminates in zeros.

We shall start with the unit interval MN of a p-axis and the square $ABCD$ which, for convenience, is placed one unit above the segment MN. Thus $0 \le p \le 1$ on MN and $0 \le x \le 1$, $0 \le y \le 1$ for the square. Any number for which $0 < p \le 1$ can be represented decimally as $.a_1 a_2 a_3 \cdots$. For example, consider a specific point $p = .210700345020 \cdots$ on the line MN. Separate the digits of this number into groups as follows: $2/1/07/003/4/5/02/ \cdots$ the rule being that the nonzero digits are grouped individually, and zeros can occur only at the beginning of a group. However, no group can consist entirely of zeros. A set of one or more consecutive zeros must be grouped with the first nonzero digit which follows them. We now assign alternate groups to x starting with the first group, and alternate groups to y starting with the second one. Thus $x = .207402 \cdots$ and $y = .10035 \cdots$. The point q having coordinates $(.207402 \cdots,$ $.10035 \cdots)$ is a point inside the square. If q is given, reverse this process to obtain p. Thus to each point p, where $0 < p \le 1$, there corresponds one and only one point q with coordinates (x, y) such that $0 < x \le 1$ and $0 < y \le 1$, and to each point q satisfying these restrictions there corresponds one and only one point p. To see why we do not use a simple alternation of digits, including zeros, notice that

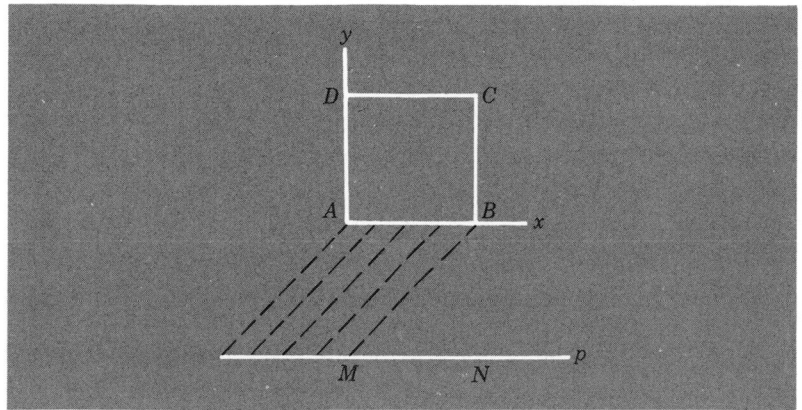

FIG. 32

such a procedure would make both .51010101 $\cdots$ and .4191919 $\cdots$ correspond to the same point (.5000 $\cdots$, .1111 $\cdots$) or (.4999 $\cdots$, .1111 $\cdots$).

Observe that a point on CD such as (.10803450 $\cdots$, .999 $\cdots$) corresponds to the point .19089039495 $\cdots$ and a point on BC such as (.9999 $\cdots$, .700680 $\cdots$) corresponds to the point .979006989 $\cdots$. Since the rule cannot be applied to the point zero on MN nor to the points on AB and AD which have one zero coordinate, it is necessary to find some other way to set up a correspondence for these points. First, observe that the rule sets up a 1–1 correspondence between MN, except for the left endpoint, and the square plus its interior, except for the sides AB and AD. The reader should convince himself that this assertion is true. The point C corresponds to the point N. By drawing lines parallel to BM the line segment AB can be put into 1–1 correspondence with the points p such that $-1 \le p \le 0$. By drawing lines parallel to AN the segment AD, except for the endpoint A, can be put into 1–1 correspondence with the points p such that $1 < p \le 2$. Therefore the square plus its interior can be put into 1–1 correspondence with a segment three units long and this portion of the plane has cardinal number C.

For additional information about cardinal numbers see Section 31.

EXERCISES

1. (*a*) Explain the difference between equivalent sets and equal sets.

(*b*) If sets are equal are they necessarily equivalent?

(*c*) If sets are equivalent are they necessarily equal?

*2. Show that the interior of a square is equivalent to the entire xy-plane.

*3. Show that a square plus its interior is equivalent to the entire xy-plane.

*4. Show that a cube plus its interior is equivalent to a line segment.

22. DUALITY

In certain branches of mathematics new theorems are obtained by interchanging certain words or phrases in established theorems. Let us consider some of the statements which we have already discussed in detail and therefore have reason to believe are generally true for sets. We shall list these statements on the left and shall list on the right the statements that we get from them by interchanging $\cup$ and $\cap$, $\supset$ and $\subset$, $\supseteq$ and $\subseteq$, and U and $\varnothing$.

(1) $A \subseteq A$.	(1*a*) $A \supseteq A$.
(2) If $A \subseteq B$ and $B \subseteq C$, then $A \subseteq C$.	(2*a*) If $A \supseteq B$ and $B \supseteq C$, then $A \supseteq C$.
(3) $A \cap B \subseteq A$.	(3*a*) $A \cup B \supseteq A$.
(4) If $A = B$, then $A' = B'$.	(4*a*) If $A = B$, then $A' = B'$.
(5) If $A \subseteq B$, then $B' \subseteq A'$.	(5*a*) If $A \supseteq B$, then $B' \supseteq A'$.
(6) If $A \subset B$, then $B' \subset A'$.	(6*a*) If $A \supset B$, then $B' \supset A'$.
(7) $A \cap (B \cap C) = (A \cap B) \cap C$.	(7*a*) $A \cup (B \cup C) = (A \cup B) \cup C$.
(8) $A \cap (B \cup C) = (A \cap B) \cup (A \cap C)$.	(8*a*) $A \cup (B \cap C) = (A \cup B) \cap (A \cup C)$.
(9) $(A \cup B)' = A' \cap B'$.	(9*a*) $(A \cap B)' = A' \cup B'$.

We now observe that (1) and (1a) are the same statement, and since $X \supseteq Y$ is equivalent to $Y \subseteq X$, (2) and (2a) are the same. Similarly, (4), (5), and (6) remain the same after these interchanges. On the other hand, these interchanges have produced new statements from (3), (7), (8), and (9). Are these statements true? They are true and the reader has been asked to establish their validity in some of the preceding exercises.

We next ask whether such interchanges made in a true statement about sets will always produce a true statement. The following principle of duality for sets is a statement which gives an affirmative answer to this question. We shall accept it without proof.

The Principle of Duality for Sets. *If a statement involving sets is true then the statement obtained from it by interchanging $\cup$ and $\cap$, $\supset$ and $\subset$, $\supseteq$ and $\subseteq$, and U and $\varnothing$ is also a true statement.*

Not only is it possible to convert established set statements into new set statements by means of the Principle of Duality but the proof used to establish the original statement can be transformed into the proof of the new statement by means of the same interchanges. Since the proofs are also dual the usual procedure is to establish a set statement and accept its dual as true without additional argument. Therefore, the Principle of Duality greatly reduces the number of proofs. In addition to producing new statements and reducing the number of proofs it assists us in remembering long lists of true statements about sets.

Statements like (1), (2), (5), and (6) are called self-dual statements, since the dual statement is the same as the original statement.

23. RUSSELL'S PARADOX

Our approach to set theory has been more or less intuitive thus far, but there are certain dangers in relying too much on intuition in answering some questions concerning sets.

Given a certain property, such as having four legs, does there exist a set of all objects having four legs? We are inclined to answer "yes" to this question. Should we go so far as to accept the following statement?

(1)   Given a property there exists a set whose elements are just those things that have this property.

Can a set be an element of itself? Does the set of all abstract ideas exist, and if it exists, is this set an abstract idea? Does the set of all concepts exist? If it exists is it a concept? Is the set of all cats a cat? The answer to the last question is obviously "No", but what can be said about the others? Does the set of all sets exist? Is it an element of itself?

Mathematicians, and perhaps some logicians, first assumed that a given property did define a set of those objects, and only those, having this property. Furthermore they assumed that some sets could be elements of themselves while others could not. They called those sets which were not elements of themselves *ordinary sets*. Using these assumptions the question arose as to how the set Z of all ordinary sets should be classified. Should it be considered an ordinary set or not an ordinary set? Let us assume for the moment that Z is an ordinary set, then since Z is the set of all ordinary sets it must be an element of itself. But if it is an element of itself then it is not an ordinary set. Therefore assuming that it is an ordinary set leads to the conclusion that it is not an ordinary set, and we have reached a contradiction.

If, on the other hand, we start the argument from the other direction and assume that Z, the set of all ordinary sets, is not itself ordinary, then it does not belong in the set of all ordinary sets, and therefore Z is not an element of Z. But if Z is not an element of itself it is by definition an ordinary set. Therefore assuming that it is not ordinary leads to the conclusion that it is ordinary and again a contradiction is reached. This paradox* is known as Russell's Paradox, for it was proposed by the famous mathematician Bertrand Russell in 1902. It shows that some of the basic assumptions are at fault. We cannot assume statement (1) as it stands. We must work within a set that we know exists. For this reason mathematicians have confined each

---

* Further information concerning Russell's Paradox can be found in Eves and Newsom, *An Introduction to the Foundations and Fundamental Concepts of Mathematics* (New York, Holt, Rinehart, and Winston, 1958), pp. 281–285; and Patrick Suppes, *Axiomatic Set Theory* (Princeton, N. J., Van Nostrand, 1960), pp. 5–8.

of their discussions to some universal set or a universe of discourse. Within this framework all goes well. Statement (1) has to be rephrased as follows:

Axiom. *Given a set A and a property p, then there exists a set S which has as its elements exactly those elements of A that have property p.*

Knowing that the set of all elephants in the world exists we can safely say that the set of all elephants weighing two tons exists.

Many versions of Russell's Paradox have been given. One of the most popular, also attributed to Russell, is the story of the barber whose superior ordered him to shave those men, and only those, who did not shave themselves. Could he obey orders by shaving himself? Could he obey orders by not shaving himself?

EXERCISES

1. Find the dual of each of the following statements.

(a) $A \cup A' = U$.

(b) $A \cap (B \cup A)' = \varnothing$.

(c) $(A' \cap B) \cup (B' \cup A) = U$.

(d) If $A = C$ and $B = C$, then $A \cap B = C$.

(e) $(A \cap B') \cap (A \cup B) = A \cap B'$.

(f) $(A \cap B')' \cup B = A' \cup B$.

(g) If $A \supseteq B$, then $A \cup B = A$ and $A \cap B = B$.

2. Replace each step of the discussion of Statement 7, p. 31, by its dual statement and verify that the resulting discussion establishes the truth of the dual of Statement 7. (Each "and" in the definitions must be changed to an "or".)

24. OPERATIONS

In Section 9, the operations of intersection, union, and complementation were introduced. These operations are usually referred to as set operations since the objects involved are sets. There are many other types of operations, some of which involve the elements of the sets rather than the sets themselves. In this section we shall discuss more general types of operations, along with some of their classifications and properties.

Operations are frequently classified according to the number of objects involved. The basic definitions of the four fundamental operations of arithmetic; namely, addition, subtraction, multiplication and division, are given in terms of two objects; that is, we tell how to add, subtract, multiply, or divide two objects in a given order. Since *two* objects are involved, these four fundamental operations are referred to as *binary* operations. In this section we shall not confine ourselves to operations on two objects but shall consider also operations on any finite number of objects starting with one.

In Section 15, an ordered pair was defined. Recall that an unordered pair is merely a set of two objects, while an ordered pair is two objects arranged so that one object is designated as the first object and the other as the second object. The reader can probably anticipate the definition of an ordered triple, quadruple, or quintuple. We can save time by defining an ordered set of n objects, usually referred to as an n-tuple.

Definition. *An* **n-tuple,** *or an* **ordered set of n objects,** *is a set of n objects arranged in a specific order so that there is a first object, a second object, $\cdots$, and an nth object.*

An n-tuple can be denoted by the symbol $(a_1, a_2, a_3, \cdots, a_n)$. Every 1–1 correspondence between a set of n objects and the set consisting of the first n integers produces an n-tuple, it being understood that the kth object is the object corresponding to the integer k.

Example **1.** The 3-tuple, or ordered triple, $(2, 3, -1)$ is different from the ordered triple $(-1, 3, 2)$ and from each of the other four orderings of the elements in the set $\{2, 3, -1\}$.

Example **2.** The 4-tuple, or ordered quadruple, $(1, 5, -2, 7)$ is different from each of the other twenty-three arrangements of the elements in the set $\{1, 5, -2, 7\}$.

Definition. *A* **unary operation** *is a correspondence which assigns to each individual element in a set D exactly one element of a set S. The element of S which is assigned to an element x of D is the* **image** *of x under* *the operation.* For a unary operation the set D is the ***domain*** of the operation and the set R, of all images, is the ***range*** of the operation.

***Example* 3.** The operation of taking the principal square root of an integer which is a square is a unary operation. Thus $\sqrt{9} = 3$. Here $D = \{0, 1, 4, 9, 16, 25, \cdots\}$ and $R = \{0, 1, 2, 3, 4, 5, \cdots\}$. The set S can be any superset of R, such as the set of all integers J, or the set of all nonnegative integers.

***Example* 4.** Set complementation is a unary operation which assigns to each subset A of a given universe U its complementary set A'. Here D is the set of all subsets of U, known as the power set of U, and R is the same set.

Definition. *A **binary operation** is a correspondence which assigns to each ordered pair of objects in a set D exactly one element of a set S.*

***Example* 5.** The operation of addition which is indicated by $+$ assigns the number 8 to the ordered pair of integers $(1, 7)$, since $1 + 7 = 8$. Thus addition is a binary operation on the integers.

Observe that the ordered pairs of integers are elements of $J \times J$ and the example just given could be considered as a unary operation on $J \times J$ instead of a binary operation on J. Then the domain is $J \times J$ and the range is J.

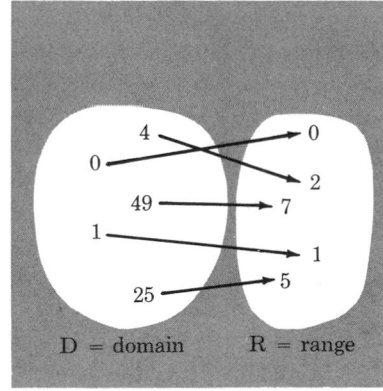 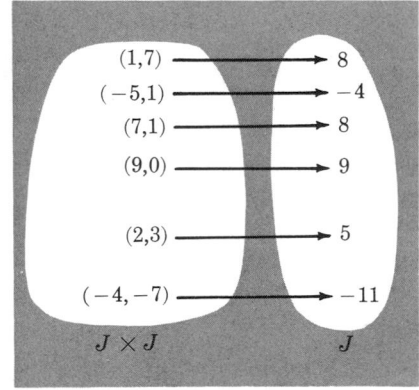

FIG. 33   FIG. 34

Example 6.   The operation of division assigns to the ordered pair (3, 4) the number 3/4, since $3 \div 4 = 3/4$. Observe that division assigns to the ordered pair (4, 3) a different number 4/3, since $4 \div 3 = 4/3$. If all pairs of integers (a, b) are used except those for which $b = 0$, then the operation produces all rational numbers.

Example 7.   The operation $\cup$ applied to the ordered pair of sets (A, B) produces $A \cup B$. If P represents the power set of the universal set U, then the subsets are elements of P. This operation assigns an element of the power set to an ordered pair of elements of the power set.

Example 8.   The operation "$-$" as applied to sets A and B gives $A - B$, which is the set of all elements that are in A but not in B, since, by definition, $A - B = A \cap B'$. This operation also assigns an element of the power set to an ordered pair of elements of the power set.

The definitions of ternary and quaternary operations can be obtained by replacing "ordered pair" in the definition of a binary operation by the words "ordered triple" and "ordered quadruple", respectively. In general, we can define an n-ary operation.

Definition.   *An* **n-ary operation** *is a correspondence which assigns to each n-tuple of objects from a set D exactly one element of a set S.*

Example 9.   The process which assigns to the triple of vertices (P_1, P_2, P_3) the area of the triangle with these vertices is a ternary operation.

Example 10.   Let S, T, W, and Z represent four points in space. The process of finding the average temperature at these four points is a quaternary operation.

Example 11.   For a fixed integer n, the process of finding the perimeter of an n-sided polygon is an n-ary operation.

Mathematicians find it very useful to indicate an n-ary operation by $T(a_1, a_2, a_3, \cdots, a_n)$. Thus when the operation is addition $T(x, y) = x + y$ and $T(3, -2) = 1$. When the operation is division $T(x, y) = x/y$ and $T(5, 7) = 5/7$. When the operation is set union then $T(A, B) = A \cup B$. If E is the set of even integers and J is the set of integers, then $T(E, J) = E \cup J = J$. The operation $T(x, y, z) = 2x - y + z$ makes the triple $(1, -1, 0)$ correspond to 3, the triple

$(0, 1, -1)$ correspond to -2, and the triple $(-1, 0, 1)$ correspond to -1. Thus $T(1, -1, 0) = 3$, $T(0, 1, -1) = -2$, and $T(-1, 0, 1) = -1$, when $T(x, y, z) = 2x - y + z$.

It is frequently convenient to indicate a binary operation by "$\circ$". Then $a \circ b$, which is read by pronouncing the letters "a", "$\circ$", "b", indicates the element obtained when the operation is applied to the ordered pair (a, b). Thus when the operation is addition, $a \circ b = a + b$, and when the operation is taking the average, $a \circ b = (a + b)/2$. Specifically, $3 \circ 7$ represents 10 if the operation is addition; -4, if the operation is subtraction; 21, if the operation is multiplication; and $3/7$, if the operation is division. If $a \circ b = 3a - b$, then this operation multiplies the first element of the ordered pair by three and subtracts the second element from the resulting product. Under this operation $3 \circ 7 = 2$. The accompanying chart shows how the value of $3 \circ 7$ depends upon the operation $\circ$.

$\circ$	$3 \circ 7$
$+$	10
$-$	-4
$\times$	21
$\div$	$3/7$

We now consider some properties of operations.

Closure. Let I represent the set of positive integers. If $a \in I$ and $b \in I$, for which of the four fundamental operations of arithmetic is $a \circ b \in I$? Is the sum of two positive integers a positive integer? Experience tells us that it is, and we describe this fact by saying that *the set of positive integers is closed with respect to addition.* Is $a \circ b \in I$ if the operation is subtraction? Not necessarily, for $3 - 5 = -2$ is not a positive integer. Therefore I is not closed with respect to subtraction. Similarly, the reader will observe that I is closed with respect to multiplication but not with respect to division, for $2 \div 3 = 2/3 \notin I$.

If S consists of all of the points inside a certain square and $T(P_1, P_2, P_3) = P$ represents the point P equidistant from three non-collinear points P_1, P_2, and P_3 in S, we can ask whether or not S is closed with respect to this ternary operation T. This question rephrased asks whether the circumcenter of every triangle with vertices in the square lies inside the square. The answer is negative. Use a sketch to verify this answer.

Definition. *The set S is **closed** with respect to an n-ary operation T if $T(a_1, a_2, a_3, \cdots, a_n)$ is in S, whenever $a_1, a_2, \cdots, a_n$ are in S.*

The set of all subsets of a given set is closed with respect to set union, for the union of two subsets is also a subset.

Commutative Law.   Certain properties of binary operations are frequently used. We may observe that the order of adding two numbers does not affect their sum, but the order of subtracting them does affect the difference. Therefore, for some operations it is always true that $a \circ b = b \circ a$. These operations are commutative operations. For other operations there are at least two elements in the given set for which $a \circ b \neq b \circ a$, and these operations are noncommutative. The addition of numbers is commutative while subtraction is not, for $2 - 5 \neq 5 - 2$.

Definition. *A binary operation $\circ$ defined on a set S is **commutative** if $a \circ b = b \circ a$, whenever a and b are in S.*

Set union is commutative since $A \cup B = B \cup A$, but relative complementation is noncommutative for $A - B \neq B - A$, in general.

Associative Law.   We also observe that grouping does not affect the sum of three numbers, for $(a + b) + c = a + (b + c)$. That is, we may add a and b to obtain a sum and then add this sum to c. The final result will be the same as that obtained by adding a to the sum of b and c. Since this is true for every triple of numbers we say that addition is an associative operation. For a general operation $\circ$ the associative law states that $(a \circ b) \circ c = a \circ (b \circ c)$. Let us consider the operation of subtraction. We do this by replacing every operation symbol by the subtraction symbol. Is it true that $(a - b) - c = a - (b - c)$ for all choices of a, b, and c? A specific example will show that it is not, for $(5 - 3) - 2 = 0$, but $5 - (3 - 2) = 4$. Therefore, subtraction is not an associative operation.

Definition. *A binary operation defined on a set S is* **associative** *if* $(a \circ b) \circ c = a \circ (b \circ c)$, *whenever a, b, and c are in S.*

Set intersection is associative since $(A \cap B) \cap C = A \cap (B \cap C)$.

Distributive Law. One of the fundamental laws of arithmetic is the distributive law of multiplication with respect to addition which states that $a(b + c) = ab + ac$, for all numbers a, b, and c used in arithmetic. This law holds, not only for the positive real numbers used in arithmetic, but also for all rational numbers, real numbers, and complex numbers. The reader, no doubt, is familiar with the fact that this law provides us with two methods of computation from which we can select the simpler one. For example, $21(\frac{1}{7} + \frac{1}{3}) = 21(\frac{1}{7}) + 21(\frac{1}{3}) = 3 + 7 = 10$, is more easily computed by using the right side of the law. On the other hand $(89)(23) + (89)(27) = 89(23 + 27) = 89(50) = 4450$ is more readily computed by factoring out the common number, thus using the left side of the law for the computation.

We can generalize this distributive law by asking whether or not two operations $\circ$ and $\ominus$ defined on a set S will satisfy some type of distributive law. Since the operations may not be commutative there are four possibilities:

$$a \ominus (b \circ c) \overset{?}{=} (a \ominus b) \circ (a \ominus c),$$
$$(b \circ c) \ominus a \overset{?}{=} (b \ominus a) \circ (c \ominus a),$$
$$a \circ (b \ominus c) \overset{?}{=} (a \circ b) \ominus (a \circ c),$$
$$(b \ominus c) \circ a \overset{?}{=} (b \circ a) \ominus (c \circ a).$$

Let us replace the operations $\circ$ and $\ominus$ by addition and multiplication, respectively. This produces:

$$a(b + c) \overset{?}{=} ab + ac,$$
$$(b + c)a \overset{?}{=} ba + ca,$$
$$a + bc \overset{?}{=} (a + b)(a + c),$$
$$bc + a \overset{?}{=} (b + a)(c + a).$$

In a set where multiplication is commutative, such as the set of rational numbers, $a(b + c) = (b + c)a$, $ab = ba$, and $ac = ca$; therefore, for such a set the first two statements amount to the same statement; namely, $a(b + c) = ab + ac$. This statement we recognize as the distributive law of multiplication with respect to addition which we have discussed. The rational numbers are also a commutative set with respect to addition. Thus for this set $a + bc = bc + a$, $a + b = b + a$, and $a + c = c + a$. Therefore, for the set of rational numbers, the last two statements amount to the same statement; namely, $a + bc \overset{?}{=} (a + b)(a + c)$. This statement does not appear to be true. Let us give specific values to a, b, and c to show that it is not true. When we use the numbers 5, 2, and 3, we obtain $5 + (2)(3) = 11$, but $(5 + 2)(5 + 3) = 56$. This shows that for the numbers with which we are accustomed to working there is no distributive law of addition with respect to multiplication. Multiplication distributes through addition, but addition does not distribute through multiplication.

Definition. *Given two binary operations* $\circ$ *and* $\ominus$ *defined on the set S, the operation* $\circ$ *is* **left distributive with respect to the operation** $\circ$ *if*

$$a \circ (b \circ c) = (a \ominus b) \circ (a \ominus c);$$

and it is **right distributive with respect to the operation** $\circ$ *if*

$$(b \circ c) \ominus a = (b \ominus a) \circ (c \ominus a),$$

whenever a, b, and c are in S.

It should be observed that there are two distributive laws for sets; namely,

$$A \cup (B \cap C) = (A \cup B) \cap (A \cup C)$$

and $$A \cap (B \cup C) = (A \cap B) \cup (A \cap C).$$

We see then that set union distributes through intersection and set intersection distributes through union.

25. ALGEBRAS OF SETS

Various applications of set theory do not involve all of the subsets of a given set. Rephrased this means that only certain elements of the power set are considered. For example, some administrator may be interested in obtaining information about German and French classes in a certain university. If E is the set of all students enrolled, G is the set of those taking German and F is the set of those taking French, it is not unlikely that certain other sets, such as $G' =$ those not taking German, $F' =$ those not taking French, $G \cup F =$ those taking German or French, and $G \cap F =$ those taking both German and French, will be needed also. It is frequently convenient to require that the set of subsets under consideration be closed with respect to set union, intersection, and complementation. If these closure requirements are satisfied, the set of subsets is called *an algebra of sets*. In the specific example at hand, if H designates the algebra of sets, then

$$H = \{G, G', F, F', G \cup F, G \cap F, G' \cap F, G \cap F', G' \cup F, G \cup F',$$
$$G' \cup F', G' \cap F', E, \varnothing\}.$$

The reader should consider various expressions obtained from union, intersection, and complementation, such as $G \cap (G \cup F) = G$, $G' \cap (G \cup F) = (G' \cap G) \cup (G' \cap F) = G' \cap F$, and $G' \cup (G \cup F) = E$ in order to verify that H has closure with respect to the three named operations.

Definition. *A subset H of the power set of a given set U is an* **algebra of sets** *if H is closed with respect to the operations of union, intersection and complementation.*

Is there an algebra of sets containing only two elements? The reader has observed that the union of a set and its complementary set is the universal set and their intersection is the null set. Therefore, every algebra of sets must contain the universal set and the null set. If the algebra of sets is to contain only two elements then it must be the set consisting of the null set and the universal set. Is this set of two elements closed with respect to union, intersection, and complementation? One can readily verify that it is and therefore $H = \{\varnothing, U\}$ is the desired algebra of sets.

In the preceding definition it would have been sufficient to require closure with respect to set union and complementation. For if A and B are elements of the algebra then so are A', B', $A' \cup B'$, and $(A' \cup B')' = A \cap B$.

26. SUCCESSOR SETS

Given a set it is always possible to build up a set having just one more element than the given set. For example, if $A = \{r, s\}$, then the set $B = \{r, s, A\}$ can be formed. Set A has two elements but set B has three elements; namely, r, s, and the set $\{r, s\} = A$. Set $C = \{r, s, A, B\}$ is a set of four elements. Observe that C could be written in the more complicated form $C = \{r, s, \{r, s\}, \{r, s, \{r, s\}\}\}$. Also observe that $B = A \cup \{A\}$ and $C = B \cup \{B\}$.

The set $A \cup \{A\}$ is called the successor set of A and is frequently denoted by A^+.

Definition. *The successor set of the set A is* $A^+ = A \cup \{A\}$.

It is interesting to start with $\varnothing$, the empty set, and build up sets from it. Then $\varnothing^+ = \varnothing \cup \{\varnothing\} = \{\varnothing\}$ is a set of one element, $\{\varnothing\}^+ = \{\varnothing, \{\varnothing\}\}$ is a set of two elements, and so on. A 1–1 correspondence can be set up between the set of nonnegative integers $\{0, 1, 2, 3, 4, \cdots\}$ and the set consisting of the null set and the successor sets formed by starting with the null set. In the following correspondence the nonnegative integer corresponding to the set indicates the number of objects in the set.

0	1	2	3	. . .
$\updownarrow$	$\updownarrow$	$\updownarrow$	$\updownarrow$	
$\varnothing$	$\{\varnothing\}$	$\{\varnothing, \{\varnothing\}\}$	$\{\varnothing, \{\varnothing\}, \{\varnothing, \{\varnothing\}\}\}$	. . .

EXERCISES

1. With respect to which of the following operations is the power set of a given set S closed?

    (*a*) Complementation in S.   (*c*) Set intersection.

    (*b*) Set union.   (*d*) Relative complementation.

2. Which of the following sets are closed with respect to all four of the fundamental operations of arithmetic? Give counter examples to indicate nonclosure.

    (*a*) $\{1, 3, 5, 7, \cdots\}$.   (*c*) The rational numbers.

    (*b*) $\{1, 2, 3, 4, 5\}$.   (*d*) The integers.

3. Indicate several binary operations which are noncommutative.

4. Indicate several binary operations which are nonassociative.

5. Let U be a universal set and $\varnothing \subset F \subset U$. Find the smallest algebra of sets containing F.

6. Let $U = \{a, b, c, d\}$. Find the smallest algebra of sets containing the sets $\{d\}$ and $\{c, d\}$.

7. (a) Give five examples of operations and classify them as unary, binary, ternary, or n-ary for a specific n.

   (b) Does a unary operation necessarily set up a 1–1 correspondence between some pair of sets? Why?

27. MODERN MATHEMATICAL REASONING

The term "modern mathematics" usually refers to the mathematics of the nineteenth and twentieth centuries.

When, in 1830, Lobachevsky (1793–1856), a Russian, and J. Bolyai (1802–1860), a Hungarian, presented their non-Euclidean geometries to the scientific world, mathematicians began to realize that a valid mathematical argument need not be based on so-called "true-to-life" statements; that is, need not agree with our interpretation of the world around us. This realization liberated mathematics from the domination of "self-evident truths" and allowed it to grow as an abstract creation of the human mind.

The axiomatic or postulational approach which is the accepted type of mathematical reasoning today was passed down to us in Euclid's "Elements", written about 300 B.C. Undoubtedly this ancient Greek geometer's greatest contribution to mathematics was his idea of a postulational approach, which showed how to draw conclusions from given assumptions. Judged by modern day standards Euclid's works were not perfect, but they embodied the basic idea on which later mathematicians have built a solid structure. Probably no other work has had a greater influence on scientific thought.

The renaissance of Greek culture followed by the tremendous development of mathematical ideas in the seventeenth and eighteenth centuries revived the question of Euclid's fifth postulate, which had been a subject of controversy as far back as Proclus (A.D. 410–485).

The question was whether Euclid's parallel postulate could be proved from the other postulates or whether it was independent of them. Euclid's parallel postulate is equivalent to the following statement: Through a given point not on a line there is one and only one line parallel to the given line.

During the eighteenth and nineteenth centuries, a host of mathematicians of many countries made great contributions to mathematical knowledge. Many of them advanced our understanding of the nature of proof. Euclid's assumptions—usually referred to as axioms or postulates—were the subject of much discussion during the seventeenth, eighteenth, and nineteenth centuries. Likewise the assumptions, definitions, and proofs of other mathematicians, such as those used in the new magnificent tool, the calculus, came under close scrutiny.

Mathematicians began to see the true nature of mathematical reasoning. They observed that it is necessary to use undefined terms. The non-Euclidean geometries* had shown them that the basic assumptions need not "fit" the world around them. They had learned from Euclidean geometry† that it is very easy to make the error of using, in a proof, statements which were never stated explicitly as assumptions and which had never been proved from the given assumptions.

The type of mathematical reasoning which the modern mathematician considers acceptable consists of four parts: (1) *undefined*

---

* Non-Euclidean geometries were produced by Lobachevsky, Bolyai, Gauss, and Riemann. Gauss never published his work on this subject. Bolyai and Lobachevsky replaced Euclid's fifth postulate by one which assumed *more* than one parallel to the given line through a point not on the line, and in 1854, Riemann produced his second type of non-Euclidean geometry by assuming that there is *no* line parallel to the given line. Riemann was the originator of a whole class of non-Euclidean geometries. For further information see Richardson, *Fundamentals of Mathematics*, rev. ed. (New York, Macmillan, 1958), Chapter XVI; Eves and Newsom, *Foundations and Fundamental Concepts of Mathematics* (New York, Holt, Rinehart, and Winston, 1958), Chapter 3; Courant & Robbins, *What is Mathematics?* (New York, Oxford University Press, Inc., 1941), pp. 218–227; Kasner & Newman, *Mathematics and the Imagination* (New York, Simon and Schuster, Inc., 1940), Chapter IV.

† For information on the shortcomings of Euclidean geometry see Eves and Newsom, *op. cit.* pp. 37–41; Allendoerfer, "Deductive Methods in Mathematics," *Twenty-Third Yearbook, NCTM*, pp. 94–97.

terms, (2) *definitions*, (3) *axioms*, and (4) *theorems*. The definitions must be stated by combining the undefined terms with simple English; the axioms must be stated in terms of the undefined terms and the definitions; and each theorem, or conclusion, must be obtained logically from the definitions, the axioms, and the theorems previously proved from the definitions and axioms. This type of approach is referred to as the *axiomatic approach*, the *postulational approach*, or the *deductive method*. For emphasis we state this concept again as follows:

The modern mathematician starts with certain undefined terms which he combines with simple English to state a set of definitions and axioms. From these he draws conclusions by applying the rules of logic. This process of drawing conclusions from undefined terms, definitions, and axioms is called *mathematical reasoning*.

Undefined Terms.   One reason for using undefined terms is that it is impractical to define every word. When one consults a dictionary he usually finds that one of two things happens. His attempt to define a given word leads him, in circular fashion, back to the same word, or it produces a list of definitions as he looks up each new word that arises. As an example of the circular situation let us define the word "person". From the American College Dictionary we obtain the following definitions which bring us again to the word "person".

> person—a human being
> human—of, pertaining to, or characteristic of man
> man—a human being, a person
> being—a living thing, a human being, a person

As an example of the type that produces a list of definitions let us consult the dictionary for the meaning of "pedometer". A pedometer is an instrument for recording the number of steps taken in walking. An instrument can be defined as a mechanical device. A device can be described as an invention or contrivance. A contrivance can be defined as something contrived. To contrive is to plan, to plan is to design, and to design is to form or conceive in the mind. If the reader wants to assume that he knows what "to form" means, he can stop there. If not, he can continue the chain of definitions until he does find a word that he *assumes* that he knows. This word, that he assumes that he knows the meaning of, is then taken without definition and hence may be considered as an undefined term. From these two examples it is quite apparent that we cannot define *every* word without using some type of circular thinking, or becoming involved in a chain of definitions. *These difficulties can best be overcome by starting with certain words which we make no attempt to define.*

A second reason for using undefined terms is that different interpretations may be given to the undefined terms. This means that the results will be valid for *all* interpretations of the undefined terms for which the basic assumptions are true. This produces an abstract approach having interpretations which are concrete examples of the abstract thinking. This is a very powerful tool which produces great economy in mathematics.

Definitions. If certain undefined terms are given, it is possible to define other terms. For instance, if the terms "point" and "between" are undefined notions, one might define the line segment joining the two given points A and B as follows:

Definition. *The **line segment** AB is the set of points consisting of A and B and all points between A and B.*

The triangle ABC can also be defined.

Definition. *The **triangle** ABC is the set of points in the line segments AB, BC, and CA.*

Axioms. Axioms are unproved statements on which mathematical reasoning is based. The mathematician usually has some concrete example in mind which helps him choose the axioms; however, he may not reveal this example until some of the theorems have been proved in a purely abstract way. Then he may reveal the example as an interpretation.*

---

* We shall not discuss here the properties of axiom systems such as interpretation, independence, consistency, completeness, categoricalness, and equivalence. The interested reader can see Eves and Newsom, *op. cit.*, pp. 161–170; and R. L. Wilder, *Foundations of Mathematics* (New York, Wiley, 1952), pp. 23–40.

Definition. *An **axiom**, a **postulate**, or an **assumption**, is a statement which is accepted without proof as a basis for argument.*

It should be observed that each definition is a type of axiom. For example, let us discuss the definition of the line segment AB just given. This definition indicates that if the line segment AB is given, then it is the points A and B and all points between A and B. Thus we *assume* that the line segment AB is the set of points just described. The definition also indicates that if the set having A and B and all points between A and B as its elements is given, then this set is the line segment AB. Thus we *assume* that if the set of points just described is given, then it is the line segment AB. This discussion shows that a definition is an "if and only if" statement which is really a *double assumption*. It can, in fact, be rephrased to emphasize this double assumption as follows.

A set of points is the line segment AB if and only if the set has as its elements only the points A and B and all points between A and B.

Definitions also serve the purpose of simplifying a discussion by replacing a group of words which present a concept, by a shorter group of words. Thus "the points A and B and all points between A and B" is replaced by "the line segment AB". These "mental bundles" promote efficiency.

Theorems.   The ultimate objective of mathematical reasoning is to obtain conclusions from given assumptions. If, by using the basic assumptions, a logical argument, or proof, is produced which shows that a general statement is true, the statement is called a theorem, or proposition, and may be used as a new tool to help establish other theorems. (Sometimes a general statement which is conjectured to be true is also referred to as a "theorem" even though no proof of it has been discovered. But, of course, until it is proved, such a theorem cannot be used in other proofs.) Modern rigor demands that in the proof of a theorem only those statements be used which are direct consequences of the given assumptions. Euclid's proofs often used statements which he had neither assumed explicitly nor proved. He continued to "borrow" from the world around him many facts which were not consequences of his assumptions. He did not hesitate to state that between two points on a line there is always a third point, or that there is a point which does not lie on a given line. We now know that there are geometries in which these statements are not necessarily true.

Remarks. The position of the mathematician attempting to follow the path of modern mathematical reasoning is similar to that of a man shipwrecked on an uninhabited island with only a limited amount of equipment. His job is to work with what he has at hand; that is, what he had with him upon arrival and what he finds on the island. He cannot use the metal hammer that he left at home, but must build up his supplies from what he has. If he succeeds in making a new "tool" it is added to his equipment and used to help make other tools. Just as there are many possible sets of "tools" which fate may have provided for the shipwrecked man, there are many sets of assumptions with which a mathematician can start. What he can get from them depends to some extent upon his ingenuity.

To make this example more specific let us assume that x, y, z, and w indicate objects involved in our discussion of the shipwrecked man. Then x, y, z, and w will be the undefined terms. When we say that z exists we mean that z is on the island. As axioms we choose the following:

Ax. 1.   The object z exists.
Ax. 2.   If x exists, then y exists.
Ax. 3.   If y and z exist, then w exists.

From these the following theorem can be proved.

Thm. If x exists, then w exists.

We shall not prove this theorem, but shall show some of the interpretations. If we let z, x, y and w represent "burning glass", "Friday July 7", "sunshine", and "fire" (can be produced), respectively, then the translation of the axioms and the theorem produces the following:

Ax. 1.   There is a burning glass.
Ax. 2.   If it is Friday, July 7, then there is sunshine.
Ax. 3.   If there is sunshine and a burning glass then fire can be produced.

Thm. If it is Friday, July 7, then fire can be produced.

As a second interpretation let z, x, y and w be "man", "mosquitoes", "malaria germs", and (there may be) "fever", respectively.

Then we have the following:

Ax. 1.   There is a man.
Ax. 2.   If there are mosquitoes then there are malaria germs.
Ax. 3.   If there are malaria germs and a man then there may be fever.

Thm.   If there are mosquitoes then there may be fever.

There are many other interpretations that can be given. If the original theorem is proved from the original set of axioms then the corresponding theorem in the interpretation is true, without proof.

A few additional historical remarks are in order. After discovering flaws in Euclid's arguments several mathematicians worked diligently to produce a rigorous postulational treatment of Euclidean geometry. Among those who succeeded were the German Pasch, in 1882, the Italians Peano and Piere, in 1889, and the German Hilbert, in 1899. Hilbert's *Grundlagen der Geometrie* (Foundations of Geometry), a classical example of the modern mathematical method, is a small book most of which can be read by an intelligent student of high school geometry. There are French and English translations of this work.

Just as non-Euclidean Geometry liberated geometry by showing the world that there are many possible geometries, so Hamilton's quaternions, which he was forced to invent in 1843 to deal with certain physical phenomena, liberated algebra by showing that there are many possible algebras. Thus whole new worlds of mathematical research were opened.

Although we have mentioned especially the branches of mathematics known as geometry and algebra, there are others that are equally fruitful. For example, the branch called analysis, which has its origin in the calculus, has been very productive in its applications to many fields of learning, especially the natural sciences and engineering. Applied mathematics, also considered as a branch of mathematics, combines the theoretical concepts of mathematics and the sciences to solve various practical problems. The tree of mathematics has spread its branches in many directions. The twentieth century exceeds any preceding century in its wealth of mathematical research.

Those who plan to participate in it should be well versed in the modern axiomatic approach.

We summarize this discussion by saying that modern mathematical reasoning is the type of mathematical reasoning which was perfected in the nineteenth century. Regardless of whether we refer to this modern type of reasoning as the axiomatic, the postulational, or the deductive method, it should be emphasized that it consists of four parts: (1) undefined terms, (2) definitions and (3) axioms stated in terms of the undefined terms and simple English, and (4) theorems which are obtained from these undefined terms, definitions and axioms by applying the rules of logic.

28. A SEMIRIGOROUS APPROACH TO SETS

Our approach to set theory has been an intuitive one. We have formulated some opinions as to how sets behave under set operations, what concepts concerning them are simple, how our concept of cardinal number is related to 1–1 correspondence, and how to avoid the major paradoxical pitfall "the set of all sets".

Since one of our main objectives is to produce an understanding of the axiomatic method, let us attempt an approach which will be more nearly rigorous than our intuitive study was. We shall outline a semirigorous approach and leave many proofs to the reader.

The procedure should be clear. We must have some undefined terms, perhaps some defined terms, and some axioms. From these we must be able to reason logically, being careful not to take for granted anything that we have not assumed in the axioms.

Undefined Terms.   We shall use as undefined terms:

set,   is an element of.

As before, we agree to represent sets by capital letters such as A, B, and C, and shall frequently represent elements by small letters such as x, y, and z. The Greek letter ϵ will mean "is an element of" and $\notin$ will mean "is not an element of". Therefore, $x \epsilon A$ will indicate that the object x is an element of the set A, and $x \notin A$ will indicate that x is not an element of A. We shall also use the set designations indicated in Section 2.

Definitions.

Def. 1. The set A is a *subset* of the set B if and only if $x \in B$ whenever $x \in A$. (If A is a subset of B we shall write $A \subseteq B$.)

Def. 2. The sets A and B are *equal* sets if and only if $A \subseteq B$ and $B \subseteq A$. ($A = B$ will denote that A and B are equal sets; $A \neq B$ will denote that the sets are not equal.)

Def. 3. The set A is a *proper* subset of the set B if and only if $A \subseteq B$ and $A \neq B$. (If A is a proper subset of the set B we shall write $A \subset B$.)

Def. 4. A property p is *determinate in a set S* if and only if, whenever $x \in S$, one and only one of the two following statements is true.

(1) x has property p,

(2) x does not have property p.

Axioms.

Ax. 1. If A is a set, then $A \not\in A$.

Ax. 2. (Axiom of Separation) Given a set A and a property p determinate in A, there exists a set C such that $x \in C$ if and only if $x \in A$ and x has property p.

Ax. 3. If A and B are sets, then there exists

(1) a set $A \cup B$, called the *union* of A and B, such that $x \in A \cup B$ if and only if $x \in A$ or $x \in B$;

(2) a set $A \cap B$, called the *intersection* of A and B, such that $x \in A \cap B$ if and only if $x \in A$ and $x \in B$;

(3) a set $A-B$, called the *relative complement* of B in A, such that $x \in A-B$ if and only if $x \in A$ and $x \not\in B$. If A and B are subsets of the same set U, we shall use the notation $U-A = A'$ and $U-B = B'$.

Ax. 4. For each set S there exists a *power set* P such that $A \in P$ if and only if A is a subset of S.

Ax. 5. If A and B are sets, then

(1) for each $a \in A$ and each $b \in B$ there exists an ordered pair (a, b);

(2) there exists a set $A \times B$, called the *Cartesian Product* of A and B, such that $y \in A \times B$ if and only if y is an ordered pair (a, b) where $a \in A$ and $b \in B$.

Ax. 6. There exists a set $\varnothing$ such that for every x, $x \notin \varnothing$.

This set is called the *empty set*. Any set not equal to $\varnothing$ is a *nonempty* set.

Ax. 7. For every set A there exists a set $\{A\}$ such that A is the only element of $\{A\}$.

Ax. 8. If A and B are sets, there exists a set $X = \{A, B\}$ such that A and B are the only elements of X.

Ax. 9. If X is a set such that every A which is an element of X is a set, then there exists a set $\underset{A \in X}{\cup} A$, called the *union of the sets in X*, such that y is an element of this union if and only if there is at least one $A \in X$ for which $y \in A$.

Ax. 10. If X is a nonempty set, and every A which is an element of X is a set, then there exists a set $\underset{A \in X}{\cap} A$, called the *intersection of the sets in X*, such that y is an element of this intersection if and only if $y \in A$ for every $A \in X$.

A few remarks are in order at this point. There is always the question of how many axioms to use. We would like to assume enough to allow us to establish certain properties of sets that we discovered in our intuitive approach. The less we assume the harder it is to establish these properties, but there is a certain satisfaction in being able to build up a theory from only a few axioms.

We have assumed more than we need here in order to make our work easier, and also to provide food for thought for the reader. He should be reminded that in applying the axioms we cannot assume as true anything that we have not stated in them. For example, we cannot assume that there are any sets unless some axiom states that some sets exist. Observe that practically all of the axioms are conditional statements which give us information *if* one or more sets exist. Only Axiom 6 states that a set exists; in fact, it states that the empty set exists.*

---

* We could have assumed that some set, such as T exists. Knowing that one set exists we could apply the Axiom of Separation, letting p be the condition that an element x is not equal to itself, and in this way obtain the empty set. In other words, if a set T exists then the empty set ϕ, defined by $\phi = \{x \mid x \in T \text{ and } x \neq x\}$, exists.

We cannot assume that any of the familiar sets that we are accustomed to will exist. We have no axiom saying that the integers or the rational numbers exist. Assuming only that the empty set exists, how can we get other sets? By Axiom 7 we can obtain $S = \{\varnothing\}$. By Axiom 8 we can get $R = \{\varnothing, S\}$. We can also form $\{S\}$ and $\{R\}$ which are different from S and R. The set $T = R \cup \{R\} = \{\varnothing, S, R\}$ exists. In our first discussion of sets this was called the successor set of R. Similarly, $T \cup \{T\} = \{\varnothing, S, R, T\}$ exists and contains an additional element. Its power set exists. If we let $K = \{\{S\}, \{R\}\}$, then $R \cup K = \{\varnothing, S, \{S\}, \{R\}\}$ but $R \cup K \neq T \cup \{T\}$. Since various Cartesian Product sets exist, it is evident that enough sets are available to make a discussion of them worthwhile. Observe that we have carefully avoided talking about the number of elements in a set since we are not assuming that the set of counting numbers exists. Furthermore, we do not have definitions for finite or infinite sets.

It should be observed that Axiom 3, part (1) could be omitted because of Axioms 8 and 9, also that Axiom 3, part (2) could be omitted because of Axioms 8 and 10, but we have chosen to include them since simpler notation is used for the union and intersection of a few sets.

Axiom 5, part (1) could be replaced by a definition of ordered pairs in terms of sets. Thus the ordered pair (a, b) can be defined as $\{\{a\}, \{a, b\}\}$; however, we have chosen not to do this.

Using this semirigorous approach we can establish Statements 1 through 9 of Section 13 as theorems. The proofs are not essentially different from the discussions already given. Certain statements that were given as exercises also can be established. We shall assume that the reader knows what is meant by the hypothesis and the conclusion of a theorem and that he can establish the following important statements in Theorem 1, within the framework of this approach.

Theorem 1. *Let A, B, and C be subsets of a given set U. Let P denote the power set of U. Then the following statements are true.*

S1. $A \cup B \in P$.   (Closure Law for $\cup$)

S2. $A \cup B = B \cup A$.   (Commutative Law for $\cup$)

S3. $(A \cup B) \cup C = A \cup (B \cup C)$.   (Associative Law for $\cup$)

S4. $\varnothing \cup A = A \cup \varnothing = A$.   (Identity Law for $\cup$)

S5. $A \cup A' = A' \cup A = U$.   (Complement Law for $\cup$)

S6. $A \cup A = A$.   (Idempotent Law for $\cup$)

S7. $A \cap B \in P.$ (Closure Law for $\cap$)

S8. $A \cap B = B \cap A.$ (Commutative Law for $\cap$)

S9. $(A \cap B) \cap C = A \cap (B \cap C).$ (Associative Law for $\cap$)

S10. $U \cap A = A \cap U = A.$ (Identity Law for $\cap$)

S11. $A \cap A' = A' \cap A = \varnothing.$ (Complement Law for $\cap$)

S12. $A \cap A = A.$ (Idempotent Law for $\cap$)

S13. $A \cap (B \cup C) = (A \cap B) \cup (A \cap C).$
          (Distributive Law of $\cap$ with respect to $\cup$)

S14. $A \cup (B \cap C) = (A \cup B) \cap (A \cup C).$
          (Distributive Law of $\cup$ with respect to $\cap$)

S15. $(A \cap B)' = A' \cup B'.$ $\left.\right\}$ (De Morgan's Laws)

S16. $(A \cup B)' = A' \cap B'.$

S17. $(A')' = A.$ (Law of Involution)

S18. If one of the following statements is true then the other two must also be true.

$A \subseteq B, \quad A \cup B = B, \quad A \cap B = A.$ (Consistency Principle)

S19. If $A \subseteq B$ and $B \subseteq C$, then $A \subseteq C.$ (Transitive Law for $\subseteq$)

S20. $A \subseteq A.$ (Reflexive Law for $\subseteq$)

From these twenty statements we can prove every statement that can be proved by referring to the given definitions and axioms, and this can be done *merely by manipulating these statements*. The following theorems show how this can be done *without returning to the basic definitions*. (Since there are many statements in Theorem 1 and they will be used frequently we shall refer to them by number only. Thus, "by S3" means "by statement S3 of Theorem 1".)

We shall often use the symbol ∎ to mark the end of a proof or argument.

Theorem 2. $A \cap B \subseteq A.$

Proof.

$A \cap (A \cap B) = (A \cap A) \cap B.$ (By S9)

$\therefore A \cap (A \cap B) = A \cap B.$ (Substitute A for $A \cap A$, by S12)

$A \cap B \subseteq A.$ (By S18)   ∎

Theorem 3. $A \cap \varnothing = \varnothing.$

Proof.

$$
\begin{aligned}
A \cap \varnothing &= (A \cap \varnothing) \cup \varnothing & \text{(By S4)} \\
&= (A \cap \varnothing) \cup (A \cap A') & \text{(Substitute } A \cap A' \text{ for } \varnothing, \text{ by S11)} \\
&= A \cap (\varnothing \cup A') & \text{(By S13)} \\
&= A \cap A' & \text{(Substitute } A' \text{ for } \varnothing \cup A', \text{ by S4)} \\
&= \varnothing & \text{(Substitute } \varnothing \text{ for } A \cap A', \text{ by S11)} \ \blacksquare
\end{aligned}
$$

Corollary. $\varnothing \subseteq A$.

Proof.

$$
\begin{aligned}
A \cap \varnothing &= \varnothing. & \text{(By Theorem 3)} \\
\therefore \varnothing &\subseteq A. & \text{(By S18)} \qquad\qquad \blacksquare
\end{aligned}
$$

Theorem 4.   (Law of Absorption)

$$A \cup (A \cap B) = A \cap (A \cup B) = A.$$

Proof.

$$
\begin{aligned}
A \cup (A \cap B) &= (A \cup A) \cap (A \cup B). & \text{(By S14)} \\
\therefore A \cup (A \cap B) &= A \cap (A \cup B). & \text{(Substitution, by S6)} \\
\text{Now} \quad A \cap B &\subseteq A. & \text{(By Theorem 2)} \\
\therefore A \cup (A \cap B) &= A & \text{(By S18)} \\
\text{and} \quad A \cup (A \cap B) &= A \cap (A \cup B) = A. & \text{(Equal sets)} \qquad \blacksquare
\end{aligned}
$$

Theorem 5. $U' = \varnothing$.

Proof.

$$
\begin{aligned}
U \cap U' &= U'. & \text{(By S10)} \\
U \cap U' &= \varnothing. & \text{(By S11)} \\
\therefore \qquad U' &= \varnothing. & \text{(Equal sets)} \qquad\qquad \blacksquare
\end{aligned}
$$

Theorem 6.   If $R \cap A = T \cap A$ and $R \cup A = T \cup A$ for some A, then $R = T$.

Proof.

$$
\begin{aligned}
R &= R \cap (R \cup A) & \text{(By Theorem 4)} \\
&= R \cap (T \cup A) & \text{(Substitute from hypothesis)} \\
&= (R \cap T) \cup (R \cap A) & \text{(By S13)} \\
&= (R \cap T) \cup (T \cap A) & \text{(Substitute from hypothesis)} \\
&= (T \cap R) \cup (T \cap A) & \text{(By S8)} \\
&= T \cap (R \cup A) & \text{(By S13)} \\
&= T \cap (T \cup A) & \text{(Substitute from hypothesis)} \\
&= T. & \text{(By Theorem 4)} \qquad \blacksquare
\end{aligned}
$$

6 states that two sets are equal if their intersections with
~~~et are equal and their unions with the same set are equal.

Theorem 7. If $A = B$, then $A' = B'$.

Proof.

$\qquad A' \cap A = \varnothing$ and $B' \cap B = \varnothing$. (By S11)

$\qquad \therefore A' \cap B = \varnothing$ and $B' \cap B = \varnothing$, (Substitute B for A)

and $\quad A' \cap B = B' \cap B$. (Equal sets)

(Therefore, the intersections of A' and B' with the set B are equal.)

$\qquad A' \cup A = U$ and $B' \cup B = U$. (By S5)

$\qquad \therefore A' \cup B = U$ and $B' \cup B = U$, (Substitute B for A)

and $\quad A' \cup B = B' \cup B$. (Equal sets)

(Therefore, the unions of A' and B' with the same set B are equal.)

$\qquad A' = B'$. (Theorem 6) ∎

Theorem 8. If $A \subseteq B$, then $B' \subseteq A'$.

Proof.

$\qquad$ Since $A \subseteq B$, $A \cap B = A$. (By S18)

$\qquad \therefore (A \cap B)' = A'$. (By Theorem 7)

$\qquad A' \cup B' = A'$. (By S15)

$\qquad \therefore \qquad B' \subseteq A$. (By S18) ∎

Corollary. If $B' \subseteq A'$, then $A \subseteq B$.

Proof.

$\qquad$ If $B' \subseteq A'$, then $(A')' \subseteq (B')'$. (By Theorem 8)

$\qquad \therefore A \subseteq B$. (By S17) ∎

Theorem 9. If $A \subseteq B$, then $A \cap B' = \varnothing$.

Proof.

$\qquad$ If $A \subseteq B$, then $A \cap B = A$. (By S18)

$\qquad A \cap B' = (A \cap B) \cap B'$ (Substitute $A \cap B$ for A)

$\qquad \qquad = A \cap (B \cap B')$ (By S9)

$\qquad \qquad = A \cap \varnothing$ (By S11)

$\qquad \qquad = \varnothing$. (By Theorem 3) ∎

Theorem 10. If $A \cap B' = \varnothing$, then $A \subseteq B$.

Proof.

$$A \cap B = (A \cap B) \cup \varnothing \qquad \text{(By S4)}$$
$$= (A \cap B) \cup (A \cap B') \quad \text{(Substitute } A \cap B' \text{ for } \varnothing)$$
$$= A \cap (B \cup B') \qquad \text{(By S13)}$$
$$= A \cap U \qquad \text{(By S5)}$$
$$= A. \qquad \text{(By S10)}$$

Since $A \cap B = A$, then $A \subseteq B$.   (By S18)   ∎

EXERCISES

Using only Theorems 1 through 10 prove the following statements.

1. $\varnothing' = U$.

2. $A \cup U = U$. (Observe that this is the dual of Theorem 3.)

3. If $A \subseteq \varnothing$, then $A = \varnothing$.

4. If $A = \varnothing$, then $A \subseteq \varnothing$.

5. If $B' \subseteq A'$, then $A \cap B' = \varnothing$.

6. If $A \cap B' = \varnothing$, then $B' \subseteq A'$.

29. AN AXIOMATIC APPROACH

We have already learned that modern mathematical reasoning can be based on various combinations of undefined terms and axioms. The mathematician is free to choose the tools with which he will start, but once these tools are chosen he must accept the conclusions which follow logically from them. We observed that after certain set properties are established other set properties can be proved from them without returning to the basic definitions. This suggests a new approach.

By using the parts of Theorem 1 in the preceding section as basic assumptions or axioms we can move one step further from the intuitive approach which we used in most of the preceding sections. We ask, "What collections P will satisfy the following conditions?" Until we find a better name we shall refer to these conditions as the Z-axioms.

Z-axioms. *P is a collection of objects A, B, C, $\cdots$ with two binary operations, denoted by $\cup$ and $\cap$, and one unary operation, denoted by ', such that P is closed with respect to the unary operation; P contains two special objects $\varnothing$ and U, where $\varnothing \neq U$; and P satisfies statements S1 through S20 of Theorem 1.*

Since "collection" and "object" are not defined here they are undefined terms. Similarly, all three of the operations are undefined even though we are using familiar symbols to represent them. However, statements S1 through S20 impose certain conditions on the objects with respect to these operations. As an interpretation we can choose P to be any collection which satisfies all of the stated requirements with respect to two binary operations and one unary operation.

We now take the attitude that the Z-axioms are a set of abstract conditions. We assume that our intuitive approach taught us how sets behave under set union, intersection and complementation, and thus provided a stockpile of information from which examples can be drawn. We therefore conclude that if P denotes the power set of a given set U with subsets A, B, C, $\cdots$; and $\cup$, $\cap$, and ' represent set union, intersection and complementation, respectively, then the Z-axioms will be satisfied. Of course, this is not a surprising conclusion because we drew our ideas for the Z-axioms from sets; however, we did not know how much of the set theory was captured by the abstract net of the Z-axioms.

It is more interesting to find that there are other interpretations of the Z-axioms. Readers familiar with logic will find that A, B, C, $\cdots$ can be interpreted as true-false statements of logic if $\cup$ and $\cap$ are interpreted as the connectives "or" (denoted by $\vee$) and "and" denoted by $\wedge$), respectively, and ' is interpreted as the negation modifier "not" (denoted by $\sim$).

Theorems 2 through 10 follow immediately from the Z-axioms and their proofs remain unchanged. In our semirigorous treatment of sets these theorems were established by using the results of previously proved theorems. In this section they follow directly from the Z-axioms. These theorems hold not only for the first interpretation, but also for the second interpretation which involves concepts of logic. Each can be translated into a statement of logic which will be true because the proof was given in abstract form and is therefore valid for every interpretation of the Z-axioms.

In the event that another interpretation is found for the Z-axioms the theorems will hold for this interpretation also. Thus by using an abstract approach involving undefined terms and operations we are able to prove theorems for sets and logic at the same time and possibly for other interpretations, some of which may not even be known to us at the time that the theorems are being proved.

Mathematicians refer to a collection P which satisfies the Z-axioms with respect to two binary operations and a unary operation as a Boolean Algebra. However some of the Z-axioms can be proved from the others. In the next section we shall show that it is possible to start with fewer axioms and still achieve the same results.

30. BOOLEAN ALGEBRAS

A *Boolean Algebra* is a collection of objects, a, b, c, $\cdots$ with two binary operations, $\circ$ called "cup" and $*$ called "cap", and a unary operation $\sim$ called "opp", which satisfy the following conditions:

B0　The collection S is closed with respect to $\circ$, $*$, and $\sim$.

B1　Each of the operations $\circ$ and $*$ is commutative; that is

$$a \circ b = b \circ a \text{ and } a * b = b * a$$

for all objects a and b in S.

B2　There exist in S, distinct elements $\oplus$ and I, $\oplus \neq I$, such that $a \circ \oplus = a$ and $a * I = a$, for every a in S.

B3　Each binary operation is distributive relative to the other one; that is, $a \circ (b * c) = (a \circ b) * (a \circ c)$ and $a * (b \circ c) = (a * b) \circ (a * c)$.

B4　For each element a in S there exists an element $\tilde{a}$ such that $a \circ \tilde{a} = I$ and $a * \tilde{a} = \oplus$.

Though these requirements are set up in the form of a definition a bit of consideration will show that the objects a, b, c, $\cdots$ of the collection S are undefined objects and that the statements B1, B2, B3, and B4 are axioms which these undefined objects must satisfy relative to the three operations, which are also undefined.

In order to obtain a clearer idea of what a Boolean Algebra is we seek some interpretation of this definition. Do we know of any set of objects, along with the right type of operations that satisfy all of the stated requirements? It should not be too difficult for the reader to guess that S can be interpreted as the power set of a universal set I, with subsets a, b, c, $\cdots$ and empty set $\oplus$, on which $\circ$, $*$, and $\sim$ are interpreted as union, intersection and complementation, respectively. Thus the set of all subsets of a given set is a Boolean Algebra. In fact every algebra of sets is a Boolean Algebra. Observe that there is a Boolean Algebra containing exactly two elements. What is I in this case?

You may feel more at home with this definition if you rewrite it, replacing the objects and operations by the more familiar ones used in set theory. It should be kept in mind, however, that the definition does not restrict us to a set interpretation.

We observe also that if $\circ$ and $*$ are interchanged, and $\oplus$ and I are also interchanged, then the definition remains *unchanged*. This means that the dual of a theorem can be obtained by these same interchanges, and that the proof of the dual theorem is obtained by making the same interchanges in the proof of the original theorem.

It is now possible to prove the following theorems for Boolean Algebras. The proof of Theorem 1 is given as an example. (The proofs of the remaining theorems can be obtained from pages 232–235 of *An Introduction to the Foundations and Fundamental Concepts of Mathematics* by Eves and Newsom. It is suggested that the reader make an honest attempt to prove these theorems before consulting this reference.)

Theorem 1.   (*Idempotent Laws*) $a \circ a = a$ *and* $a * a = a$.

Proof.

$$
\begin{aligned}
a &= a \circ \oplus & \text{(By B2)} \\
&= a \circ (a * \tilde{a}) & \text{(By B4)} \\
&= (a \circ a) * (a \circ \tilde{a}) & \text{(By B3)} \\
&= (a \circ a) * I & \text{(By B4)} \\
&= a \circ a & \text{(By B2)} \quad\blacksquare
\end{aligned}
$$

Since $a * a = a$ is the dual statement the proof is the dual of the proof just given. This proof is left for the reader.

Theorem 2. $a \circ I = I$ *and* $a * \oplus = \oplus$.

Theorem 3. (*Laws of Absorption*) $a * (a \circ b) = a$ *and*
$a \circ (a * b) = a$.

Theorem 4. (*Associative Laws*) $a \circ (b \circ c) = (a \circ b) \circ c$ *and*
$a * (b * c) = (a * b) * c$.

Theorem 5. $\tilde{a}$ *is unique*.

Theorem 6. (*De Morgan's Laws*) $\widetilde{(a \circ b)} = \tilde{a} * \tilde{b}$ *and*
$\widetilde{(a * b)} = \tilde{a} \circ \tilde{b}$.

The following definition introduces the concept of inclusion.

Definition. $a \subseteq b$ *if and only if* $a \circ b = b$.

Theorem 7. $a \subseteq a$.

Theorem 8. *If* $a \subseteq b$ *and* $b \subseteq a$,   *then* $a = b$.

Theorem 9. *If* $a \subseteq b$ *and* $b \subseteq c$,   *then* $a \subseteq c$.

Theorem 10. $\oplus \subseteq a \subseteq I$ *for each object a of S*.

Theorem 11. *If* $a \subseteq x$ *and* $b \subseteq x$,   *then* $a \circ b \subseteq x$.

From the definition of a Boolean Algebra many additional theorems can be proved. All such theorems are true for the set of subsets of a given set, because the power set is a Boolean Algebra.

Many other sets of axioms have been given for Boolean Algebras. The one used here was given by E. V. Huntington in 1904. Boolean Algebras are named for the English logician and mathematician George Boole (1815–1864) who did much work toward setting up an algebra of logic. Additional information about Boolean Algebras can be found in *Some Basic Mathematical Concepts* by R. D. Luce, pages 151–162. (School Mathematics Study Group)

EXERCISES

1. Write out the proof of $a * a = a$.

2. Complete the proofs for the theorems listed for Boolean Algebras.

*31. ADDITIONAL PROPERTIES OF CARDINAL NUMBERS

If the first of two finite sets cannot be put into 1–1 correspondence with a subset of the second set, but the second set can be put into 1–1 correspondence with a subset of the first set, then the cardinal number of the first finite set is *larger* than the cardinal number of the second finite set. The cardinal numbers of two infinite sets are compared in the same way. The following definition applies to any two sets, finite or infinite.

Definition. *The cardinal number of a set H is greater than the cardinal number of a set S if S is equivalent to a subset of H but H is not equivalent to a subset of S.*

What conclusion can be drawn if the set H is equivalent to a subset of S and S is equivalent to a subset of H? Mathematicians have shown that such sets are equivalent. We shall accept the following theorem without proof and without indicating what undefined terms, definitions and assumptions precede it.

Schroeder-Bernstein Theorem. *If a set H is equivalent to a subset of a set S and S is equivalent to a subset of H then H is equivalent to S.*

Let us again consider the sets $I = \{x \mid x \text{ is a positive integer}\}$ and $T = \{x \mid 0 \leq x \leq 1 \text{ and } x \text{ is a real number}\}$. The set I has cardinal number $\aleph_0$ and T has cardinal number C. Is one of these cardinal numbers greater than the other? The correspondence $n \leftrightarrow 1/n$ sets up a 1–1 correspondence between I and the subset of T consisting of the points 1, 1/2, 1/3, 1/4, $\cdots$. Thus I is equivalent to a subset of T. If T were equivalent to a subset of I then by the Schroeder-Bernstein Theorem I and T would be equivalent sets. However, we have shown that there is no 1–1 correspondence between I and T. Therefore T is not equivalent to a subset of I and C is a greater cardinal number than $\aleph_0$.

---

* This section contains supplementary material based on Section 21. It can be omitted in a short course.

The power set P of a set S of three elements has 2^3 or 8 elements in it. The power set N of P has 2^{2^3} or $2^8 = 256$ elements in it. The power set R of N has 2^{256} elements in it. The number 2^{256} is an extremely large number, having 78 digits to the left of the decimal point. The power set of R has even more elements in it. Thus if one finite set is given, larger and larger finite sets can be obtained by using the power sets. For a finite set the cardinal number of the power set is always greater than the cardinal number of the set. Is this true of infinite sets? The following statement shows that it is.

Statement. *The cardinal number of the power set of a nonempty set is greater than the cardinal number of the set.*

Discussion. Let S represent the given set and P represent its power set. The correspondence $x \leftrightarrow \{x\}$, where $x \in S$ and $\{x\} \in P$, is a 1–1 correspondence between S and a proper subset of P; namely, the collection of unit sets in P. Therefore S is equivalent to a subset of P.

In order to show that P is not equivalent to a subset of S we shall use the indirect method of assuming that it is. Then there is a 1–1 correspondence between the elements of P and some, or all, of the elements of S. The elements of P are sets. The elements of these sets are elements of S. The 1–1 correspondence assumed matches a set Z in P with an element x in S. We now form a set W consisting of all elements x of S which are not elements of the sets to which they correspond. Thus $x \in W$ if $x \leftrightarrow Z$ and $x \notin Z$. The set W contains at least one element because $\varnothing \in P$ and is matched with an element t of S under the 1–1 correspondence. Since $\varnothing$ contains no elements, $t \notin \varnothing$, $t \leftrightarrow \varnothing$, and therefore $t \in W$. Every element of W is in S, therefore W is a subset of S and $W \in P$. Therefore, W must be matched with some element $y \in S$ under the assumed 1–1 correspondence. Since W is a subset of S and $y \in S$, then $y \in W$ or $y \notin W$.

Assume that $y \in W$. Then $y \in W$, $y \leftrightarrow W$, and y belongs to the set to which it corresponds. On the other hand W contains only those elements that do not belong to the set to which they correspond. Therefore, $y \notin W$. This is a contradiction.

Assume that $y \notin W$. Then $y \notin W$, $y \leftrightarrow W$, and y does not belong to the set to which it corresponds. On the other hand W contains all elements that do not belong to the set to which they correspond. Therefore, $y \in W$. This is a contradiction.

The original assumption that there is a 1–1 correspondence between P and a subset of S leads to contradictions and therefore must be discarded. Since there is no 1–1 correspondence between P and a subset of S, but there is a 1–1 correspondence between S and a subset of P, the cardinal number of the power set is greater than the cardinal number of the set.

The preceding statement and discussion assures us that there are an unlimited number of infinite cardinal numbers. The power set of an infinite set has a greater cardinal number than the set. The power set of the power set has a greater cardinal number than the power set, and so on.

When we started with a set of three elements and considered the number of elements in successive power sets, some of the numbers that we obtained were 3, 8, 256, and 2^{256}. The entire list of the numbers thus obtained does not contain all of the positive integers. There are two positive integers less than 3; there are four integers between 3 and 8, and 247 integers between 8 and 256. If we have several infinite cardinal numbers will there be other infinite cardinal numbers between them? Specifically, is there an infinite cardinal number between $\aleph_0$ and C? Mathematicians have not yet been able to answer these questions.

We are now in a position to define cardinal numbers. For convenience, we shall speak of a "class of sets" rather than a "set of sets". This will make it easier for the reader to tell when the collection is being referred to rather than the elements in the collection.

What property is possessed by the sets $\{5, 2, 4\}$, $\{tire, mile, nail\}$ and $\{James, Frank, Tom\}$? The property of being equivalent sets. Does the set $\{a, b\}$ possess this property? Since it is not equivalent to any one of these sets it does not have the property of threeness. It is this property of threeness that we want to capture in the definition of cardinal number. Some mathematicians feel that the property of threeness can best be captured by defining the cardinal number of a set as the class of all sets equivalent to that set.

Definition. *The **cardinal number** of a set S is the class of all sets equivalent to S.*

This definition indicates that we should think of all unit sets as forming one class, or set; all sets containing a pair of elements as forming another class; all sets containing a triple of numbers as forming still another class, and so on. These classes themselves are the cardinal numbers. Since there is only one null set the cardinal number for $\varnothing$ is the unit class $\{\varnothing\}$. The cardinal number for the set I of positive integers is the class of all sets equivalent to I, and the cardinal number of the set T, the set of real numbers in the unit interval, is the class of all sets equivalent to T.

We shall refer to a specific set in a class as a *representative* of the class. Thus {tire, mile, nail} is a representative of the set of triples.

Definition. *A **representative** of the cardinal number M is a set S in M.*

What rule shall we use for adding two cardinal numbers? If M denotes the class of all triples and N denotes the class of all pairs how can M be added to N? Let $A = \{a, b, c\}$ be a representative of M and $B = \{\text{Sam, Paul}\}$ be a representative of N, such that $A \cap B = \varnothing$. Form $A \cup B$. The cardinal number of $A \cup B$ is the sum of M and N. Thus the class of all sets equivalent to $\{a, b, c, \text{Sam, Paul}\}$ is the sum of M and N.

To find the product of M and N find the cardinal number of the Cartesian product set $A \times B$. Thus the product of M and N is the class of all sets equivalent to

$$A \times B = \{(a, \text{Sam}), (a, \text{Paul}), (b, \text{Sam}), (b, \text{Paul}), (c, \text{Sam}), (c, \text{Paul})\}.$$

Let A^B denote the set of all functions* with domain B and range C, where $C \subseteq A$. The power M^N is the class of all sets equivalent to

$$A^B = \left\{ \binom{S, a}{P, a}, \binom{S, b}{P, b}, \binom{S, c}{P, c}, \binom{S, a}{P, b}, \binom{S, a}{P, c}, \right.$$
$$\left. \binom{S, b}{P, c}, \binom{S, b}{P, a}, \binom{S, c}{P, a}, \binom{S, c}{P, b} \right\},$$

where S denotes Sam and P denotes Paul.

Definitions. Let A and B be two disjoint sets which are representatives of the cardinal numbers M and N, respectively. Let R be the

---

* See the section on functions, p. 136.

cardinal number of $A \cup B$, H be the cardinal number of $A \times B$, and K be the cardinal number of A^B, then $M + N = R$, $MN = H$, and $M^N = K$.

It can easily be shown that cardinal numbers obey the five fundamental laws of arithmetic as well as many of the laws of exponents.

Let C_1 denote the class of unit sets, C_2 denote the class of sets consisting of pairs, and, in general, let C_n denote the class of all sets equivalent to the set $\{1, 2, \cdots, n\}$, where n is an integer. Since the cardinal number of a set is the class of all sets equivalent to the given set, $C_1, C_2, \cdots, C_n, \cdots$ are the cardinal numbers for the finite sets. These behave exactly like the positive integers as to addition, multiplication, and raising to powers, therefore we can use either C_n or n as the cardinal number of a set of n elements.

Working with transfinite cardinals produces some new and interesting results. We have agreed to let $\aleph_0$ denote the cardinal number of the set of positive integers and C denote the cardinal number of the set of points on a line segment. The following conclusions can easily be reached by applying the definitions of addition, multiplication, and raising to powers. In some cases results already obtained are useful. For example, $C \cdot C = C$ follows immediately from the fact that a unit square plus its interior has cardinal number C and the square is equivalent to the Cartesian product of two unit intervals, each having cardinal number C.

$$\aleph_0 + n = \aleph_0 \qquad C + n = C \qquad \aleph_0 \cdot C = C$$
$$\aleph_0 + \aleph_0 = \aleph_0 \qquad C + \aleph_0 = C \qquad C \cdot C = C$$
$$n \cdot \aleph_0 = \aleph_0 \qquad C + C = C$$
$$\aleph_0 \cdot \aleph_0 = \aleph_0 \qquad n \cdot C = C$$

More difficult results have been obtained by mathematicians. Some of them are

$$2^{\aleph_0} = C, \qquad C^{\aleph_0} = C, \qquad 2^C = F$$

where F is the cardinal number of the power set of the set of real numbers.

Remark. When the power set of a set S was defined, it was remarked that 2^S is frequently used to denote the power set. It was found that if S is a finite set of n elements, then 2^n is the number of elements in the power set. In forming subsets from n elements, two decisions are possible for each element; namely, *take* or *leave* the element. Thus the number of choices is 2 for each of the n objects, or a total of 2^n subsets. As a specific example, let $n = 3$ and let the set be $S = \{a, b, c\}$. Then we can represent the number of subsets by a tree diagram where 1 means take the object and 2 means leave the object.

a	b	c	Corresponding subset

		1	$\{a, b, c\}$
		2	$\{a, b\}$
		1	$\{a, c\}$
		2	$\{a\}$
		1	$\{b, c\}$
		2	$\{b\}$
		1	$\{c\}$
		2	$\varnothing$

This tree diagram can also be interpreted as the set of functions from the set $\{a, b, c\}$ into the set $\{1, 2\}$. To obtain one of these functions we assign to a one of the numbers 1 or 2, then do the same for b, and for c. How many functions are possible. Obviously $2 \cdot 2 \cdot 2 = 8$ functions. Therefore 2^S can be interpreted as the set of functions from S into the set $\{1, 2\}$. This was the type of definition used in defining M^N, where M and N are any cardinal numbers whatsoever. Interpreted in this way, the statement $2^{\aleph_0} = C$ says that the cardinal number of the power set of I, the set of positive integers, is C, the cardinal number of the set of real numbers. Also 2^C is the cardinal number of the power set of the real numbers and is greater than C, the cardinal number of the set.

Supplements

I. Relations

Using nontechnical language we often say that two or more elements of a set are related in some way or that they have some relationship to each other. If the elements are integers, one integer may be larger than the other, the first integer may be an integral divisor of the second, or the integers may be relatively prime to each other. If the elements are people, one person may be the uncle of another, or the spouse of another, two people may be siblings, one may be subordinate to the other in authority, or two people may be the parents of a third person. If the elements are lines, one may be parallel or perpendicular to the other; if they are triangles one may be congruent or similar to the other; and if they are sets one may be a subset of the other or the complement of the other. Our everyday experiences provide an abundance of additional examples.

BINARY RELATIONS

Before giving a definition of a relation let us consider some specific examples involving two elements. Relations involving two elements are *binary* or *dyadic* relations.

Example 1.   In the set of integers, certain integers are the squares of other integers. For example, the square of 3 is 9 and the square of 7 is 49. If we use ordered pairs such as (3, 9) and (7, 49) to indicate an integer and its square we can systematically indicate all pairs by (n, n^2), where n is an integer. They form the set $\{(0, 0), (1, 1), (-1, 1), (2, 4), (-2, 4), (3, 9), (-3, 9), \cdots\}$. This set of ordered pairs can be indicated in two ways as shown in Figures 35 and 36.

The graph emphasizes the fact that the set is a set of ordered pairs, and the second representation emphasizes the correspondence between the elements of the ordered pairs. Observe that it is impossible to graph all of the pairs or to represent them as corresponding values, but enough points can be used to show the general nature of the graph or correspondence.

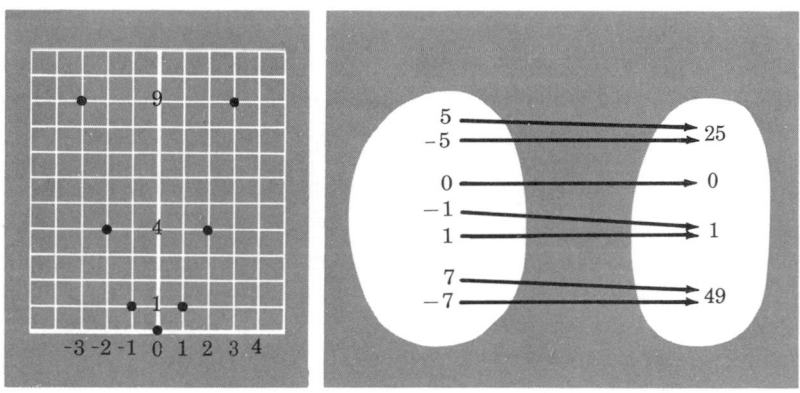

FIG. 35   FIG. 36

Example 2. If the ordered pairs are reversed the set consisting of the ordered pairs (n^2, n) is obtained; namely,

$$\{(0, 0), (1, 1), (1, -1), (4, 2), (4, -2), (9, 3), (9, -3), \cdots\}.$$

It is easy to see that the first element of each ordered pair is followed by one of its square roots. This set of ordered pairs can also be indicated in two ways as shown in Figures 37 and 38, the first emphasizing the ordered pairs and the second emphasizing the correspondence.

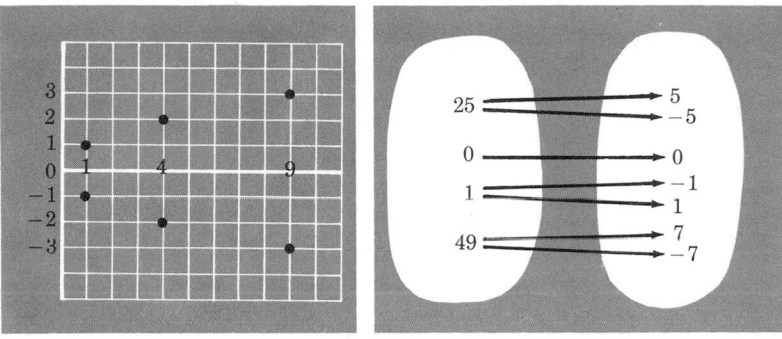

FIG. 37   FIG. 38

***Example* 3.** Let $C = \{c_1, c_2, c_3\}$ represent a set of three children and $B = \{b_1, b_2, b_3, b_4, b_5\}$ represent a set of five books. The books are given to the children according to the following pattern:

$$\{(c_1, b_3), \ (c_2, b_2), \ (c_2, b_5), \ (c_3, b_1), \ (c_3, b_4)\}.$$

The two representations of these ordered pairs are given in Figures 39 and 40.

In each of these examples our discussion of a relation involves a set of ordered pairs. Let J represent the set of integers and recall that $J \times J$ is the Cartesian product which consists of all ordered pairs of integers. The set of all ordered pairs of integers of the form (n, n^2) which we obtained from the first example is a subset of $J \times J$. Likewise, the set of ordered pairs of integers of the form (n^2, n) obtained from the second example is a subset of $J \times J$. The set of pairs obtained in the third example is a subset of the Cartesian product $C \times B$. Since C and B are sets of three and five elements, respectively, $C \times B$ is a set of fifteen elements. Five of these ordered pairs are involved in Example 3. Since the squaring relation in the set of integers is completely determined by the set of ordered pairs (n, n^2), where n is an integer, we *define* the squaring relation to be the set of all ordered pairs (n, n^2). If then S represents the squaring relation, we define this squaring relation as follows: $S = \{(n, n^2) \mid n \ \epsilon \ J\}$. Then Figure 35 is the graph of the squaring relation. Similarly we *define* the square root relation R to be the set of ordered pairs (n^2, n). Thus $R = \{(n^2, n) \mid n \ \epsilon \ J\}$, and its graph is given in Figure 37. Finally we define

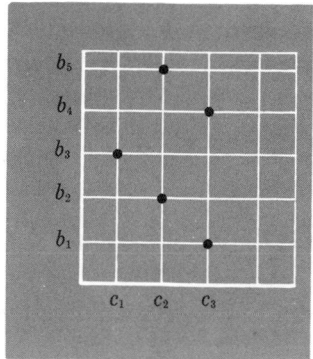 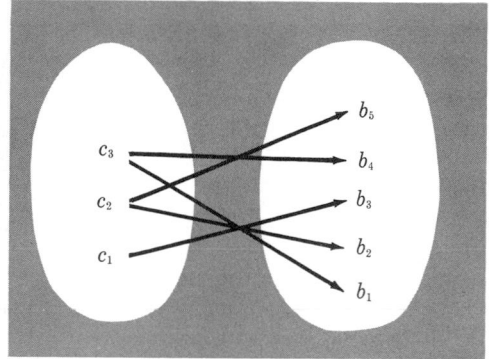

FIG. 39   FIG. 40

the giving relation G as the set of ordered pairs displayed in Example 3. Thus $G = \{(c_1, b_3), (c_2, b_2), (c_2, b_5), (c_3, b_1), (c_3, b_4)\}$ and its graph is given in Figure 39. We have therefore defined each of the relations in Examples 1, 2, and 3 as a set of ordered pairs.

In general, we can think of a relation as a set of ordered pairs and therefore a subset of some Cartesian product. We then ask if every subset of a Cartesian product should be accepted as a relation. For example, consider the set

$$T = \{(-1, -1), (2, 1), (5, 3)\}.$$

Is this a relation? Listing the ordered pairs shows which second element is matched with each first element, therefore, the relationship between elements is exhibited. The reader may feel that some rule of correspondence should be produced, but it is important to understand that the correspondence exists and is displayed by listing the ordered pairs. Thus -1 corresponds to -1, 1 corresponds to 2, and 3 corresponds to 5. No better rule is needed as long as the elements are definitely paired. The set T is accepted as a relation in $J \times J$. It happens that T consists of the set of all pairs (x, y) satisfying $2x - 3y = 1$, in $A \times D$, where $A = \{-2, -1, 0, 1, 2, 3, 4, 5\}$ and $D = \{-1, 0, 1, 2, 3\}$, but this information is not necessary to decide that T should be accepted as a relation. Even if someone prefers not to accept every subset of a Cartesian product as a relation it is extremely difficult, if not impossible, to find a rule which separates the acceptable subsets from the unacceptable ones. For this reason mathematicians accept every subset of a Cartesian product $A \times B$ as a relation from A to B.

Definition. *A **binary relation** from the set A to the set B is a subset of $A \times B$.*

This definition allows the empty subset of $A \times B$ to be a relation. This relation does not contain any ordered pairs and is referred to as the *null relation* or the *empty relation* in $A \times B$. It also allows $A \times B$ as a relation which is referred to as the *universal relation* from A to B.

If $A = B$ we often say that the *relation is in A* rather than that it is from A to A, nevertheless it is still a subset of $A \times A$.

If R is a subset of $A \times B$ and (x, y) is in R, using set notation, we write $(x, y) \in R$.

Definition. *The **domain** of a binary relation is the set of all first elements of the ordered pairs in the relation. The **range** of a binary relation is the set of all second elements of the ordered pairs in the relation.*

We shall denote the domain of a relation R by $d(R)$ and the range by $r(R)$.

In the examples at the beginning of this section we have:

for S, the squaring relation in J,

$$d(S) = J, \quad r(S) = \{0, 1, 4, 9, 16, \cdots\};$$

for R, the square root relation in J,

$$d(R) = \{0, 1, 4, 9, 16, \cdots\}, \quad r(R) = J;$$

for G, the relation of giving, $d(G) = C$, and $r(G) = B$.
These results can also be tabulated as follows.

Relation	Domain	Range
S	J	$\{0, 1, 4, 9, 16, 25, \cdots\}$
R	$\{0, 1, 4, 9, 16, 25, \cdots\}$	J
G	C	B

Let us now consider the possibility of defining a relation as a correspondence. Is it possible to have a set of ordered pairs without having a correspondence? We have just stated that if (x, y) is an ordered pair then it makes y correspond to x. Therefore, if we have a set of ordered pairs, the ordered pairs show how the elements of the range are paired with the elements of the domain, and thus establish a correspondence. Hence every set of ordered pairs determines a correspondence between the elements involved in the ordered pairs. On the other hand, is it true that a set of ordered pairs is determined by a set A, a set B, and a rule of correspondence which assigns one or more elements of B to each element of A? If b, t, n, q, $\cdots$ in B correspond to a in A, then the pairs (a, b), (a, t), (a, n), (a, q), $\cdots$ are determined. Therefore, a correspondence determines a set of ordered pairs.

If the domain of a binary relation is a finite set as was the case for the relation T, it is possible to display all of the ordered pairs in the relation. If, however, the domain is an infinite set, as was the case for the relation S in J, it is not possible to write down all of the ordered pairs of the relation. It is then necessary to give the rule of correspondence by which one can find the element or elements of the range that correspond to an arbitrary element of the domain. Thus, the set of ordered pairs $\{(0, 0),\ (1, 1),\ (-1, 1),\ (2, 4)\}$ defines a certain squaring relation having the finite domain $A = \{0, 1, -1, 2\}$. However, to define the squaring relation for the domain of all integers, it is necessary to use the rule of correspondence, (n, n^2), where $n \in J$. Thus $n^2 = n \cdot n$ is the rule for finding the element of the range that corresponds to an arbitrary element n of the domain J. Without such a rule one cannot find the element corresponding to certain specific elements such as $n = 9876$.

Our discussion shows that even though the concept of a correspondence is not identical with the concept of a set of ordered pairs, these two concepts are logically equivalent. By this we mean that these two concepts produce the same set of relations. An object, or set of objects, is a relation according to the concept of ordered pairs if and only if it is a relation according to the concept of a correspondence from one set to another. As another example of logically equivalent concepts consider the concept of a parallelogram defined first as a quadrilateral having its opposite sides parallel and secondly as a quadrilateral having its opposite sides equal. In plane geometry it is possible, by using the proper assumptions, to show that a quadrilateral with the opposite sides parallel must have its opposite sides equal and that a quadrilateral with its opposite sides equal must have its opposite sides parallel. Therefore, these two definitions are logically equivalent even though they are not identical definitions. If, in the plane, X

is the set of all geometric figures which are parallelograms according to the first definition and Y is the set of all geometric figures which are parallelograms according to the second definition, then $X = Y$.

We now state a second definition of a relation which is logically equivalent to the first definition.

Definition. *A **binary relation** from A to B is a correspondence which makes one or more elements of B correspond to each element of some subset of A.*

When a relation is considered as a correspondence, a notation emphasizing the correspondence is often used. Examples 1 and 2 of this section can be represented as follows:

$$S: n \rightarrow n^2, \text{ where } n \ \epsilon \ J.$$
$$R: n^2 \rightarrow n, \text{ where } n \ \epsilon \ J.$$

These statements can be read "S makes the integer n^2 correspond to the integer n" and "R makes the integer n correspond to the integer n^2". Sometimes a more direct left to right reading is preferred such as "S sends n into n^2" and "R sends n^2 into n". In general, if a relation W sends x into y we write

$$W: x \rightarrow y$$

and refer to x as an *object* and y as an *image* of x under the correspondence. If x is paired with more than one y it is sometimes convenient to speak of the images of x; however, it frequently is convenient to refer to the set of images merely as *the image* of x. For example, the images of 25 as indicated in Figure 38 are 5 and -5 since $(25, 5)$ and $(25, -5)$ are in the relation. The set of images, or briefly, the image of 25 is $\{5, -5\}$. It is easy to see that the domain of the relation is the set of all objects and the range of the relation is the set of all images. The range can also be considered as the union of all of the image sets.

WAYS OF DETERMINING A RELATION

A relation is defined or determined if enough information is given to indicate which ordered pairs belong to the relation. A relation can be determined by (1) an equation or an inequality, (2) a graph, (3) a chart or table, or (4) a statement.

Example 4. In the set of integers the equation $y = -\sqrt{25 - x^2}$ determines the relation $C = \{(x, y) \mid y = -\sqrt{25 - x^2}, x$ and y in $J\}$. The domain $d(C) = \{-5, -4, -3, 0, 3, 4, 5\}$ and the range $r(C) = \{0, -3, -4, -5\}$. Its graph is given in Figure 41.

The reader should be careful not to say that $y = -\sqrt{25 - x^2}$ is the relation. It merely determines the correspondence in the set of integers. This equation will produce a different relation if x is in a different universal set, such as the set of real numbers.

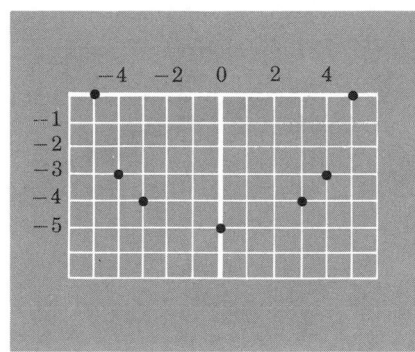
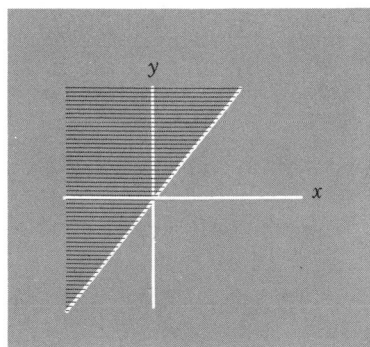

FIG. 41   FIG. 42

Example 5. The inequality $y \geq x$ determines a relation in the set of real numbers. This relation is indicated by the horizontal shading in Figure 42. Its domain is the set of all real numbers and its range is the same set.

Example 6. The graph in Figure 43 determines a relation with domain $\{x \mid -8 \leq x \leq 7\}$ and range $\{y \mid -2 \leq y \leq 4\}$.

Example 7. The chart in Figure 44 determines a relation from A to B where $A = \{-2, -1, 0, 1\}$ and $B = \{-4, -2, 0, 1, 3\}$.

Example 8. Let x represent the value in dollars of the Siamese imports coming into New York City in each of the years from 1940 to 1960. Let y represent the number of marriage licenses issued in Chicago for each of the same years. If the values of x and y are paired for the same year, the resulting pairs are a relation.

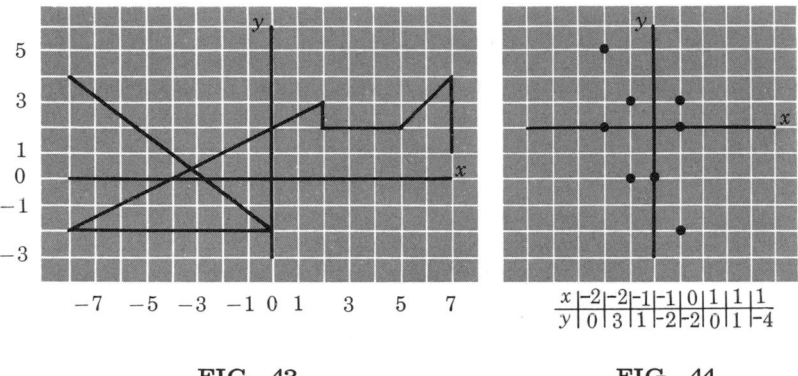

FIG. 43   FIG. 44

Example 9. Let x and y represent people in the United States such that y is the father of x. Then the ordered pairs (x, y) are a relation. The domain is the set of all children in the United States who have living fathers in the United States and the range is the set of all fathers in the United States who have at least one living child in this country.

Example 10. If A is the set of all residences in Miami, Florida, and B is the set of all men in the same city, then let $a \in A$ be paired with $b \in B$ if and only if b is the sole owner of a. The set of all pairs (a, b) for which $a \in A$, $b \in B$, and b is the sole owner of a, is a relation from A to B. It is a subset of $A \times B$. The domain is the set of those residences in Miami each of which is owned individually by a man in Miami, and the range is the set of all men in Miami each of whom is the sole owner of a residence in that city.

A ternary or triadic relation can be defined as a set of ordered triples, a quaternary or tetradic relation can be defined as a set of ordered quadruples, and, in general, an n-ary relation can be defined as a set of n-tuples. By grouping the elements of an ordered triple (x, y, z) it is possible to consider it as an ordered pair such as $((x, y), z)$ or $(x, (y, z))$. In this way the theory of ordered pairs can be extended to ordered triples. Likewise, the theory of ordered triples can be extended to ordered quadruples; and, in general, the theory of n-tuples can be extended to $(n + 1)$-tuples.

EQUIVALENCE RELATIONS

Some relations have special properties which make them useful in mathematics. In discussing these special properties it will be convenient to write $x \, R \, y$ if (x, y) is an ordered pair in the relation R and $x \, \not\!\!R \, y$ if (x, y) is not an ordered pair in the relation R. Thus $x \, R \, y$ and $(x, y) \, \epsilon \, R$ both mean that the ordered pair (x, y) belongs to the relation R.*

If C represents the relation of cubing and W represents the relation of being the wife of, then

$$2 \, C \, 8, \quad 3 \, \not\!\!C \, 6, \quad \text{and} \quad (\text{George V}) \, W \, (\text{Queen Mary})$$

indicate, respectively, that the cube of 2 is 8, the cube of 3 is not 6, and that Queen Mary was the wife of George V.

Equivalence relations are of prime importance in mathematics.

Definition. *A relation R is an* **equivalence relation** *in a set D if it has the following properties*:

Reflexive: $x \, R \, x$, *for all x in D,*
Symmetric: *If $x \, R \, y$, then $y \, R \, x$, for all x and y in D,*
Transitive: *If $x \, R \, y$ and $y \, R \, z$, then $x \, R \, z$, for all x, y, and z in D.*

Example **11.** The identity relation is an equivalence relation on any set D. If $x \, \epsilon \, D$, then x is identical to x. If x is identical to y, then x and y are the same element, and therefore y is identical to x. If x and y are identical, and y and z are identical, then x and z are identical. Therefore the relation is reflexive, symmetric, and transitive and is an equivalence relation.

Example **12.** The set of all pairs of equal rational numbers is an equivalence relation, for if a, b, and c are integers such that $b \neq 0$ and $d \neq 0$, then $a/b = c/d$ if and only if ad and bc are identical integers. The verification is left to the reader.

Example **13.** The set of all pairs of similar triangles is an equivalence relation. The verification is left to the reader.

* Some authors use $y \, R \, x$ instead of $x \, R \, y$. We have chosen the order which agrees with the order of the coordinates in the ordered pair (x, y).

Example 14. Let $x R y$ if and only if $x - y = 3n$, where x, y, and n are integers. Then R is reflexive, for $x - x = 3 \cdot 0 = 0$; and R is symmetric, for if $x - y = 3n$ for some integer n, then $y - x = 3(-n)$ for the integer $-n$. Finally, R is transitive, for if $x R y$ and $y R z$, then $x - y = 3n$ and $y - z = 3m$, where n and m are integers. Adding these statements we obtain $x - z = 3(n + m)$, where $n + m$ is an integer, and therefore $x R z$.

Definition. *If R is an equivalence relation and $x R y$, then $x* **is** *equivalent to* y *in R.*

If R is an equivalence relation in a set D, and if $x \in D$, the set of all elements equivalent to x forms an *equivalence class* of which x is an element. *The equivalence relation R separates the elements of D into disjoint equivalence classes.* For, if an element w is in D but is not equivalent to x it determines another equivalence class. These two classes cannot have a common element t, for if $x R t$ and $t R w$ then $x R w$, contrary to the fact that w is not equivalent to x. Therefore if $x \not R w$ the equivalence classes determined by x and w are disjoint.

Example 15. For the relation defined by similarity of triangles, a typical equivalence class is the set of all isosceles right triangles. Another equivalence class is the set of all triangles having angles of $20°$, $30°$, and $130°$. Still another is the set of all equilateral triangles. In fact, every set of three positive angles A, B, and C such that $A + B + C = 180°$ determines an equivalence class of triangles. The set of all triangles is the union of these disjoint equivalence classes.

Example 16. For the relation in Example 14 we have an equivalence class determined by 0, which consists of all elements equivalent to 0; namely, $\{0, 3, -3, 6, -6, \cdots\}$; an equivalence class determined by 1; namely, $\{1, 4, -2, 7, -5, \cdots\}$; and an equivalence class determined by 2; namely, $\{2, 5, -1, 8, -4, \cdots\}$. These classes are disjoint and their union is J, the set of all integers. Thus this relation separates the set of integers into three disjoint equivalence classes.

Definition. *A set of subsets of a set S is a* **partition** *of S, if the subsets are disjoint and S is the union of these subsets.*

Example 17. The sets $A = \{0, 3, -3, 6, -6, \cdots\}$, $B = \{1, 4, -2, 7, -5, \cdots\}$ and $C = \{2, 5, -1, 8, -4, \cdots\}$ form a partition of J

since $A \cap B = \varnothing, A \cap C = \varnothing, B \cap C = \varnothing$, and $A \cup B \cup C = J$. This partition was induced by the relation R in J where $x \mathrel{R} y$ if and only if $x - y = 3n$ and $n \in J$.

Not only does every equivalence relation on a set S induce a partition of S, but every partition of S determines an equivalence relation R in S the relation being that $x \mathrel{R} y$ if and only if $x \in S$ and $y \in S$ and x and y belong to the same subset of the partition.*

Example 18. At a given time the set of all high school students in Los Angeles is partitioned into the subsets that belong to the various high schools in that city. Then two students x and y are in the relation R if they attend the same high school. The reader can show that R is an equivalence relation.

REVERSE RELATIONS

In Example 2 of this section we considered the relation R obtained by reversing the ordered pairs in the squaring relation S of Example 1. Each of these relations is the reverse relation of the other since it can be obtained from the other relation by reversing the order of the ordered pairs.

Definition. *The relation H_r is the* **reverse relation** *of the relation H if $H_r = \{(b, a) \mid (a, b) \in H\}$.*

A reverse relation, as defined here, is also called a *converse relation*, a *transpose relation*, or an *inverse relation*, and it is also denoted by H^{-1} instead of H_r. If this notation is used it should be clearly understood that "-1" is not to be considered as an exponent.

Observe that if H is a subset of $A \times B$ then H_r is a subset of $B \times A$, and that H_r can be represented by reversing the arrows in the representation of H, as indicated in Figures 45 and 46.

If $(b, a) \in H_r$ then a is an image of b under H_r and a *reverse image* of b under H. Thus under H the reverse image of -7 is $\{2, 5, -3\}$; the reverse image of 0 is $\{1, 8\}$; and the reverse image of 11 is $\{-3\}$. We

---

* The statements $x \in S$ and $y \in S$ will often be shortened to $x, y \in S$. Similarly $x \in S, y \in S, z \in S, \cdots$ will be written $x, y, z \cdots \in S$.

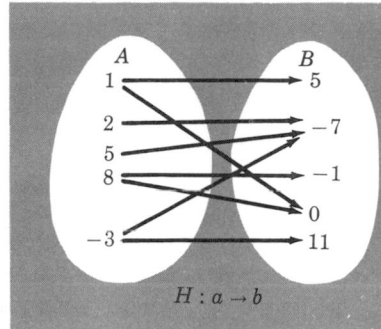 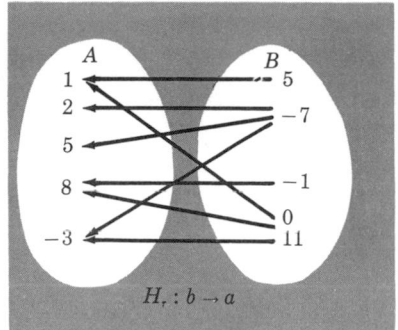

FIG. 45   FIG. 46

can also define the reverse image of a subset C of B if every element of C is an image of some element in A under the relation H. Thus the reverse image of the set $C = \{-7, 0, 11\}$ is the set $\{-3, 1, 2, 5, 8\}$ which is the union of the reverse images $\{2, 5, -3\}$, $\{1, 8\}$, and $\{-3\}$ of -7, 0 and 11, respectively. We indicate the reverse image set of C by writing $H_r(C) = \{-3, 1, 2, 5, 8\}$.

If two relations H and K are subsets of the same Cartesian Product set, the definitions of equality, inclusion, intersection, union, and complementation can be applied to them as sets. Thus it is meaningful to say that two relations are equal or that one relation is included in the other. It is also meaningful to speak of $H \cap K$, $H \cup K$, and H', as well as $(H \cap K)_r$, $(H \cup K)_r$, and $(H')_r$, or to say that $H \subseteq K$, or $H \subset K$.

Example 19.

If $\qquad\qquad S = \{(n, t) \mid t \geq n^2, n, t \in J\}$

and $\qquad\qquad K = \{(n, n^2) \mid n \text{ is a real number}\}$,

and $\qquad S \cap K = \{(n, n^2) \mid n \in J\}$,

then $\qquad S \cap K_r = \{(0, 0), (1, 1)\}$.

In sketching the reverse of a relation it is often helpful to observe that the line $y = x$ is the perpendicular bisector of the line segment which joins the point P, with coordinates (x, y), to the point Q, with coordinates (y, x). If the graph is folded along the line $y = x$, the

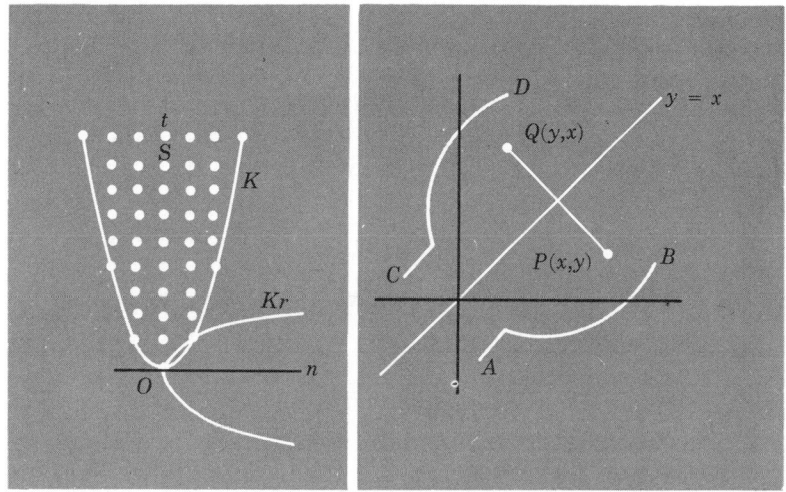

FIG. 47   FIG. 48

points P and Q coincide. (See Figure 48.) Such points as P and Q are symmetric with respect to the line $y = x$.

Definition.   *Two points P and Q in the xy-plane are* **symmetric** *with respect to a line L if L is the perpendicular bisector of the line segment PQ.*

If a two-sided mirror is placed on the line $y = x$ the reflection of P appears to be at Q and the reflection of Q appears to be at P. This type of mechanical device readily shows that the reverse of the relation represented by the curve AB in Figure 48 is the relation represented by the curve CD. It also is true that AB represents the relation that is the reverse of the relation represented by CD.

Symmetry with respect to other lines is also important. The points (x, y) and $(x, -y)$ are symmetric with respect to the x-axis, and the points (x, y) and $(-x, y)$ are symmetric with respect to the y-axis. A relation S is *reflected in a line L* when the points in the graph of S are replaced by the points which are symmetric to them with respect to L. The resulting relation R is the *reflection* of S in L, and S is also the reflection of R in L.

In summary, a relation involves three things; namely, two sets A and B and a correspondence between some or all of the elements in these sets. The correspondence produces ordered pairs, and the set of all ordered pairs thus produced is a subset of $A \times B$. When we define a relation from A to B as a subset of $A \times B$ we automatically have the three things mentioned; that is, we have A, B, and the correspondence which produces the ordered pairs. Some authors prefer to define a relation as a *system* consisting of these three things; namely, two sets and a rule of correspondence, or equivalently, two sets and a set of ordered pairs obtained from them.

EXERCISES

In the following exercises J denotes the set of integers and Q denotes the set of real numbers. If no restrictions are indicated, the xy-plane will be considered as $Q \times Q$; that is, the set of all ordered pairs of real numbers, and x and y will denote the objects in the ordered pairs (x, y).

1. Give at least three ordered pairs which belong to the relation determined by each of the following statements in the universe of all real or fictitious people, except those living.

(a) x was of the same nationality as y.

(b) x and y participated in the same sport.

2. Give at least three ordered pairs of integers belonging to the relation determined by the following statements.

(a) x is exactly divisible by y.

(b) x is the remainder when y is divided by 7.

(c) x exceeds y by an even integer.

(d) $3x$ equals $5y$.

3. Graph each of the following relations and give its domain and range.

(a) $R = \{(x, x^4) \mid x \in Q\}$.

(b) $R = \{(x^4, x) \mid x \in Q\}$.

(c) $R: x \to 2x$, where $x \in J$; where $x \in Q$.

(d) $R: x \to x^3$, where $x \in J$; where $x \in Q$.

(e) $R = \{(x, y) \mid x^2 + y^2 \leqq 2$, where $x, y \in J\}$: where $x, y \in Q$.

4. Give the domain and range of each of the following relations. Graph all pairs for which $n \leqq 15$.

(a) Let n be an integer greater than 1 and let p be a prime integer dividing n. Then the set of pairs (n, p) is a relation in J.

(b) Let n be the same as in part (a), except that p is the largest prime integer dividing x.

5. Sketch the relation consisting of all ordered pairs (x, y) satisfying each of the following conditions, where x and y are real numbers. Also give the domain and the range of the relation. Bounding lines or curves whose points do not belong to the relation should be indicated by dotted lines or dotted curves.

(a) $y < 4 - x$.   (d) $y > 6 - 2x$.
(b) $y \geqq x^2$.   (e) $3x - 2y - 12 \geqq 0$.
(c) $y \leqq x^3$.   (f) $x^2 + y^2 \geqq 9$.

6. Repeat Exercise 5 replacing the universal set of real numbers by the universal set $S = \{0, 1, 2, 3\}$.

7. By sketching each of the sets R, S, and T show that they are disjoint sets whose union is the entire plane.

(a) $R = \{(x, y) \mid y = -5\}, S = \{(x, y) \mid y > -5\}$,
    $T = \{(x, y) \mid y < -5\}$.
(b) $R = \{(x, y) \mid y = 7x - 14\}, S = \{(x, y) \mid y > 7x - 14\}$,
    $T = \{(x, y) \mid y < 7x - 14\}$.
(c) $R = \{(x, y) \mid y = x^2\}, S = \{(x, y) \mid y > x^2\}$,
    $T = \{(x, y) \mid y < x^2\}$.

8. Indicate the set of ordered pairs which are real numbers and which satisfy each of the following equations or inequalities. Is each a relation?

(a) $x^2 + y^2 = 25$.   (b) $x^2 + y^2 < 25$.   (c) $x^2 + y^2 > 25$.
(d) What is the union of the sets in (a), (b), and (c)?

9. Express each of the following sets as a union of sets from the preceding exercise.

(a) $x^2 + y^2 \leqq 25$.   (b) $x^2 + y^2 \geqq 25$.

10. Let $R = \{(x, y) \mid y \geqq x^2 \text{ and } x, y \epsilon Q\}$.
    Let $S = \{(x, y) \mid x + y \leqq 3 \text{ and } x, y \epsilon Q\}$.

Sketch each of the following and determine whether it is a relation.

(a) $R \cap S$.   (b) $R \cup S$.   (c) $R \cap S$, if $x, y \epsilon J$.
(d) $R \cup S$, if $x, y \epsilon J$.

11. Let R be the set of points in the xy-plane such that $x \leqq -2$, S be the set of points for which $y \geqq -1$, and T be the set for which $x - y + 5 > 0$. Sketch $R \cap S \cap T$. Is it a relation?

12. Determine whether each of the following relations R is an equivalence relation. If it is, indicate the partition induced; that is, indicate the equivalence classes.

(a) Let $x\,R\,y$ if and only if $x - y = 2n$, where $x, y, n \in J$.

(b) Change (a) so that $x\,R\,y$ if and only if $x - y = 5n$.

(c) Let S be the set of books in a specific college library. If $x, y \in S$ then $x\,R\,y$ if the books x and y have the same number of pages in them.

(d) In the set of all people let $x\,M\,y$ if and only if y is the mother of x.

(e) Let $x, y \in Q$ and let $x\,R\,y$ if and only if $x - y > 0$.

(f) Let U be the set of all furniture in a specific furniture store and let $x\,R\,y$ if and only if x and y are the same type of furniture; that is, chairs, tables, beds, etc.

13. Show that a partition of a set S determines an equivalence relation in S.

14. Recall that a relation is a *set* of ordered pairs. Determine which of the following are relations in J. Be sure to distinguish between the set and the elements of the set, especially when the set is a unit set.

(a) $(5, -7)$.

(b) $\{(5, -7)\}$.

(c) $\{\{(5, -7)\}\}$.

(d) $\{\{\{(5, -7)\}\}\}$.

(e) $(1, -5), (2, 3)$.

(f) $\{(1, -5), (2, 3)\}$.

15. Two ordered pairs (a, b) and (c, d) are equal if and only if $a = c$ and $b = d$. Use this definition to show that the ordered quadruples (a, b, e, f) and (c, d, r, s) are equal if and only if $a = c$, $b = d$, $e = r$, and $f = s$.

16. Find an equation which defines each of the following relations. Give the domain and the range.

(a) $\{(0, 3), (1, 4), (2, 5), (-1, 2)\}$.

(b) $\{(-3, 9), (\sqrt{2}, 2), (2, 4)\}$.

(c) $\{(0, 1), (1, \sqrt{2}), (-1, \sqrt{2}), (2, \sqrt{5}), (-2, \sqrt{5})\}$.

17. Let R be a relation from T to S; that is, a subset of $T \times S$. What is defined by each of the following statements?

(a) $X = \{t \mid t \epsilon T$ and there is an $s \epsilon S$ such that $t R s\}$.

(b) $Y = \{s \mid s \epsilon S$ and there is a $t \epsilon T$ such that $t R s\}$.

18. Let $D = \{a, b\}$. List all relations in D, then indicate those which are

(a) Reflexive in D.

(b) Symmetric in D.

(c) Transitive in D.

(d) Equivalence relations in D.

19. If R is a relation from A to B and D is a subset of B, what is defined by

$$\{x \mid (x, y) \epsilon R \quad \text{and} \quad y \epsilon D\} \text{ ?}$$

II. Functions

The concept of a function is widely used throughout mathematics. In order to emphasize different aspects of this concept a function is sometimes called a mapping, an operation*, or a transformation. For easy reference we shall define a function as follows.

Definition. *A **function** from the set A to the set B is a set of ordered pairs (a, b), where $a \in A$ and $b \in B$, such that no two distinct ordered pairs have the same first element.*

Since every subset of $A \times B$ is a relation from A to B and a function from A to B is a special type of subset of $A \times B$, then every function is a relation. However, a relation may not be a function, for the same element of A may be paired with several elements in B in a relation.

Throughout this section we shall let Q denote the set of real numbers.

***Example* 1.** The set of ordered pairs (t, t^2), where $t \in Q$, is a function because each real number has exactly one square. However, the set of ordered pairs (t^2, t), where $t \in Q$, is not a function since different ordered pairs such as $(4, 2)$ and $(4, -2)$ have the same first element. Every nonzero real number has two square roots.

The *domain* of a relation was defined as the set of first elements in the ordered pairs and the *range* was defined as the set of second elements in the ordered pairs. Since every function is a relation these

---

* The word "operator" is frequently used instead of "operation."

definitions are applicable to functions. Similarly the definitions of object and image, as given for a relation, can be used for functions. Thus, in a function the first element of an ordered pair is called an *object* and the second element of the ordered pair is called its *image*. Observe that in a relation an object may have an image set consisting of several elements. In a function the image set of an object is always a unit set; that is, each object has a unique element as its image.

Like relations, functions can be defined by equations, graphs, tables, or statements, though it may not be possible nor convenient to define a specific function in all of these ways. The alert reader can find examples of these various ways of defining a function among the illustrations and exercises.

Since each ordered pair in a function consists of an object and its unique image, the graph of a function never has more than one point on any one vertical line. This means that if a vertical line in the xy-plane intersects the graph of a function it intersects it in exactly one point.

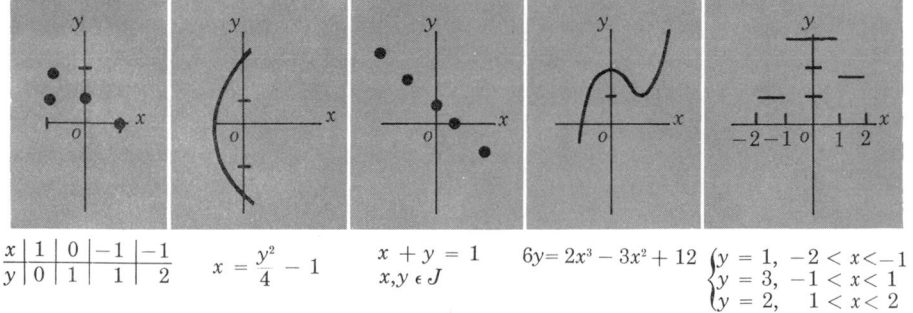

$$\begin{array}{c|c|c|c|c} x & 1 & 0 & -1 & -1 \\ \hline y & 0 & 1 & 1 & 2 \end{array}$$

$$x = \frac{y^2}{4} - 1$$

$$\begin{array}{l} x + y = 1 \\ x, y \, \epsilon \, J \end{array}$$

$$6y = 2x^3 - 3x^2 + 12$$

$$\begin{cases} y = 1, & -2 < x < -1 \\ y = 3, & -1 < x < 1 \\ y = 2, & 1 < x < 2 \end{cases}$$

FIG. 49

The first two graphs in Figure 49 do not represent functions. In the first graph a vertical line drawn through $(-1, 0)$ intersects the graph in two points. In the second graph the vertical line through the origin intersects the graph in two points. The last three graphs represent functions.

A function is also a correspondence. In the preceding section we showed that every set of ordered pairs defines a correspondence between the set of first elements of the ordered pairs and the set of second elements; and, conversely, every correspondence determines a set of ordered pairs. For this reason the following definition of a function is logically equivalent to the definition given at the beginning of this section.

Definition. *A function from the set A to the set B is a correspondence which pairs exactly one element of B with each element of some subset of A.*

If $A = B$, the function is *in* A. Frequently every element of A is used in the correspondence. Then A, rather than a proper subset of A, is the *domain* of the function and the function is *on* A. Some authors define a function so that A is the domain, rather than a proper subset of A.

A function is often called a mapping. If the domain of the function is all of A and the range is all of B then the function is a *mapping* of A *onto* B. If the range is a proper subset of B then the function is a *mapping* of A *into* B.

If a specific function is denoted by f and (a, b) is in f, then the image of the object a is denoted by $f(a)$, read "the value of f at a", or "f at a", or "f of a". Since b and $f(a)$ are names of the same element, $b = f(a)$ and $(a, b) = (a, f(a))$. To emphasize that a function is a correspondence we can write $f: a \rightarrow b$, $f: a \rightarrow f(a)$, $f: x \rightarrow y$, or $f: x \rightarrow f(x)$. Each of these notations can be read in many ways. For example, the last one can be read "the function f sends x into $f(x)$", "$f(x)$ is the image of x under f", "$f(x)$ corresponds to x under f", or "f maps x into $f(x)$".

Definition. *If f is a function from A to B which pairs the object $a \,\epsilon\, A$ with the image $b \,\epsilon\, B$, then the notation $b = f(a)$ is **functional notation**.*

Care should be taken not to say that $b = f(a)$ is the function. It merely indicates that b is the image of a for the function f. In some cases the information is specific enough to define a function if the domain is also indicated; nevertheless, even in such cases $b = f(a)$ is not the function but merely defines the function.

Functional notation provides a concise way of indicating the ordered pairs in a function. If $f: x \rightarrow 2x - 3$, where x is a real number, then using the functional notation we can write $f(x) = 2x - 3$. The value of the function at $x = 0$, denoted by $f(0)$, is obtained by replacing every x in this notation by 0. Thus

$$f(0) = 2(0) - 3 = -3.$$

The value of f at $x = -1$ is obtained by replacing every x by -1. Thus

$$f(-1) = 2(-1) - 3 = -5.$$

Similarly, $f(2) = 1$. Every x can also be replaced by an algebraic expression such as $t + 2$ or $1/r$. Thus

$$f(t + 2) = 2(t + 2) - 3 = 2t + 4 - 3 = 2t + 1,$$

and

$$f(1/r) = 2(1/r) - 3 = (2 - 3r)/r.$$

The results of these last two substitutions could be read "f of $t + 2$ is $2t + 1$" and "f of $1/r$ is $(2 - 3r)/r$".

If a function F assigns to an ordered pair (x, y) the image z, this can be indicated as $z = F(x, y)$, and this notation is also called functional notation. Actually this is a special case of the notation $z = f(a)$, where $a = (x, y)$. Direct substitution gives $z = F((x, y))$, which, for simplicity, is written as $z = F(x, y)$. If, for example, $F(x, y) = 2x - 3y$ then the ordered pair $(2, 4)$ has -8 as its image and we write $F(2, 4) = -8$. Similarly, if an ordered triple (x, y, z) has u as its image in the function G we write $u = G(x, y, z)$. If $G(x, y, z) = x - 2y + z$, then $G(0, 1, 1) = -1$.

The graphical representation of a function as a correspondence has only one arrow drawn from each object. However, more than one arrow may point to the same image. The functions

$$f = \{(1, 1), (2, 1), (5, 1), (-3, 1)\},$$
$$g = \{(1, 5), (2, 3), (4, 0), (-3, 1)\},$$

and $\quad h = \{(\text{Anne, doll}), (\text{James, car}), (\text{Karen, doll})\}$

can be represented as in Figure 50.

Since each function is a relation its reverse relation exists. Is the reverse relation of a function also a function? In order to answer this question let us consider the reverse relations corresponding to the functions f, g, and h. Representations of the reverse relations can be obtained by reversing the direction of the arrows in Figure 50. We

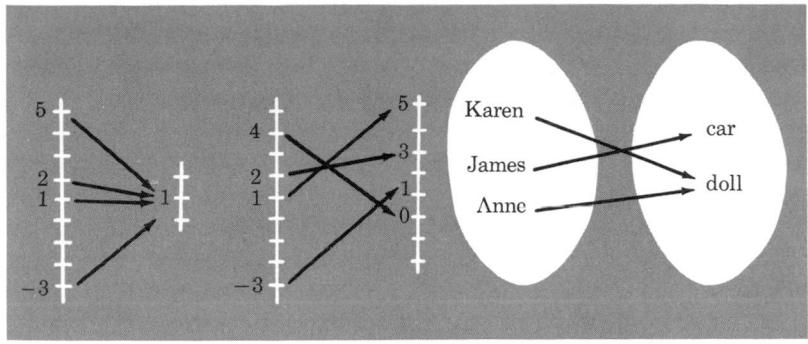

FIG. 50

see that $f_r = \{(1, 1), (1, 2), (1, 5), (1, -3)\}$ which is not a function; $g_r = \{(5, 1), (3, 2), (0, 4), (1, -3)\}$ which is a function; and $h_r = \{(\text{doll, Anne}), (\text{car, James}), (\text{doll, Karen})\}$ which is not a function. What property does g have which causes g_r to be a function? The domain of g which is the set $\{1, 2, 4, -3\}$ is in 1–1 correspondence with the range of g which is $\{5, 3, 0, -1\}$. This is shown by the fact that no two arrows in the representation of g terminate in the same point. A bit of reflection will convince the reader that, in general, f_r is a function if and only if the function f is a 1–1 correspondence between its domain and its range. Such a function f is often called a *1–1 function* or a *1–1 mapping*. Graphically this means that f_r is a function if and only if no horizontal line intersects the graph of the function f in more than one point. As examples, let us graph the functions f and g, in Figure 50, and their reverse relations.

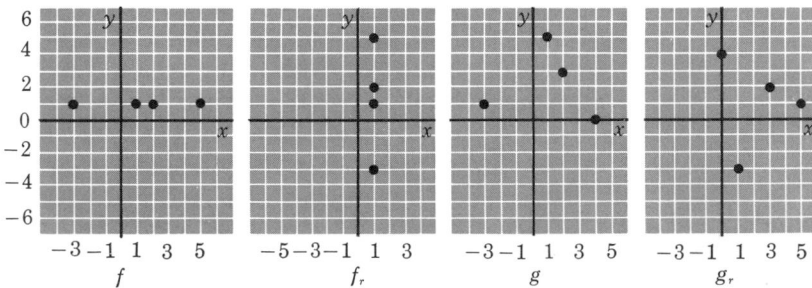

FIG. 51

There are four points of the function f on the horizontal line $y = 1$. Reversing the coordinates produces f_r which has four points on the line $x = 1$. Therefore f_r is not a function. No horizontal line cuts the graph of g in more than one point. Therefore no vertical line cuts g_r in more than one point, and g_r is a function.

TYPES OF FUNCTIONS

Certain types of functions are of sufficient importance to be given individual attention.

The *identity function* on a set S is $f: x \rightarrow x$, which pairs each object with itself. It can also be indicated as $f = \{(x, x) \mid x \in S\}$, or can be defined by $f(x) = x$, where $x \in S$.

A *constant function* is a function whose range is a unit set. As an example, if $A = \{$John, Frank, Sarah, Mary$\}$ and $B = \{$S, E, G, F, D$\}$, where the elements of B are grades, a function g which assigns the same grade to every person in the set A is a constant function. If the grade made by each is E then the range is $\{E\}$, a unit set.

Many of the functions in mathematics are subsets of $Q \times Q$. We shall now discuss some of them. Constant functions on the real numbers occur frequently. For example, $f: x \rightarrow 2$ pairs every real number with 2. Thus $(1, 2)$, $(\sqrt{2}, 2)$, and $(-5, 2)$ are in this function. Its graph is the horizontal line parallel to the x-axis, two units above this axis. This line is usually indicated by the equation $y = 2$.

A *linear function* on the real numbers is of the form $f: x \rightarrow sx + c$. If $s = 1$ and $c = -2$, then $f(x) = x - 2$. The graph of this function is the straight line through the points $(0, -2)$ and $(2, 0)$, frequently indicated by the equation $y = x - 2$.

A *quadratic function* on the real numbers is a function of the form $f: x \rightarrow mx^2 + sx + c$. If $m = 2$, $s = 4$, and $c = -6$, then $f(x) = 2x^2 + 4x - 6$. Its graph is a parabola passing through the points $(0, -6)$, $(1, 0)$, and $(-3, 0)$, usually indicated by $y = 2x^2 + 4x - 6$. The last two points are easily found by factoring $2x^2 + 4x - 6$ into $(2x - 2)(x + 3)$ and setting each factor equal to zero.

Constant functions, linear functions, and quadratic functions in $Q \times Q$ are special types of polynomial functions.

Definition.* *A **polynomial in x of degree n** is an expression which can be put into the form*

$$a_0 x^n + a_1 x^{n-1} + a_2 x^{n-2} + \cdots + a_n$$

*where n is zero or a positive integer, the a's are constants, and $a_0 \neq 0$. The **leading coefficient** of the polynomial is a_0, the **constant term** is a_n, and the **leading term** is $a_0 x^n$.*

Observe that polynomials of zero degree are nonzero constants since the leading coefficient $a_0 \neq 0$.

Definition.   *The **zero polynomial** is the number 0. It does not have any degree.*

Definition.   *A function p is a **polynomial function** of x if $p : x \to p(x)$, where $p(x)$ is a polynomial.*

This definition tells us that a specific nth degree polynomial function pairs x with the value of that nth degree polynomial at x. A constant function in $Q \times Q$ is the zero polynomial or a polynomial function of degree zero, a linear function is a first degree polynomial function, and a quadratic function is a second degree polynomial function. A specific fourth degree polynomial function is

$$f : x \to 5x^4 - 3x^3 - 22x^2 + 12x + 8.$$

The reader will find it instructive to sketch the graphs of the specific polynomial functions given here. Graphs of polynomial functions will be discussed in detail in a later section.

The *absolute value function* for real numbers pairs zero and each positive real number with itself, and pairs every negative number with its negative. The absolute value of x is denoted by $|x|$.

Definition. $|x| = x$, *if* $x \geqq 0$; $|x| = -x$, *if* $x < 0$.

Thus $|0| = 0$, $|5| = 5$, and $|-7| = 7$. (Since -7 is a negative number its negative is $-(-7) = 7$.) Geometrically the absolute value of a number is its distance from the origin when it is represented as a real

---

* This general definition of a polynomial includes polynomials with complex coefficients; however, we shall require that the a's, as well as x, be real numbers and this will keep the functions in $Q \times Q$.

number on the x-axis. Observe that 7 and -7 are each seven units from the origin, therefore $|7| = 7$, and $|-7| = 7$.

It can be proved that $|ab| = |a||b|$, $\left|\dfrac{a}{b}\right| = \dfrac{|a|}{|b|}$, and $|a + b| \leqq |a| + |b|$.

The graph of the function determined by $y = |x|$, where x is a real number, is shown in Figure 52. It can be obtained from the graph of the line $y = x$ by retaining all points of the line $y = x$ which are on the x-axis or above it, and reflecting in the x-axis that portion of the line which lies below the x-axis. Figure 52 shows how this graph and the graphs of other equations involving absolute values can be obtained by omitting the absolute value bars, sketching the resulting curves, and then reflecting certain portions of the curves in the x-axis. In order to sketch $y = |x^2 - 4|$ quickly, we sketch $y = x^2 - 4$, retain the part of this curve where $y \geqq 0$, and reflect, in the x-axis, that part where $y < 0$; that is, we reflect the portion below the x-axis.

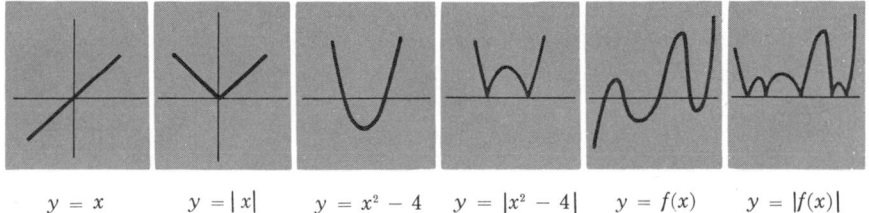

$y = x$ $y = |x|$ $y = x^2 - 4$ $y = |x^2 - 4|$ $y = f(x)$ $y = |f(x)|$

FIG. 52

The reader may understand this process of reflection in the x-axis better if he places one edge of a rectangular mirror along the x-axis, holds it perpendicular to the xy-plane, and observes the position of the image of that portion of the curve which is below the x-axis. This image appears to be above the x-axis. A purely mechanical procedure for getting the graph of $y = |x^2 - 4|$ is to cut the graph of $y = x^2 - 4$ along the parabola and fold it along the x-axis so that the part which is below the axis is folded up above the axis.

To sketch the function $|x| + |y| = 2$ we consider the case where $x \geqq 0$ and $y \geqq 0$. This means that we are restricting the discussion to the first quadrant* of the xy-plane. Since the absolute value of a

---

* The coordinate axes divide the xy-plane into four parts called *quadrants*. These are numbered I, II, III, and IV starting with I in the upper right hand corner and proceeding counterclockwise around the origin.

positive or zero quantity is the quantity itself, in this section of the plane $|x| = x$ and $|y| = y$. Therefore in the first quadrant the equation becomes $x + y = 2$. The graph of this equation in the first quadrant is the line segment joining the points $(2, 0)$ and $(0, 2)$. In the second quadrant $x \leq 0$ and $y \geq 0$. Since the absolute value of a negative quantity is the negative of this quantity, we have in this quadrant $|x| = -x$. Therefore in the second quadrant the equation becomes $-x + y = 2$, which has as its graph the line segment joining $(-2, 0)$ to $(0, 2)$. Proceeding in this fashion in quadrants three and four we find that the graph of $|x| + |y| = 2$ is a square with vertices at $(2, 0)$, $(0, 2)$, $(-2, 0)$ and $(0, -2)$.

The *sum, difference, product* and *quotient* of two functions are defined as follows.

Definition.   *If* $f: x \rightarrow f(x)$ *and* $g: x \rightarrow g(x)$, *then*

the **sum of f and g** *is* $f + g: x \rightarrow f(x) + g(x)$,

the **difference of f and g** *is* $f - g: x \rightarrow f(x) - g(x)$,

the **product of f and g** *is* $f \cdot g: x \rightarrow f(x) \cdot g(x)$,

and, if $g(x) \neq 0$,

the **quotient of f and g** *is* $\dfrac{f}{g}: x \rightarrow \dfrac{f(x)}{g(x)}.$

Each of these functions has as its domain the intersection of the domains of f and g; namely, $d(f) \cap d(g)$, except for the quotient function which is not defined when $g(x) = 0$. If S is the set of points where $g(x) = 0$ then f/g has $[d(f) \cap g(g)] - S$ as its domain.

Example 2.   If $f: x \rightarrow x^2 + 1$ and $g: x \rightarrow x$, where $x \in Q$, then $f + g: x \rightarrow x^2 + x + 1$, $f{-}g: x \rightarrow x^2 - x + 1$, $f \cdot g: x \rightarrow x^3 + x$, and $f/g: x \rightarrow x + (1/x)$. The domain of each of these functions is the set of all real numbers except for the quotient function f/g. Its domain is the set of all real numbers except zero. (See Figure 53.)

If $f = \{(-5, -4), (-2, -4), (-1, 0), (2, 1), (-3, 5), (5, 3)\}$ and $g = \{(-4, -3), (-2, 3), (0, 2), (2, 0), (3, 2)\}$, the numbers $-4, 0$, and 3 are in the range of f and also in the domain of g. The following sketch shows that -5 is sent into -4 by f and -4 is sent into -3 by g. The combined result is that -5 is paired with -3. Similarly -2 is paired with -3, -1 is paired with 2, and 5 is paired with 2. The set

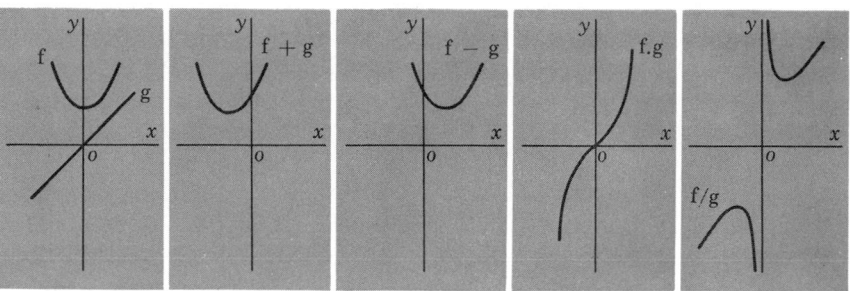

FIG. 53

of ordered pairs which results is a composite function of f and g, which we shall denote by gf. Thus

$$gf = \{(-5, -3), (-2, -3), (-1, 2), (5, 2)\}.$$

Similarly, the numbers -3 and 2 are in the range of g and also in the domain of f, and the composite function is fg. Thus

$$fg = \{(-4, 5), (0, 1), (3, 1)\}.$$

In general, if $f: x \rightarrow f(x)$ and $g: x \rightarrow g(x)$ are two functions, the *composite functions of f and g* are $gf: x \rightarrow g(f(x))$ and $fg: x \rightarrow f(g(x))$. The function gf has as its domain those elements x in the domain of f for which $f(x)$ is in the domain of g. The function fg has as its domain those elements x in the domain of g for which $g(x)$ is in the domain of f. A composite function is frequently called a function of a function.

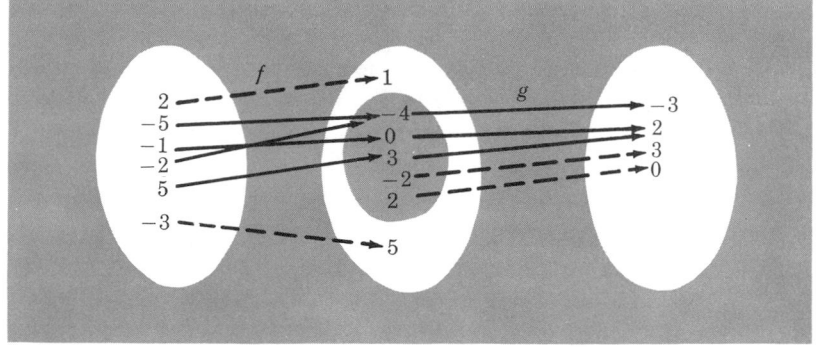

FIG. 54

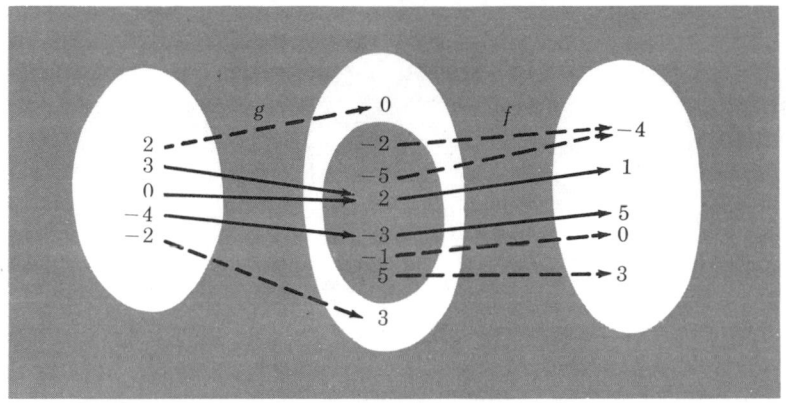

FIG. 55

Observe the difference between $f \cdot g$ which is the product function, and fg which is the composite function.

It has been pointed out that the reverse of a function f is a relation but not necessarily a function. If, however, it is a function the composites of f and f_r have special properties. If (a, b) is in f then (b, a) is in f_r. The function f sends a into b and the function f_r sends b into a; therefore the composite function $f_r f$ sends a into a and is the identity function on the domain of f. Also the composite function $f f_r$ sends b into b and is the identity function on the range of f. A bit of reflection should convince the reader that there is at most one such function. If there is such a function it is called the inverse function of f and is often denoted by f^{-1}.

Definition. *If for two functions f and g the composite function gf is the identity function on the domain of f and fg is the identity function on the domain of g, then each of the functions f and g is the* **inverse function** *of the other.*

This inverse relationship between the functions can be denoted by $f^{-1} = g$ and $g^{-1} = f$.

Example 3. If $f: x \to x + 5$, where x is a real number then the image of each real number a is $a + 5$. If the function $g: x \to x - 5$ is applied to this image the result is $(a + 5) - 5 = a$, the original number, Therefore $gf: x \rightarrow x$. Under g, the image of b is $b - 5$. If f is applied to this image the result is $(b - 5) + 5 = b$. Therefore $fg: x \rightarrow x$ and f and g are inverse functions.

Example 4. Similarly, the function which multiplies a given real number by 3 and the function which divides it by 3 are inverse functions. The first is $f: x \rightarrow 3x$ and the second is $g: x \rightarrow x/3$. Thus $f(a) = 3a$ and $g(3a) = 3a/3 = a$. Therefore gf is the identity function. Also $g(b) = b/3$ and $f(b/3) = 3(b/3) = b$. Therefore, fg is the identity function.

If f is a 1–1 function its inverse function exists. We shall denote it by f^{-1}. If the ordered pairs in f are known, then the ordered pairs in f^{-1} can be obtained by reversing the ordered pairs in f, regardless of what type of elements are involved in the ordered pairs. Also the graph of the inverse function can be obtained by reflecting the graph of the function in the line $y = x$.

When a 1–1 function f is a set of ordered pairs of real numbers defined by an equation $y = f(x)$ the equation which defines the inverse relation can be obtained by interchanging x and y to obtain $x = f(y)$. If $y = 2x - 3$, then interchanging x and y produces $x = 2y - 3$. If the second equation is solved for y it gives $y = (x + 3)/2$. The image of a real number a according to the first equation is $2a - 3$, and the image of $2a - 3$ according to the second equation is $[(2a - 3) + 3]/2 = a$, which is the original element. Also, starting with the second equation, we find that the image of an element b is $(b + 3)/2$. Under the first equation the image of $(b + 3)/2$ is $2[(b + 3)/2] - 3 = b$, the original element.

Similarly, $y = x^3$ and $x = y^3$ define inverse functions over the real numbers. The second equation, when solved for y, is $y = \sqrt[3]{x}$. The reader can verify that the cube root of the cube of a is a, and that the cube of the cube root of a is a.

Some functions are identical with their inverses. If $g: x \rightarrow 1/x$, where $x \neq 0$ is a real number, then $y = 1/x$. Interchanging x and y gives $x = 1/y$ and when this is solved for y it gives $y = 1/x$, which defines the original function. This function pairs x with its reciprocal. Since the reciprocal of the reciprocal is the original number the mapping applied twice brings us back to the original element.

Occasionally the domain of a function must be restricted in order for it to be the inverse function of a given function. The inverse of the function defined by $y = \sqrt{x}$ is such an example. The graph of the function is half of a parabola. The graph of the inverse function is obtained by reflecting this graph in the line $y = x$ and is therefore half of a parabola. If we interchange x and y in the equation $y = \sqrt{x}$ we obtain $x = \sqrt{y}$. If we try to solve this for y we obtain $y = x^2$. However, this is the equation of an entire parabola. Therefore, this equation alone cannot represent the inverse function. We can, however, obtain the correct graph from this equation and a restriction on x by stipulating that $y = x^2$ and $x \geq 0$. The fact that x must be positive or zero comes from the equation $x = \sqrt{y}$ since the radical indicates that the square root must be nonnegative. This restriction was lost in the process of squaring to find y.

OTHER NAMES FOR FUNCTIONS

Near the beginning of this section we stated that a function is often called a *mapping*. Because a function assigns exactly one element of a second set to each element of a first set it resembles the mapping process which assigns exactly one point on a piece of paper to each point of some portion of the earth's surface. When this property of the function concept is to be emphasized we call the function a mapping.

Operations were discussed in Section 24. The reader should have no trouble understanding that every operation is a function and that every function is an operation. Therefore they are the same concept. However, when we speak of a function as an *operation* or an *operator* we are emphasizing that it behaves like some of the operations with which we are familiar, such as addition, or taking a square root of a number, or finding the complement of a given set. An operation such as addition assigns a specific sum to an ordered pair of real numbers. Therefore it is a function from $Q \times Q$ to Q.

Functions are also called *transformations*. This terminology suggests a change in position or shape of certain geometric figures. Thus the function $f: x \to x + 3$, where x is a real number, assigns to every real number an image which exceeds the number by 3. If the real numbers are represented on a horizontal line as indicated in Figure 56, then every point corresponds to a point three units to the right. The images of the points in the set $\{x \mid -1 < x < 1\}$ are the points in the set $\{x \mid 2 < x < 4\}$. This suggests a "mechanical" procedure for matching an object with its image. Imagine that instead of one horizontal line there are two coincident wires of "infinite" length, identically marked as x-axes, and placed so that the origins match and each real number r on one wire coincides with the same real number r on the other. Let one wire represent the object set and the other represent the image set. If the object wire is slid three units to the right along the image wire each object will coincide with its image. The segment between -1 and 1 will also coincide with the segment between 2 and 4. Because this type of "mechanical" procedure will match each object with its image we sometimes say that this function or transformation shifts the x-axis 3 units to the right. This is a quick, though slightly inaccurate, way of indicating which values are paired in this function. Similarly, we shall say that the transformation $T: x \rightarrow x - 5$, where x is real, shifts the x-axis 5 units to the left.

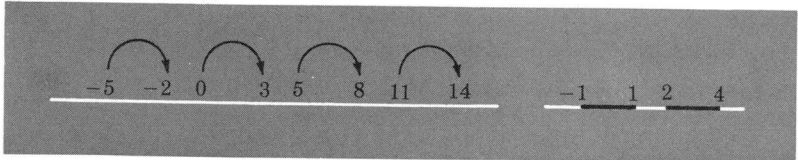

FIG. 56

In the plane the transformation

$$T: \begin{array}{l} x \rightarrow x + 4 \\ y \rightarrow y - 2 \end{array}$$

pairs the object point (x, y) with the image point $(x + 4, y - 2)$. It can also be indicated by $T: (x, y) \rightarrow (x + 4, y - 2)$. It transforms the circle of radius 2 with center at the origin into the circle of radius 2 with center at $(4, -2)$. This means that the images of the points on the first circle are the points that lie on the second circle. It shifts the entire xy-plane 4 units to the right and 2 units down, so that the origin has as its image the point $(4, -2)$. The y-axis transforms into the line $x = 4$ and the x-axis transforms into the line $y = -2$. The reader can verify these statements by checking a number of images of

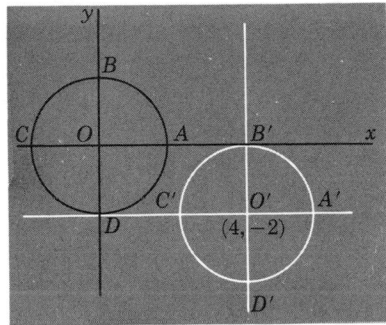 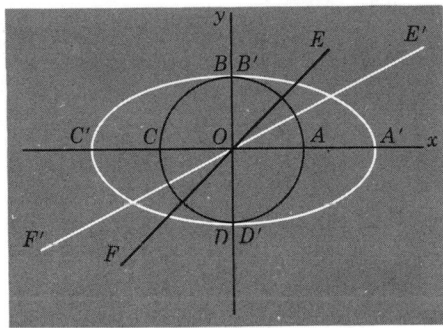

FIG. 57   FIG. 58

specific points. It is often convenient to indicate the image of a point A by A'. This should not be confused with the set notation for complementation.

In the plane, the transformation $T: (x, y) \rightarrow (2x, y)$ transforms the circle with center at the origin and radius 2 into the ellipse shown in Figure 58. It transforms the line $y = x$ into the line $y = x/2$. Where are the points that map into themselves?

EXERCISES

Throughout this set of exercises Q will denote the set of all real numbers, J will denote the set of all integers, and x and y will denote the objects in the ordered pairs (x, y).

1. Tell which of the graphs in Figure 59 are graphs of functions and which are graphs of relations that are not functions.

Indicate those functions which have inverses.

2. Tell which of the following define functions $f: x \rightarrow y$ over the indicated universe.

(a) x is the child of y. U = all people in China.

(b) y is the father of x. U = all people in the United States.

(c) $x = y^2$; $x, y \, \epsilon \, Q$.   (d) $x^2 + y^2 = 25$; $x, y \, \epsilon \, Q$.

(e) $y = (2 - x)(x + 1)(x - 5)$; $x, y \, \epsilon \, Q$.

(f) $3y = 2x - 12$; $x, y \, \epsilon \, Q$.

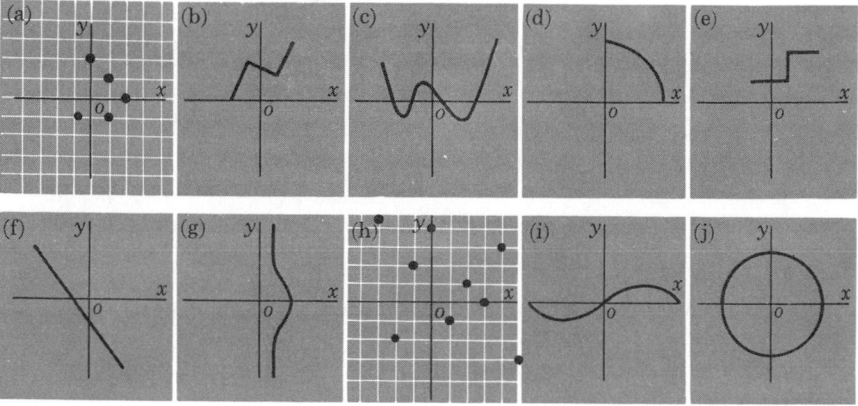

FIG. 59

3. Explain the difference between the following, where f and g are functions, and $f - g$ is the difference between the functions f and g.

(a) $f \cup g$ and $f + g$.　　(c) $f \cap g'$ and $f - g$.

(b) $f \cap g$ and $f - g$.　　(d) $f \cdot g$ and fg.

4. Give the domain and the range of the function defined by each of the following, where x and y are real numbers.

(a) $y = 3x - 2$.

(b) $y = \sqrt{x}$.

(c) $y = \sqrt{x^2 - 9}$.

(d) $y = \sqrt{9 - x^2}$.

(e) $y = x^2 - 3$.

(f) $y = \dfrac{x}{x - 1}$.

5. Give the domain and the range of the function defined by each of the following, where x and y are integers.

(a) $y = 2x - 7$, $|x| < 4$.

(b) $\{(-2, 7), (3, -2), (5, -1), (8, 2)\}$.

(c) $y = |x - 2|$.

(d) $|x| + |y| = 6$, $x \geq 0$, $y \leq 0$.

(e) $y = |x^2 - 3|$.

6. Sketch the graphs of the functions defined by the following, where $x, y \in Q$.

(a) $y = x(2 - x)(x + 3)$.

(b) $y = |x^2 - 9|$.

(c) $y = (x - 1)^2(x + 2)^2$.

(d) $y = x/|x|$.

(e) $y = \sqrt{25 - x^2}$.

(f) $\begin{cases} y = -2, \text{ if } x \leq 0, \\ y = 2x - 3, \text{ if } 0 < x \leq 3, \\ y = x, \quad \text{if } x > 3. \end{cases}$

7. Let $D: cx^n \to cnx^{n-1}$, where x is a real number, n is a nonnegative integer and c is a fixed constant. Find the image of each of the following under this mapping.

　(a) x^3.　　(b) $5x^2$.　　(c) $-3x^7$.　　(d) $-7x^0$.　　(e) $6x^5$.

8. Find the following, given that

$$F(x) = 3x^2 - 2x - 3, \quad G(x) = 3 - x^2, \quad H(x, y) = 7x - 3y + xy,$$

$$K(x, y, z) = 2x^2 - y^2 + 7xyz, \quad T(x, y, z, w) = xy^2 - z^2w, \quad \text{and}$$

$$f(x) = \frac{x}{x - 1}.$$

(a) $F(0)$.	(g) $K(0, -1, 2)$.	(m) $F(x + h)$.
(b) $F(-3)$.	(h) $K(a, b, c)$.	(n) $F(x + h) - F(x)$.
(c) $G(0)$.	(i) $T(1, -1, -1, 2)$.	(o) $F(a)/G(a)$.
(d) $G(-1)$.	(j) $T(a, c, -b, t)$.	(p) $H(x + y, x - y)$.
(e) $H(0, 0)$.	(k) $G(a + b)$.	(q) $[G(x + h) - G(x)]/h$.
(f) $H(1, -2)$.	(l) $G(1/a)$.	(r) $f\left(\dfrac{a}{a - 1}\right)$.

9. For the functions defined in Exercise 8 find the following.

　(a) $F \cdot G$.　　(c) $F + G$.　　(e) FG.　　　(g) Gf.

　(b) $F \cap G$.　　(d) $K - H$.　　(f) GF.　　　(h) fG.

10. Find a relation which is not a function but whose reverse relation is a function.

11. Do the equations $y = \dfrac{x^2 - 4}{x - 2}$ and $y = x + 2$ determine the same function? Explain your answer.

12. Using the functions $f = \{(-1, 1), \ (0, 3), \ (1, 5)\}$ and $g = \{(-1, 1), (0, -2)\}$

　(a) Find $f - g$, when this notation denotes the difference function;

　(b) Find $f - g$, when this notation denotes the relative complement of g in f.

13. Which of the following are polynomials in x? Give the degree of each polynomial.

　(a) $7 - 2x - x^3$.　　　　　　　　(e) $3x^3 - x^6 + 11x^4 + 9$.

　(b) $x^{-2} + 3x^{-1} - 5$.　　　　　　(f) $5x^{3/4} + 2x^{1/4} + 5$.

　(c) $\sqrt{x} + 5$.　　　　　　　　　(g) 32.

　(d) $7 - 3x$.　　　　　　　　　　(h) $\sqrt{x + 2}$.

14. Find the inverses of the functions defined by the following equations and inequalities, where x, $y \in Q$.

(a) $y = 3x + 2$.

(c) $y = |2x - 6|$, $x \leqq 0$.

(b) $y = \sqrt{25 - x^2}$, $x \geqq 0$.

(d) $y = x^2$, $x \leqq 0$.

15. The greatest integer function is denoted by $y = [x]$, where x is real. It is defined to be the largest integer which is less than or equal to x. For example, $[2.73] = 2$ and $[-2.73] = -3$. Sketch

(a) $y = [x]$.

(b) $y = x - [x]$.

(c) $y = |[x]|$.

16. Under the transformation $T : (x, y) \to (x + 2, y + 1)$ find the image sets of the following.

(a) The origin.

(b) The y-axis.

(c) The x-axis.

(d) The circle with center at the origin and radius 2.

17. Find the reverse image of S under f, where x is a real number. Is f_r a function?

(a) $S = \{0, -1, 2\}$, $f: x \to 2x - 1$.

(c) $S = \{1\}$, $f: x \to x^3$.

(b) $S = \{5\}, f: x \to x^2$.

(d) $S = \{0, 3\}$, $f: x \to |x|$.

18. (a) List all the functions from A to B which have A as their domain if $A = \{r, s\}$ and $B = \{u, v\}$. Which of these have inverses? (b) Do the same for $A = \{r, s, t\}$ and $B = \{u, v, w\}$.

19. Determine which of the following statements define a function.

(a) A function is a set of ordered pairs in which no two distinct pairs have the same first component.

(b) A function is a correspondence which assigns to each element of a given set a unique element of some other, not necessarily distinct, set.

(c) A function F is a binary relation such that if $x R y$ and $x R z$ then $y = z$.

(d) A function is a relation which contains no ordered pairs whose second components are different but whose first components are the same.

(e) A function in $S \times T$ is a relation F in $S \times T$ such that whenever (x, y) and (x, z) belong to F then $y = z$.

(f) A subset f of $A \times B$ is a function from A into B or a mapping of A into B, if
  (i) for each $x \in A$ there is a $y \in B$ such that $(x, y) \in f$,

(ii) for each $x \,\epsilon\, A$ and for each y and $z \,\epsilon\, B$, if $(x, y) \,\epsilon f$ and $(x, z) \,\epsilon f$, then $y = z$.

20. Prove the following theorems where $\sqrt{x}$ means the real non-negative square root of x, and a, b, x, and z are real numbers.

Theorem 1. $|a| = a$ or $|a| = -a$.

Theorem 2. If $z \geqq a$ and $z \geqq -a$, then $z \geqq |a|$.

Theorem 3. $|a| \geqq a$ and $|a| \geqq -a$.

Theorem 4. $|a| + |b| \geqq |a + b|$.

Theorem 5. $|a| = \sqrt{a^2}$.

Theorem 6. $|a||b| = |ab|$.

Theorem 7. $\left|\dfrac{a}{b}\right| = \dfrac{|a|}{|b|}$.

Theorem 8. The difference between two real numbers is greater than or equal to the difference between their absolute values; that is, $|x - z| \geqq ||x| - |z||$. (Graphically, this theorem says that the points representing two real numbers on the x-axis can be farther apart than the points representing their absolute values. Briefly, but less accurately, stated: Two real numbers can be farther apart than their absolute values. *Hint for proof:* Start with the identity $(x - y) + y = x$; take the absolute value of each side. Apply Theorem 4 to the left side to obtain $|x - y| \geqq |x| - |y|$. Reverse x and y to obtain $|x - y| \geqq -(|x| - |y|)$ and then use Theorem 2.)

III. Solution Sets

Throughout this section we shall denote the set of integers by J and the set of real numbers by Q.

When a symbol, such as x, is used to represent an arbitrary element of a set T it is sometimes convenient to call this symbol a variable.

Definition. *A **variable** is a symbol which represents an unspecified or arbitrary element of a specified set, called the **replacement set**.*

If x represents an element of the set S, where S is the set of names of rivers in the world, then the declarative statement

The x river is in South America,

is true if x is replaced by "Orinoco" or "Amazon" and false if x is replaced by "Rhine", "Mississippi", "Euphrates", or "Danube". This type of statement is an open statement. It is neither true nor false but becomes true or false if x is replaced by the name of a river. A replacement, such as "Amazon", which makes the statement true is called a *solution* of the open statement. If x is replaced by "how" the sentence is neither true nor false and is considered meaningless because "how" is not the name of a river.

Open sentences can have more than one symbol in them. The statement that

x is the capital city of the state of y,

is true for some replacements of x and y but false for others. If the symbol x in this statement represents an element from the set C of names of cities in the United States and y represents an element from the set S of names of states in the United States, then x and y are variables. We shall say that $C \times S$ is the universe of discourse of the open sentence in which x and y occur.* Then the ordered pair (Tallahassee, Florida) is a replacement which makes the statement true and is therefore a solution.

Definition. *An* **open statement** *is a declarative sentence which*
(a) *contains a finite number n of variables, where* $n \geq 1$,
(b) *is neither true nor false, but*
(c) *becomes true or false when the variables are replaced by elements from their replacement sets.*

Sometimes it is difficult to see that certain open sentences are neither true nor false. The variables serve as placeholders for the elements that they represent, consequently they act as blanks in the statement. For example, "_____ is the richest man living" is neither true nor false. It is not a complete statement until the blank is filled.

Definition. *Let* v_1, v_2, v_3, $\cdots$, v_n *represent the variables in an open statement and let* R_1, R_2, R_3, $\cdots$, R_n *be their respective replacement sets. Then the* **universe of discourse** U *of the open statement is the Cartesian Product set* $R_1 \times R_2 \times R_3 \times \cdots \times R_n$. *If* $(a_1, a_2, a_3, \cdots, a_n)$ *is an element of* U *such that the open statement is true when* v_1 *is replaced by* a_1, v_2 *is replaced by* a_2, $\cdots$, *and* v_n *is replaced by* a_n, *then* $(a_1, a_2, a_3, \cdots, a_n)$ *is* **a solution** *of the open statement.*

It should be observed that a specific arrangement of the variables produces a specific universe of discourse.

Definition. *The* **solution set** *of an open statement is the set consisting of all of its solutions.*

The solution set for "The x river is in South America" is the set of all rivers in South America, and the solution set of "x is the capital

---

* The set $S \times C$ could just as well be the universe of discourse if we agree to list the state first and the city second. Regardless of which order is chosen the name of the city is substituted for x and the name of the state for y.

city of the state of y" is the set of all ordered pairs (x, y) such that x is a capital city in the United States and y is the state having x as its capital.

EQUALITIES

Consider the following equations where x, y, and z represent real numbers. They are open statements.

(1) $5x - 2 = 7$.

(2) $x(x - 3) = 2(3 + x)$.

(3) $x + y = 5$.

(4) $x(2x - 5)(5 - x) = 0$.

(5) $x - 2y + 3z = 12$.

(6) $x^2 + 5 = 0$.

(7) $(x - 3)(x + 3) = x^2 - 9$.

(8) $\dfrac{x^2 - 4}{x + 2} = x - 2$.

(9) $\dfrac{3x^2 + 2}{x - 1} = 3x + 3 + \dfrac{5}{x - 1}$.

(10) $x(x - 5) + 3 = 3(1 - x) - x(2 - x)$.

(11) $(x + y)(x - y) = x^2 - y^2$.

We are interested in finding all values of the variables for which each statement is true. The set of all such values is the solution set of the open statement. One way of finding solutions is to substitute real numbers for the variables. For example, if $x = 0$ in (1) we have $5(0) - 2 = 7$, a statement which is not true. Similarly, if $x = -2$, then $5(-2) - 2 = 7$ is not a true statement. However, $x = 1.8$ is a real number which makes the statement true, for $5(1.8) - 2 = 9 - 2 = 7$. The reader no doubt knows that further testing will not produce any other real number which will make the statement true. In fact, he would not waste time substituting numbers one at a time but would use elementary methods of algebra to obtain $5x = 9$, and $x = 1.8$. Therefore, the solution set is the unit set $\{1.8\}$. We have suggested substituting numbers one at a time in order to emphasize the basic ideas involved.

Substitution shows that -1 and 6 make statement (2) true. However, all other numbers will make the statement false. By the methods of algebra it can be shown that (2) has only two solutions and that its solution set is $\{-1, 6\}$.

The universe of discourse for statement (3) is $Q \times Q$. There are an infinite number of ordered pairs (x, y) for which this statement is true. For example, $(1, 4)$, $(-1, 6)$, $(1.5, 3.5)$, $(\sqrt{2}, 5 - \sqrt{2})$. Substitution shows that $1 + 4 = 5$, $-1 + 6 = 5$, $1.5 + 3.5 = 5$, and $\sqrt{2} + 5 - \sqrt{2} = 5$. There are also many ordered pairs which do not satisfy this equation. For example $3 + 8 = 5$ is a false statement. The best way to visualize this infinite solution set is to consider its graph which is a straight line through the points $(0, 5)$ and $(5, 0)$. If the sum of the coordinates of any point in the plane is 5 then the point is on the line, and if the point is on the line then the sum of its coordinates is 5, regardless of how complicated the coordinates may appear. For example, $(3\frac{15}{123}, 1\frac{108}{123})$ and $(-2.75432, 7.75432)$ are on this line.

Statement (4) is true only when $x = 0$, $x = 2.5$, or $x = 5$. All other values of x make it false. Therefore the solution set is $\{0, 2.5, 5\}$.

Statement (5) is true for an infinite number of ordered triples (x, y, z). For example, it is true for $(12, 0, 0)$, $(0, -6, 0)$, $(0, 0, 4)$, $(8, 1, 2)$ and $(-1, -8, -1)$, but is false for $(1, 1, 1)$ and $(0, 0, 0)$.

Equation (6) is not true for any value of x, for the square of a real number is always 0 or a positive number. Therefore, if 5 is added to 0 or a positive number the result is 5 or more, and it can never be 0. Therefore the solution set of (6) is the null set, denoted by $\emptyset$.

Equations (1), (2), (3), (4), (5) and (6) are true for some, or none, of the values of the variables and false for others. Such equations are called conditional equations.

Definition. *A statement of equality which involves variables and which is false for some of the values of the variables is a **conditional equation** over its universe of discourse.*

Another way of stating this definition is to say that a conditional equation is a statement of equality which is true only for certain values of the variables or for none of the values of the variables.

We now turn our attention to the remaining statements. Equation (7) is true for $x = 0$ since $(0 - 3)(0 + 3) = 0^2 - 9$. It is true for $x = 1$ since $(1 - 3)(1 + 3) = 1^2 - 9$. In fact, it is true for all real values of x. By using the methods of algebra, we see that since the product $(x - 3)(x + 3)$ is $x^2 - 9$, we have $x^2 - 9 = x^2 - 9$. This shows that the truth of the statement is independent of the value of x. Therefore the solution set is Q.

Equation (8) is meaningless for $x = -2$, since substituting this value into the denominator produces $-2 + 2 = 0$, and division by 0 is not defined. For every value of x other than $x = -2$ the statement is meaningful and true. Therefore the solution set is all real numbers except -2; that is, $Q - \{-2\}$.

Statement (9) is meaningless when $x = 1$, for this value produces 0 in the denominator. Algebraic simplification shows that the statement is true for all other values of x since the right side,

$3x + 3 + \dfrac{5}{x - 1}$, when simplified, produces $\dfrac{3(x + 1)(x - 1) + 5}{x - 1} =$

$\dfrac{3(x^2 - 1) + 5}{x - 1} = \dfrac{3x^2 + 2}{x - 1}$, which is the left side. The solution set is

$Q - \{1\}$.

Statement (10) is true for all values of x, for each side, when simplified, produces $x^2 - 5x + 3$.

Statement (11) is true for all ordered pairs (x, y) for the left side reduces to $x^2 - y^2$. The solution set is $Q \times Q$.

Statements (7), (8), (9), (10) and (11) are true for all real numbers for which they are meaningful. They are identities.

Definition. *A statement of equality involving variables, which is true for all values of the variables for which the statement is meaningful is an* **identity** *over its universe of discourse.*

INEQUALITIES

Now consider the following inequalities where x, y, and z are real numbers. Keep in mind that an inequality is preserved if

(a) the same quantity is added to or subtracted from both sides,

(b) both sides are multiplied or divided by the same *positive* quantity, and

(c) that multiplying an inequality by a *negative* quantity reverses the direction of the inequality.

(12) $(x + 3)(x - 5) < 0.$ (13) $(x + 3)(x - 5) > 0.$

(14) $(x - 3)^2(x + 2)(5 - x) < 0.$ (16) $|x + 1| + |x - 2| \geqq 3.$

(15) $|x + 1| + |x - 2| < 3.$ (17) $x^2 + 1 > 0.$

We can find the solution sets for (12) and (13) simultaneously. This is done by first finding the solution set for $(x + 3)(x - 5) = 0$. This is $\{-3, 5\}$. These two points divide the x-axis into three parts; namely, the part to the left of -3, the part between -3 and 5, and the part to the right of 5. (See Figure 60). We test a number to the left of -3, such as -4. If $x = -4$, then $x + 3$ is negative and $x - 5$ is negative. Therefore the product is positive. We indicate this as follows:

$$x = -4, \quad (-)(-) > 0.$$

We also observe that *any other number to the left of* -3 would make each factor negative and therefore make the product positive; that is, would produce the same result. If x is a number between -3 and 5, such as 0, then the first factor is positive and the second factor is negative. We indicate this in the same manner.

$$x = 0, \quad (+)(-) < 0.$$

Finally, if x is a number to the right of 5, such as 6, both factors are positive.

$$x = 6, \quad (+)(+) > 0.$$

Then we label each part of the figure as positive or negative. The solution set for (12) is read from the figure. It is $\{x|\ -3 < x < 5\}$. The solution set for (13) is also read from the figure. It is $\{x\ |\ x < -3\ \text{or}\ x > 5\}$.

We follow the same procedure for (14). The solution set of $(x - 3)^2(x + 2)(5 - x) = 0$ is $\{-2, 3, 5\}$. The numbers in the solution set divide the x-axis into four parts. We test a number in each part and observe the signs of the factors.

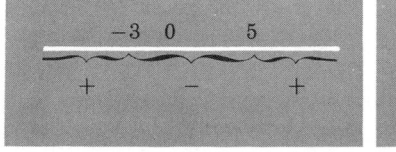   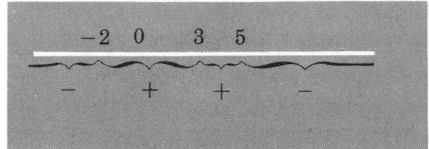

FIG. 60   FIG. 61

$$x = -3, \quad (+)(-)(+) < 0.$$
$$x = 0, \quad (+)(+)(+) > 0.$$
$$x = 4, \quad (+)(+)(+) > 0.$$
$$x = 6, \quad (+)(+)(-) < 0.$$

The solution set of (14) is $\{x \mid x < -2 \text{ or } x > 5\}$. The information obtained also shows that the solution set of $(x - 3)^2(x + 2)(5 - x)$ > 0 is $\{x \mid -2 < x < 5 \text{ and } x \neq 3\}$. We shall show later how some of these solution sets can be used to sketch the graphs of polynomials over the real numbers.

The solution set for (15) will be obtained graphically in the following section. We shall show another method of solving this inequality.* We observe first that the absolute value of a number is equal to the absolute value of its negative. Thus $|5| = |-5|$. Since $r - s$ is the negative of $s - r$, then $|r - s| = |s - r|$. Furthermore, it can be proved that $|a| + |b| \geqq |a + b|$, regardless of what real numbers a and b represent. If we use the left side of (15), first replace $x - 2$ by its negative, and then use $a = x + 1$ and $b = 2 - x$ in $|a| + |b| \geqq$ $|a + b|$, we have

$$|x + 1| + |x - 2| = |x + 1| + |2 - x| \geqq$$
$$|(x + 1) + (2 - x)| = |x + 1 + 2 - x| = |3| = 3.$$

Therefore $|x + 1| + |2 - x| \geqq 3$ for all values of x, and the left side of (15) is never less than 3. The solution set is $\varnothing$. From this discussion it also follows that the solution set of (16) is Q.

The solution set of (17) is Q because the square of a real number is zero or positive. If zero or a positive number is added to 1 the result is 1 or more, and therefore positive.

---

* A third method of finding the solution is worth mentioning because of the method involved. We first find the point where $x + 1 = 0$; namely, $x = -1$, and the point where $x - 2 = 0$; namely $x = 2$. These two points divide the x-axis into three parts. For values to the left of -1, $x + 1 < 0$ and $x - 2 < 0$. Since the absolute value of a negative quantity is the negative of the quantity, we can remove the absolute value bars and replace each quantity by its negative. Thus to the left of -1 we have $-x - 1 - x + 2 < 3$, $-2x + 1$ < 3, $-2x < 2$, $x > -1$. This is impossible if $x < -1$. For $-1 < x < 2$, $x + 1 > 0$, $x - 2 < 0$, therefore $x + 1 - x + 2 < 3$, $3 < 3$. This is impossible. For $x > 2$, $x + 1 > 0$, $x - 2 > 0$, therefore $x + 1 + x - 2 < 3$, $2x - 1 < 3$, $2x < 4$, and $x < 2$. This is impossible if $x > 2$. Therefore the solution set is ϕ.

From this discussion we can see that inequalities, like equations, can be separated into two classes according to their solution sets; namely, conditional inequalities and absolute inequalities.

Definition. *An inequality which involves variables and which is false for some of the values of the variables is a* **conditional inequality** *over its universe of discourse.*

Definition. *An inequality which involves variables and which is true for all values of the variables for which the inequality is meaningful is an* **absolute inequality** *over its universe of discourse.*

A solution set which satisfies more than one open sentence is the intersection of the solution sets of the open statements involved. A solution set which satisfies one open statement or the other is the union of the solution sets.

EXERCISES

1. Classify each of the following as a conditional equation, an identity, a conditional inequality, or an absolute inequality. Indicate the solution set, given that $x, y \in Q$.

(a) $\dfrac{x^2 - 4y^2}{x - 2y} = x + 2y$.

(b) $2x^2 + 7 < 0$.

(c) $x^2 + 4 > 0$.

(d) $x^2 + y^2 = 0$.

(e) $(x - 5)(x + 4) > 0$.

(f) $(2x - 3)(x + 5) = 0$.

(g) $(x - 2)^2(x + 3)(x + 5) > 0$.

(h) $\dfrac{24}{x + 2} + \dfrac{10}{x - 2} = \dfrac{7}{3}$.

(i) $4(x - 2) - (x - 4) > x$.

(j) $7 + x^2 + y^2 > 0$.

(k) $x^2 + y^2 - 16 > 0$.

(*l*) $\dfrac{5}{x+2} + \dfrac{3}{x} = \dfrac{8x-3}{x^2+2x}$.

(*m*) $4x^2 - 4x + 5 < 0$.

(*n*) $7x + 2 = -x + 3$.

(*o*) $2x - 3y = 6$.

(*p*) $\dfrac{x^2 - 5x + 2}{x+3} = x - 8 + \dfrac{26}{x+3}$.

(*q*) $(2x-3)(x-7) = x^2 - 7x$.

(*r*) $|x-1| + |x+3| \geq 4$.

(*s*) $x^2 - 5x + 6 = (x-1)(x-7) + 3x - 1$.

(*t*) $(x-4)(x+3)(x-1) < 0$.

(*u*) $\dfrac{4}{x-4} - \dfrac{1}{x-2} = \dfrac{x}{x^2 - 6x + 8}$.

(*v*) $(x-6)(x-2)^2(x+3)(x+1) = 0$.

(*w*) $5x^3 - 7x^2 + 2x - 1 = (x+1)(5x^2 - 12x + 14) - 15$.

(*x*) $(3x-y)(3x+y) = 9x^2 - y^2$.

(*y*) $3x^2 + 2y^2 < 0$.

(*z*) $(x-2)^2 + (y-3)^2 = 0$.

2. Find an open statement which is true of exactly n real numbers where n is (*a*) 1; (*b*) 2; (*c*) 3; (*d*) 4; (*e*) 5.

3. Prove that the following are absolute inequalities, where a, b, c, x and y are real numbers.

(*a*) $x^2 + y^2 \geq 2xy$.

(*b*) $x^2 + y^2 \geq 2|x||y|$.

(*c*) $a^2 + b^2 + c^2 \geq ab + ac + bc$.

(*d*) $\dfrac{a+b}{2} \geq \sqrt{ab}$, where $a > 0$ and $b > 0$.

(*e*) $x^3 + 4xy^2 \geq 4x^2y$ if $x > 0$.

(*f*) $x^3 + y^3 \geq x^2y + xy^2$ if $x > 0$ and $y > 0$.

IV. Graphs
of Solution Sets

Solution sets of open statements over the real numbers are often intervals.

INTERVALS

Intervals on the x-axis are classified as open, half-open, or closed according to whether they contain neither of their end points, one of the end points, or both of the end points, respectively.

Definition. *If x is a real number, the set of all x such that $a < x < b$ is the **open interval from a to b**. It is usually denoted by (a, b). The sets $a \leqq x < b$ and $a < x \leqq b$ are the **half-open intervals from a to b**. They are denoted by $[a, b)$ and $(a, b]$, respectively. The set $a \leqq x \leqq b$ is the **closed interval from a to b**. It is denoted by $[a, b]$. The sets $x > a$ and $x < a$ are the **open infinite intervals,** or **open rays,** and the sets $x \geqq a$ and $x \leqq a$ are the **closed infinite intervals,** or **closed rays**.*

Even though the notation (a, b) is also used for an ordered pair of numbers it is usually clear from the context whether it represents an ordered pair or an open interval.

For easy reference we list the information in the preceding definitions as follows along with the usual graphical representation.

$(a, b) = \{x \mid x \in Q$ and $a < x < b\}$ (open interval),

$[a, b) = \{x \mid x \in Q$ and $a \leqq x < b\}$ (half-open interval),

$(a, b] = \{x \mid x \in Q$ and $a < x \leqq b\}$ (half-open interval),

$[a, b] = \{x \mid x \in Q$ and $a \leqq x \leqq b\}$ (closed interval),

$(a, \rightarrow) = \{x \mid x \in Q$ and $x > a\}$ (open ray),

$(\leftarrow, a) = \{x \mid x \in Q$ and $x < a\}$ (open ray),

$[a, \rightarrow) = \{x \mid x \in Q$ and $x \geqq a\}$ (closed ray),

$(\leftarrow, a] = \{x \mid x \in Q$ and $x \leqq a\}$ (closed ray).

All of the intervals here defined are often referred to as intervals of the x-axis.

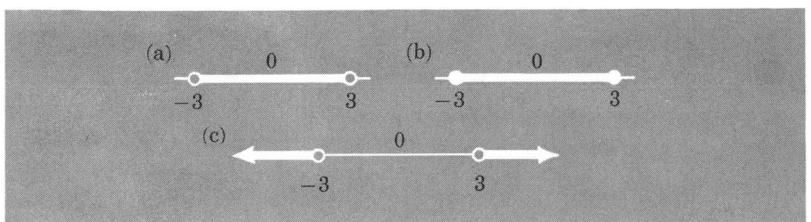

FIG. 62

Example 1. If $|x| < 3$, then $-3 < x < 3$. This open interval is indicated graphically in Figure 62a.

Example 2. If $|x| \leqq 3$, then $-3 \leqq x \leqq 3$. This closed interval is indicated in Figure 62b.

Example 3. If $|x| > 3$, then $x < -3$ or $x > 3$. This set can be indicated as in Figure 62c.

Example 4. If $z \in Q$ and $|z - 3| < 2$, we can substitute x for $z - 3$. If $|x| < 2$, then $-2 < x < 2$. Therefore, replacing x by $z - 3$ we have $-2 < z - 3 < 2$. Adding 3 to each part of this inequality we obtain $1 < z < 5$, as indicated in Figure 63a.

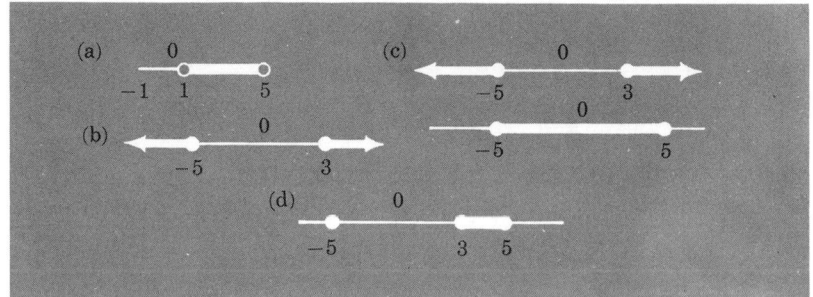

FIG. 63

Example 5. If $x \in Q$ and $|x + 1| \geq 4$, then $x + 1 \geq 4$ or $x + 1 \leq -4$. If $x + 1 \geq 4$, then $x \geq 3$. If $x + 1 \leq -4$, then $x \leq -5$. The graph is given in Figure 63b.

Example 6. Find the solution set of $\{x \mid x \in Q, |x + 1| \geq 4$ and $|x| \leq 5\}$. We separate this example into two parts and find the intersection of the solution sets for the separate parts. The real numbers for which $|x + 1| \geq 4$ are indicated in Figure 63b. We shall use this figure along with another representation of the x-axis on which we have graphed $|x| \leq 5$. The intersection of these two solution sets is $\{x \mid x = -5$ or $3 \leq x \leq 5\}$. The graphical representation of the solution set is given in 63d.

The following examples do not have intervals as their solution sets, but it is convenient to show their graphical representations at this point.

Example 7. If x is an integer and $|x| < 3$, then we can write $\{x \mid x \in J$ and $|x| < 3\}$. The solution set consists of the isolated values $\{-2, -1, 0, 1, 2\}$. Its graph is given in Figure 64a.

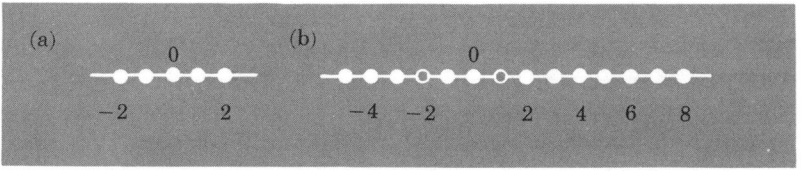

FIG. 64

Example 8. If x is an integer other than -2 or 1 we have $\{x \mid x \in J,\ x \neq -2,\ x \neq 1\}$. This set can be represented graphically by Figure 64b.

Example 9. It is not possible to draw an accurate graph of $|x| < 3$ if x is restricted to rational numbers. The reason for this is that every interval of the x-axis, however small, contains an infinite number of rational numbers. If we try to plot these points, the dots which represent them will be so close together that they form a solid line. (Points have no width but the dots drawn on paper to represent them do have width, therefore if enough points are drawn the line appears to be solid.) However, between two rational points there is always an irrational point so that two rational points should not be connected by a solid line. If the solution set is represented by a solid line we must keep mentally alert to the fact that the graph is "full of holes".

ADDITION OF ORDINATES

In connection with graphs in the xy-plane, a point is represented by an ordered pair (x, y) of real numbers, called the coordinates of the point. The number x is the abscissa and the number y is the ordinate of the point. It is frequently easy to sketch the graphs of certain functions by the method of *addition of ordinates*. For example, to sketch the graph of $y = x + 1/x$ we first dot in the functions $y_1 = x$ and $y_2 = 1/x$ on the same graph, and then add the y-values geometrically to obtain $y_1 + y_2 = x + 1/x = y$. The y-values of either curve may be added to those of the other curve. In this specific example we shall add the ordinates of the hyperbola $y_2 = 1/x$ to the ordinates of the line $y_1 = x$. The vertical line through the point A with coordinates $(1, 0)$ intersects both curves at B. If we start at the point B and measure BC above the line and equal to AB the point C will be a point on the desired graph. Similarly the vertical distances $FG = DE$, $JK = HI$, and $NR = LM$ are measured above the line $y = x$, since they represent positive values of y. The vertical distances $B'C' = A'B'$, $F'G' = D'E'$, and $J'K' = H'I'$ represent negative values of y therefore they are measured below the line $y = x$. The solid lines through the points O, C, G, K, C', G', and K' are the graph of $y = x + 1/x$.

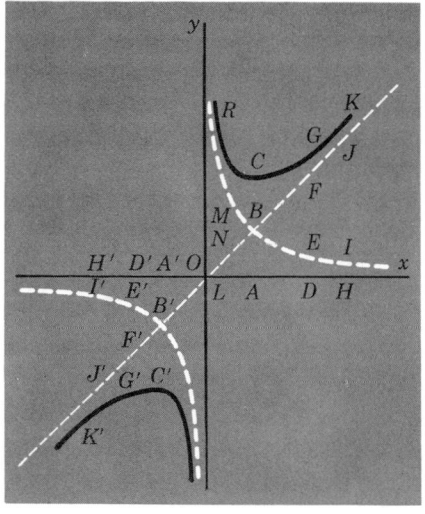

$$y = x + \frac{1}{x}$$

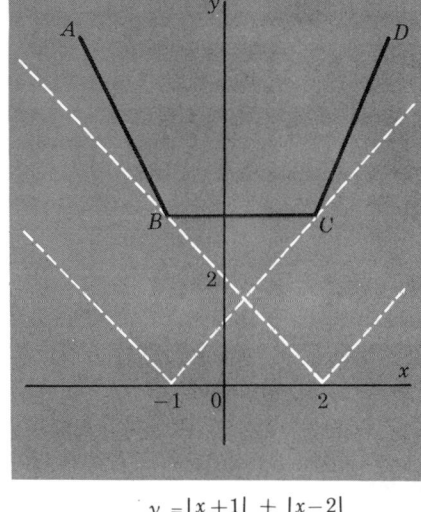

$$y = |x+1| + |x-2|$$

FIG. 65   FIG. 66

Addition of ordinates can be used to find the set of values for which $|x + 1| + |x - 2| < 3$. First we sketch $y_1 = |x + 1|$ by sketching $y_1 = x + 1$ and reflecting the negative part of the sketch in the x-axis. Then we sketch $y_2 = |x - 2|$ using the same method. Addition of ordinates then produces the sketch which passes through the points A, B, C, and D in Figure 66. This shows that $y_1 + y_2 = |x + 1| + |x - 2| \geqq 3$ for all values of x. Therefore the set of all real numbers for which the given inequality holds is the null set. Other methods for solving this problem will be given later.

From the same graph we can obtain the set of all x for which the following inequalities hold.

Inequality	Solution
(a) $|x + 1| + |x - 2| < 3$	$\varnothing$
(b) $|x + 1| + |x - 2| < 4$	$\{x \mid -\frac{3}{2} < x < \frac{5}{2}\}$
(c) $|x + 1| + |x - 2| \leqq 4$	$\{x \mid -\frac{3}{2} \leqq x \leqq \frac{5}{2}\}$
(d) $|x + 1| + |x - 2| > 4$	$\{x \mid x < -\frac{3}{2} \text{ or } x > \frac{5}{2}\}$
(e) $|x + 1| + |x - 2| > 1$	Q

POLYNOMIALS

The remainder of this section will be used to discuss the graphs of solution sets of equations of the type $y = p(x)$, where $p(x)$ is a polynomial over the set of all real numbers, and of graphs which are closely related to polynomial graphs.

It is proved in more advanced mathematics that the graph of a polynomial function over the set of all real numbers is a smooth curve without breaks, jumps, or gaps in it. Observe that this is true of first and second degree polynomial functions over the real numbers, whose graphs are straight lines and parabolas, respectively. It is also true of a constant function over the reals, since its graph is a horizontal straight line. It would not be true, however, if the domain of the function were the integers or the rational numbers. The graph of a polynomial over the set of all real numbers can be drawn with only one "stroke" of the pencil; that is, there is no need to lift the pencil from the paper while any desired portion of the curve is being drawn.

We shall assume that the reader has had some experience in sketching the graphs of straight lines, especially those written in the form $y = ax + b$. If $b \neq 0$, the intercepts frequently provide two convenient points through which the line can be drawn.

The solution sets of (12), (13), and (14), (pages 159–160) can be used to sketch the polynomial functions $y = (x + 3)(x - 5)$ and $y = (x - 3)^2(x + 2)(5 - x)$. To sketch $y = (x + 3)(x - 5)$ start with Figure 60 and observe that the curve is on the axis when $x = -3$ or 5, is below the x-axis when $-3 < x < 5$, and above the axis for all other values. Since the graph of $y = (x - a)(x - b)$ has its lowest point when x is halfway between a and b, average -3 and 5 to obtain $(-3 + 5)/2 = 1$. At $x = 1$, $y = (4)(-4) = -16$. The curve is a parabola that passes through $(-3, 0)$, $(1, -16)$ and $(5, 0)$. See Figure 67a.

To sketch $y = (x - 3)^2(x + 2)(5 - x)$ start with Figure 61. This shows where the curve is on the axis (when $y = 0$), where it is below the axis (when $y < 0$) and where it is above the axis (when $y > 0$). If we use the fact that the graph is a smooth curve we can sketch it very roughly by starting to the left of -2. Since here the values are

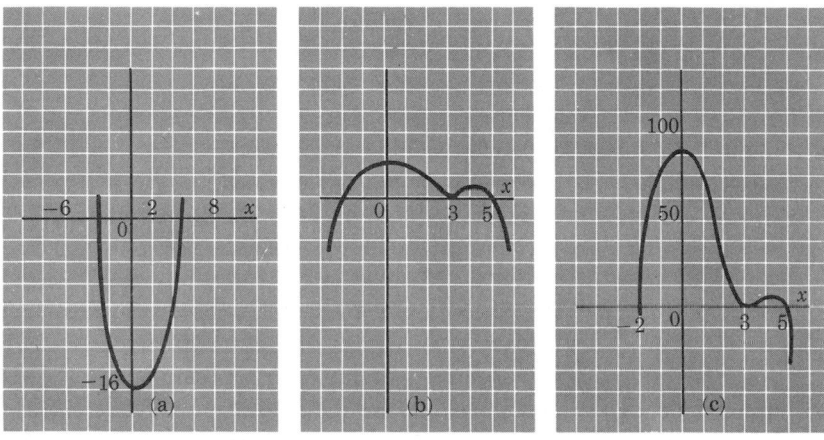

FIG. 67

negative we start below the axis and move the pencil up through the point $(-2, 0)$. Since the values are positive between -2 and 3 we make some kind of arch joining these two points, and then make another arch between 3 and 5, for the same reason. The curve is then drawn downward from $(5, 0)$ since the values are negative for $x > 5$. Perhaps the rough graph looks like Figure 67b. If there is a need for greater accuracy the sketch can be improved by finding a few values. To use functional notation we let $g(x) = (x - 3)^2(x + 2)(5 - x)$. Then $g(-1) = 96$, $g(0) = 90$, $g(1) = 48$, $g(2) = 12$, and $g(4) = 6$. With these values we obtain Figure 67c, which is the graph of $g(x)$ rather than a sketch. The rough sketch is adequate for many purposes in advanced mathematics. In such cases no additional values of the function need to be computed.

Observe that this graph did not cross the axis at $x = 3$. We can understand why if we consider where each factor changes sign. The factor $x + 2$ is zero at $x = -2$. We usually say that the zero of $x + 2$ is at -2. This point acts as an "origin" for the factor $x + 2$ in that this factor is positive to the right of $x = -2$ and negative to the left of this point. Therefore, this factor changes sign only at the point $x = -2$. Similarly, the factor $5 - x$ has its zero at $x = 5$, is negative to the right of $x = 5$ and positive to the left of this point, and changes sign only at $x = 5$. The zero of $x - 3$ is at $x = 3$. This factor is positive to the right of this point and negative to the left, and changes sign only at $x = 3$. However $(x - 3)^2$ does not change sign at $x = 3$. It is zero there but positive both to the right and to the left of this point since the square of a nonzero real number is positive. Since the factors $x + 2$ and $5 - x$ do not change sign at $x = 3$, as long as the value of x stays between -2 and 5 any changes in sign must result from the factor $(x - 3)^2$. But $(x - 3)^2$ cannot change signs. The smallest value that it can produce is zero. Therefore the curve touches the x-axis but does not cross it. In general, if $(x - c)^k$ occurs in the factored form of a polynomial we shall say that $x - c$ is a *factor of multiplicity* k. If k is even the graph does not cross the x-axis at $x = c$. If k is odd, the graph does cross the x-axis at $x = c$. Why?

If a polynomial is not in factored form it is sometimes possible to factor it and then use the methods just discussed to graph it. Some polynomials, such as $5x^4 - 3x^3 - 22x^2 + 12x + 8$, can be factored readily by first grouping the odd powered terms and factoring them. Since $-3x^3 + 12x = -3x(x^2 - 4)$ we ask whether $x^2 - 4$ is a factor of the even powered terms. Since $5x^4 - 22x^2 + 8 = (x^2 - 4)(5x^2 - 2)$, then $x^2 - 4$, the common factor, can be removed. Thus $5x^4 - 22x^2 + 8 - 3x^3 + 12x = (x^2 - 4)(5x^2 - 2) - 3x(x^2 - 4)$ $= (x^2 - 4)(5x^2 - 2 - 3x) = (x - 2)(x + 2)(5x + 2)(x - 1)$. Therefore this polynomial is 0 when $x = 2$, -2, $-2/5$, or 1.

In order to discuss the graphing of polynomials which are not easily factored we introduce the method of synthetic substitution.

Let $f(x)$ represent a polynomial in x over the real numbers. The term which contains the highest power of x is the leading term and its coefficient is the leading coefficient. The leading term determines whether the value at x is positive or negative when $|x|$ is very large. For example, if

$$f(x) = x^5 - 50x^3 - 200$$

we observe that for small numbers like 0, 1, and -1 the sign of $f(x)$ is determined by its third term. But if $x = 10$ we have $f(x) = 100,000 - 50,000 - 200 > 0$ and the sign is determined by the first term. Therefore, for very large positive numbers $f(x)$, like x^5, is positive. If $x = -4$, then $f(x) = -1024 + 3200 - 200 > 0$ and the sign is determined by the second term. But if $x = -10$ then $f(x) = -100,000 + 50,000 - 200 < 0$ and the sign is determined by the first term. If

$x < -10$, $f(x)$, like x^5, will be negative. This information helps us sketch the polynomial function.

Synthetic substitution is a method of finding the value of a polynomial at $x = a$ without substituting directly into the polynomial. If $f(x) = 5x^3 + 3x^2 - 7x - 11$ we can write

$$f(x) = (5x^2 + 3x - 7)x - 11,$$
$$= [(5x + 3)x - 7]x - 11.$$

This tells us that in order to find $f(2)$ we can

(i) multiply 2 by 5 (the coefficient of x^3) and add the result to 3 (the coefficient of x^2),

(ii) multiply this result by 2 and add it to -7 (the coefficient of x),

(iii) multiply this result by 2 and add it to -11 (the constant term).

At first sight this method may not appear to be simpler than finding the powers of 2 and substituting them into $f(x)$. However, if we look more closely at (i), (ii), and (iii) we can see a pattern. If the powers are arranged in descending order, in order to find $f(2)$ we first multiply the leading coefficient by 2 and add in the next coefficient; then multiply the result by 2 and add in the next coefficient. This procedure is followed until the constant term has been added. This result is $f(2)$. We now systematize the work as follows. First arrange the polynomial according to descending power of x, then write, in a horizontal line, the coefficients of the polynomial, being sure to enter a zero if a certain power is missing. To the right we put the number 2, since we are trying to find $f(2)$. This number is separated from the coefficients by a division line. Two lines below the coefficient line we draw a horizontal line. Below this line we shall write those numbers which are to be multiplied by 2. The first number to be multiplied by 2 is the leading coefficient 5. Therefore we begin by putting 5 below the line. Now we multiply 5 by 2 and since the result is to be added to 3, the coefficient of the next term, we put 10 under 3 and add. This produces the following.

$$\begin{array}{r} 5 + \ 3 - 7 - 11 \ \underline{\lfloor 2} \\ + 10 \\ \hline 5 + 13 \end{array}$$

The result 13 must now be multiplied by 2 and added to the next coefficient which is -7. Thus $26 + (-7) = 19$ which is then multiplied by 2 and added to -11. This gives the following completed form, which shows that 27 is $f(2)$.

$$\begin{array}{r} 5 + 3 - 7 - 11 \,\underline{\big|\,2} \\ + \,10 + 26 + 38 \\ \hline 5 + 13 + 19 + 27 \end{array}$$

This result can be checked by actual substitution.

$f(2) = 5(2^3) + 3(2^2) - 7(2) - 11 = 40 + 12 - 14 - 11 = 27.$

The next question to consider is whether this method will work on *every* third degree polynomial. If

$$f(x) = a_0x^3 + a_1x^2 + a_2x + a_3$$

and $f(c)$ is needed, can it be obtained by this method? We now compute as indicated below.

$$\begin{array}{llll} a_0 + a_1 & + a_2 & + a_3 & \underline{\big|\,c} \\ + a_0c & + a_0c^2 + a_1c & + a_0c^3 + a_1c^2 + a_2c & \\ \hline a_0 + (a_0c + a_1) + (a_0c^2 + a_1c + a_2) + (a_0c^3 + a_1c^2 + a_2c + a_3) \end{array}$$

Since $f(c)$ is the value obtained by replacing every x by c in $f(x)$, the last term below the horizontal line is $f(c)$. Therefore, this method works for every third degree polynomial. By long division the reader can show that if this general third degree polynomial is divided by $x - c$ the quotient is $a_0x^2 + (a_0c + a_1)x + (a_0c^2 + a_1c + a_2)$ and the remainder is $a_0c^3 + a_1c^2 + a_2c + a_3 = f(c)$. This shows that for a third degree polynomial the third line of synthetic substitution provides the coefficients of the quotient and also the remainder, which is equal to $f(c)$. It can be proved that this is always true for a polynomial of any finite degree n. For this reason synthetic substitution is also called *synthetic division*, for it can be used to find the quotient and the remainder which results when a polynomial is divided by $x - c$, and it eliminates the necessity of doing the division by the usual methods. For example, if the polynomial $f(x) = 5x^3 + 3x^2 - 7x - 11$ is divided by $x - 2$ our previous computation shows that the quotient is $5x^2 + 13x + 19$ and the remainder is 27. This information is read from the third line of synthetic substitution (or synthetic division).

As another example of synthetic substitution we let

$$g(x) = 3x^5 + 2x^4 + 11x^3 + 200x^2 + 27$$

and find $g(-4)$. Since the x term is missing we must use a zero coefficient in the x position.

$$
\begin{array}{r}
3 + \ \ 2 + 11 + 200 + \ \ 0 + 27 \ \underline{\big|\ -4} \\
- 12 + 40 - 204 + 16 - 64 \\
\hline
3 - 10 + 51 - \ \ \ 4 + 16 - 37
\end{array}
$$

Thus $g(-4) = -37$. This computation also shows that when $g(x)$ is divided by $x - (-4) = x + 4$ the quotient is $3x^4 - 10x^3 + 51x^2 - 4x + 16$ and the remainder is -37. The reader will appreciate this method of synthetic substitution if he computes a few values of the polynomial, such as $g(-4)$, $g(5)$, and $g(-7)$, by direct substitution.

It is easy to prove that the remainder which results from dividing a polynomial $f(x)$ by $x - c$ is $f(c)$. We have proved this only for polynomials of degree 3. The proof is based on a fact that the reader has undoubtedly used to check the answers for division problems; namely, that the dividend can be obtained by multiplying the divisor by the quotient and adding in the remainder.

Remainder Theorem. *If a polynomial $f(x)$ of positive degree is divided by $x - c$ the remainder is $f(c)$.*

Proof. Let $q(x)$ denote the quotient and R denote the remainder. Then

$$f(x) = (x - c)q(x) + R.$$

This is an identity in x. Therefore it is true for all values of x. Let $x = c$, then $f(c) = 0 \cdot q(x) + R$
or $f(c) = R.$

The Factor Theorem follows readily from the Remainder Theorem. The proof is left as an exercise.

Factor Theorem. *A polynomial $f(x)$ of positive degree has $x - c$ as a factor if and only if $f(c) = 0$.*

Let us now graph the polynomial function defined by

$$h(x) - 8x^5 + 4x^4 - 66x^3 - 37x^2 + 100x + 75,$$

where $x \in Q$. Synthetic substitution produces the following table of values. In order to plot the large values involved we shall use a different unit of measure on the y-axis from the one used on the x-axis. We know that far to the right of the origin the curve is positive and far to the left it is negative, since the sign of the entire polynomial far from the origin is determined by the leading term $8x^5$, which is positive far to the right and negative far to the left. The graph is given in Figure 68a.

It should be observed that grouping the odd and even powered terms and factoring produces

$$h(x) = 8x^5 - 66x^3 + 100x + 4x^4 - 37x^2 + 75$$
$$= x(4x^2 - 25)(2x^2 - 4) + (4x^2 - 25)(x^2 - 3)$$
$$= (4x^2 - 25)(2x^3 + x^2 - 4x - 3).$$

Dividing the second factor synthetically by -1 gives

$$
\begin{array}{r}
2 + 1 - 4 - 3 \ \lfloor -1 \\
- 2 + 1 + 3 \\
\hline
2 - 1 - 3 + 0
\end{array}
$$

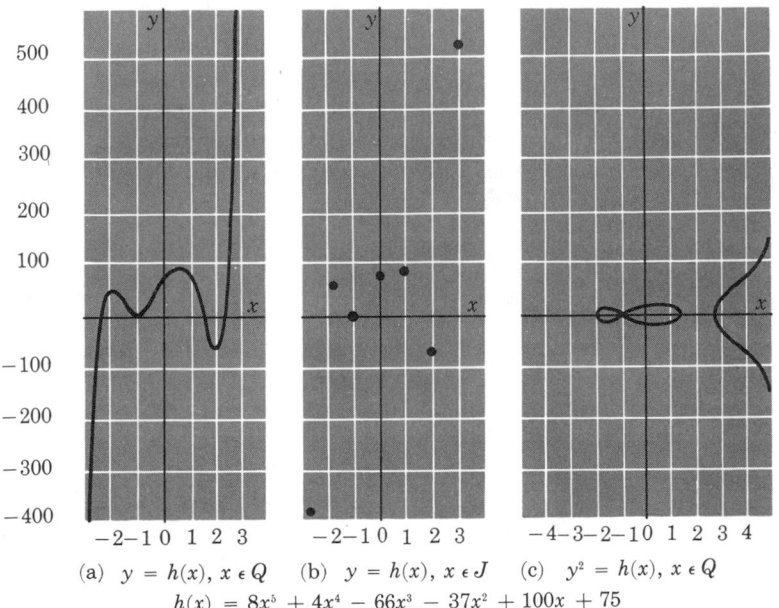

(a) $y = h(x),\ x \in Q$ (b) $y = h(x),\ x \in J$ (c) $y^2 = h(x),\ x \in Q$

$$h(x) = 8x^5 + 4x^4 - 66x^3 - 37x^2 + 100x + 75$$

FIG. 68

which shows that $x + 1$ is a factor of $2x^3 + x^2 - 4x - 3$ and that the quotient is $2x^2 - x - 3 = (2x - 3)(x + 1)$. Therefore

$$h(x) = (2x - 5)(2x + 5)(x + 1)^2(2x - 3).$$

The curve crosses the x-axis at $5/2$, $-5/2$, and $3/2$, and touches the axis at -1. This agrees with the graph in Figure 68a.

Observe that if x is restricted to the integers, the graph of this polynomial consists of isolated points which cannot be connected because no values exist between the points. See Figure 68b. If x is restricted to rational numbers any graphical representation of it looks like Figure 68a because of the physical limitations in showing the "holes" in the curve.

If we know how to sketch the graph of a polynomial function determined by $y = h(x)$ we can readily sketch the graph of $y^2 = h(x)$. As an example we shall sketch $y^2 = h(x) = 8x^5 + 4x^4 - 66x^3 - 37x^2 + 100x + 75$. For this equation $y = \pm \sqrt{h(x)}$; that is, the values of y for $y^2 = h(x)$ are the square roots of those for $y = h(x)$. This means that when $h(x) < 0$ there are no points on the graph of $y^2 = h(x)$, for there are no real square roots of negative quantities. Where $h(x) = 0$, the square root is also zero. Where $h(x) = 1$, the square roots are ± 1. In general, where $h(x) > 0$, there are two points on the graph, one above and one below the x-axis. Thus in the interval between -2.5 and -1 there is a loop of the curve. Also between -1 and 1.5 there is a loop. Corresponding to the values where $x > 2.5$ there are two values. The sketch is given in Figure 68c.

Definition.   *If $f(x)$ is a polynomial of positive degree then $f(x) = 0$ is a **polynomial equation**.*

Definition.   *The number $x = c$ is a **zero of the polynomial $f(x)$** if and only if $f(c) = 0$.*

When c is a zero of $f(x)$ then it is an element of the solution set of $f(x) = 0$, and is referred to as a *root* or *solution* of this polynomial equation. We frequently find zeros of polynomials by synthetic division. A theorem on rational roots is quite helpful and will be stated here without proof.

Rational Root Theorem. *If the rational number p/q, expressed in lowest terms, is a root of a polynomial equation of positive degree which has integral coefficients, then p is a divisor of the constant term and q is a divisor of the leading coefficient.*

We shall also use some properties of upper and lower bounds without proving these properties.

Definition. *The number M is an **upper bound** of a set S of real numbers if $M \geqq x$ for every $x \in S$.*

Definition. *The number N is a **lower bound** of a set S of real numbers if $N \leqq x$ for every $x \in S$.*

Rules for Upper and Lower Bounds. *Let $f(x)$ be a polynomial having a positive leading coefficient and have positive degree in x over the real numbers. If the third line of the synthetic division of $f(x)$ by $x - c$, where $c > 0$, does not contain any negative terms then c is an upper bound of the roots of the polynomial equation $f(x) = 0$. If $c < 0$ and the third line of synthetic division contains terms which are alternately nonnegative and nonpositive then the negative number c is a lower bound of the roots of the polynomial equation $f(x) = 0$.*

What are the roots of the polynomial equation $h(x) = 0$, where $h(x)$ is the polynomial discussed in the preceding paragraphs? They are $5/2$, $-5/2$, $3/2$, and -1. Thus the solution set of $h(x) = 0$ is $\{5/2, -5/2, 3/2, -1\}$. In this particular case the most efficient way of obtaining the roots is by factoring.

Let us consider how the roots can be obtained graphically. The graph of $y = h(x)$ as given in Figure 68a gives us a picture of *all* values that can be obtained from $h(x)$. When we consider the polynomial equation $h(x) = 0$, we restrict ourselves to the zeros of $h(x)$. Graphically, where are the values for which $h(x) = 0$? Obviously, since the graph is the set of ordered pairs (x, y) where $y = h(x)$, those where $h(x) = 0$ are those where $y = 0$, and $y = 0$ only on the x-axis. The roots are therefore those points where the curve intersects the x-axis. Therefore the graph shows that there is a zero at -1, that there is a zero between -3 and -2, a zero between 1 and 2, and a zero between 2 and 3. If the graph is drawn with sufficient accuracy it will indicate that the other roots are near $-5/2$, $3/2$, and $5/2$. These values can then be checked to show that they satisfy the equation.

It is not always possible to factor the equation nor to find the roots quickly from the graph. In such cases it usually is convenient to use the rule for rational roots. Let us assume for the moment that we do not know the roots of $h(x) = 0$ and that we choose to apply the rule for rational roots. We first list the possible rational roots. The numerator must be a divisor of the constant term; that is, an integral divisor of 75. Therefore the possible numerators are ± 1, $+3$, $+5$, $+15$, $+25$, and ± 75. Since the denominator must be a divisor of the leading coefficient the possible denominators are ± 1, ± 2, ± 4, and ± 8. Combining these numerators and denominators we have the following possible rational roots which can be tested by synthetic division.

Possible rational roots of $8x^5 + 4x^4 - 66x^3 - 37x^2 + 100x + 75$.

$$\pm 1, \ \pm 3, \ \pm 5, \ \pm 15, \ \pm 25, \ \pm 75$$
$$\pm 1/2, \ \pm 3/2, \ \pm 5/2, \ \pm 15/2, \ \pm 25/2, \ \pm 75/2$$
$$\pm 1/4, \ \pm 3/4, \ \pm 5/4, \ \pm 15/4, \ \pm 25/4, \ \pm 75/4$$
$$\pm 1/8, \ \pm 3/8, \ \pm 5/8, \ \pm 15/8, \ \pm 25/8, \ \pm 75/8$$

Usually it is easier to check 0, 1, and -1 as possible roots by actual substitution. It is easy to see that $x = 0$ is not a root since $h(0) = 75$. Also $h(1) = 84$, therefore 1 is not a root; however, $h(-1) = 0$ and $x = -1$ is a root. We now divide synthetically by -1 to find the quotient, which when it is set equal to zero is called a depressed equation of $h(x) = 0$.

Definition.   *If a polynomial equation $p(x) = 0$ of degree $n \geq 2$ has a root $x = c$, and $q(x)$ is the quotient obtained from the division of $p(x)$ by $x - c$, then $q(x) = 0$ is a* **depressed equation** *of $p(x) = 0$.*

The result of dividing $h(x) = 0$ synthetically by -1 is given below.

$$\frac{8 + 4 - 66 - 37 + 100 + 75 \ \lfloor -1}{\ \ -8 + \ \ 4 + 62 - \ \ 25 - 75}$$
$$8 - 4 - 62 + 25 + \ \ 75 + \ \ 0$$

The depressed equation is $8x^4 - 4x^3 - 62x^2 + 25x + 75 = 0$. Substitution shows that -1 is a root of this equation also. Synthetic division by -1 produces a second depressed equation; namely $8x^3 - 12x^2 - 50x + 75 = 0$.

$$
\begin{array}{r}
8 - 4 - 62 + 25 + 75 \,\lvert\,{-1} \\
-8 + 12 + 50 - 75 \\
\hline
8 - 12 - 50 + 75 + 0
\end{array}
$$

This equation can be factored as follows:

$$8x^3 - 12x^2 - 50x + 75 = 0$$
$$4x^2(2x - 3) - 25(2x - 3) = 0$$
$$(2x - 3)(4x^2 - 25) = 0$$
$$(2x - 3)(2x - 5)(2x + 5) = 0$$
$$x = 3/2,\ x = 5/2,\ x = -5/2.$$

If however, we do not use factoring we must test some of the possible rational roots. Synthetic division by 3 merely shows that 3 is not a root. The third line of synthetic division by 5 contains only positive entries. Therefore 5 is an upper bound of the roots; and 15, 25, 75, 15/2, 25/2, 75/2, 25/4, 75/4, and 75/8 can be discarded as possible rational roots. Synthetic division by -3 shows that the entries in the third line of synthetic division are alternately plus and minus. Therefore, -3 is a lower bound, and we can discard -5, -15, -25, -75, $-15/2$, $-25/2$, $-75/2$, $-15/4$, $-25/4$, $-75/4$, $-25/8$, and $-75/8$ as possible rational roots. Synthetic division shows that $1/2$ is not a root, but $3/2$ is a root. If we refrain from indicating the zero remainders and use this space for the next divisor in synthetic division, the solution can be put into the following compact form.

$$
\begin{array}{r}
8 + 4 - 66 - 37 + 100 + 75 \,\lvert\,{-1} \\
-8 + 4 + 62 - 25 - 75 \\
\hline
8 - 4 - 62 + 25 + 75 \,\lvert\,{-1} \\
-8 + 12 + 50 - 75 \\
\hline
8 - 12 - 50 + 75 \,\lvert\,3/2 \\
+ 12 + 0 - 75 \\
\hline
8 + 0 - 50
\end{array}
$$

$$8x^2 - 50 = 0$$
$$4x^2 - 25 = 0$$
$$(2x - 5)(2x + 5) = 0$$
$$x = 5/2,\ x = -5/2.$$

Roots: -1, -1, $3/2$, $5/2$, $-5/2$.

The root -1 is indicated twice because $h(x)$ has $x + 1$ as a factor of multiplicity two. Therefore, if each factor is set equal to zero, the root -1 is obtained twice.

Definition. *If a polynomial $p(x)$ has $x - c$ as a factor of multiplicity k, then it has the number c as a zero of multiplicity k and the polynomial equation $p(x) = 0$ has c as a root* of multiplicity k.*

EXERCISES

1. Graph the solution sets of the following where $x \in Q$.

(a) $|x| < 4$.

(b) $|x| \geq 4$.

(c) $|x - 2| < 3$.

(d) $|x + 4| \geq 1$.

(e) $|x + 1| \geq 2$ and $|x| < 4$.

(f) $|x + 1| \geq 4$ and $|x| \leq 3$.

(g) $|x - 2| \geq 5$ or $|x| \leq 1$.

(h) $|x + 3| < 2$ or $|x| < 1$.

2. Use addition of ordinates to graph the following.

(a) $y = 2x + \dfrac{1}{x}$.

(b) $y = x + 1 + \dfrac{2}{x}$.

(c) $y = x - \dfrac{1}{x}$.

(d) $y = |2 - x| + |3 + x|$.

(e) $y = |x| + |x^2 - 2|$.

(f) $y = |3x - 6| + |x^3|$.

3. Sketch the following where $x, y \in Q$.

(a) $y = (x - 3)(x + 1)$.

(b) $y = (3 - x)(x + 2)^2$.

(c) $y = (x + 2)(x - 5)(x^2 - 1)$.

(d) $y = (x - 1)^3(x + 5)^2$.

(e) $y = (x - 1)^4(3 - x)$.

(f) $y = (x - 1)(x + 4)(2 - x)(x + 3)^2$.

4. (a) Replace each y in Exercise 3 by y^2 and sketch the solution set of the resulting equation.

---

* It can be proved that a polynomial equation of positive degree n with real or complex coefficients has exactly n roots which are real or complex numbers, if a root of multiplicity k is counted as k roots. (A complex number is a number of the form $a + bi$ where a and b are real numbers and $i^2 = -1$.)

(b) Use the sketch of each $y = f(x)$ in Exercise 3 to obtain a sketch of $y = |f(x)|$.

5. Sketch the following where $x, y \in J$.

(a) $y = x^2 - 2$.

(b) $y = x^3 + 3$.

(c) $|x| \leq 5$.

(d) $\{x \mid x \in J, x \neq 3 \quad \text{or} \quad 7\}$.

(e) $|x + 5| > 3$.

(f) $|x + 2| < 5 \quad \text{and} \quad |x| \geq 3$.

6. Use synthetic division to find the quotient and the remainder when (a) $5x^3 - 6x^2 + 7x - 2 \div x - 1$.

(b) $7x^3 - 6x + 2 \div x + 2$.

(c) $3x^4 - 7x^2 - 5x + 3 \div x - 2$.

(d) $x^5 - 4x^4 + x^2 + 3 \div x - 3$.

7. Sketch the following where $x, y \in Q$.

(a) $y = x^3 - 3x^2 + 4x - 12$.

(b) $y = 2x^4 - 9x^3 - 6x^2 + 45x - 20$.

(c) $y = 40 - 218x + 87x^2 + 16x^3 - 5x^4$.

(d) $y = x^5 + 2x^4 - 11x^3 - 12x^2 + 36x$.

8. Sketch the following where $x, y \in Q$.

(a) $y < x^2 - 2$.

(b) $x^2 + y^2 - 16 > 0$.

(c) $y > (3 - x)(x + 4)^2$.

(d) $y < (x - 2)^2(x + 7)^2$.

(e) $|x| + |y| \leq 4 \quad \text{or} \quad |x| - |y| \geq 4$.

(f) $|xy| > 0$.

9. (a) Show that for *every* fourth degree polynomial the method of synthetic division produces the quotient and the remainder obtained by dividing the polynomial by $x - r$, where r is a constant.

(b) Do the same for polynomials of fifth degree.

10. Prove the Factor Theorem.

11. Find the roots of the following polynomial equations.

(a) $2x^3 + 7x^2 + 2x - 3 = 0$.

(b) $10x^3 + 19x^2 - 8x - 21 = 0$.

(c) $7x^3 + 9x^2 - 66x + 40 = 0$.

(d) $3x^4 - 4x^3 - 20x^2 + 28x - 7 = 0$.

(e) $10x^4 - 37x^3 - 88x^2 + 319x - 60 = 0$.

(f) $12x^4 - 23x^3 - 55x^2 + 115x - 25 = 0$.

12. Prove the Rational Root Theorem.

13. Explain why the rules given for upper and lower bounds are valid.

14. Are there an uncountable number of numbers of the following type in each interval of the x-axis?
(*a*) Rational.   (*c*) Real.
(*b*) Integers.   (*d*) Irrational.

15. (*a*) Show that if r and s are real numbers such that $|r - s| < 3$ then $r - 3 < s < r + 3$ and $s - 3 < r < s + 3$. What can be said of the distance between the points representing the real numbers r and s on the x-axis?

(*b*) Give a geometric interpretation of $|r - s| > 3$.

16. (*a*) For each $n = 1, 2, 3, 4, 5$, sketch $y = p(x)$, where $p(x)$ is a polynomial of degree n having a positive leading coefficient and n distinct real roots.

(*b*) Change "positive" to "negative" in part (*a*) and make the sketches.

V. Application of
Boolean Algebra
To Switching Networks
By L. R. Sjoblom

The following quotation reveals the nature of this section.

To me, Boolean Algebra means electrical circuits, electrical networks. Professor Wiley teaches at the University of Oklahoma during the winter and in the summer he often goes to Westinghouse. Westinghouse is delighted to have him during the summer and the University of Oklahoma is delighted to have him in the winter. A couple of years ago, when he arrived at Westinghouse, they asked him to come to building 7. The electrical engineers had a large blackboard which was filled with circuit diagrams — complicated circuit diagrams. They were pretty proud of it because they started out with a much bigger diagram and had condensed it down, and condensed it down, and condensed it down, taking out more and more relays and switches. Every time you take out a switch, not only does it save the cost of that switch, but it saves in repairs and maintenance. They triumphantly showed Professor Wiley the final diagrams. I think that they wanted to brag a bit. He sat down and covered a piece of paper with symbols involving letters and horseshoes and croquet wickets and pretty soon he said, "I think maybe you can simplify that even more." The Westinghouse engineers had been working for several weeks on the circuits and they had to be shown that further improvements were possible. Wiley pushed his pencil a little more and said,

"You can take out this switch, substitute this one in it, and hook it in this way and it will work out just the same." The engineers scratched their pencils and sure enough, they could. They were interested and they wanted to know how he did it. His answer was, "Boolean Algebra."

Before long they had actually taken out 5 switches. Five switches may not sound like very much to you, but if you eliminate five switches worth $4.00 each — that is $20. If you make 10,000 of these items, $200,000 is a rather healthy savings — the sort of thing that really pleases industry. If a man makes a discovery like this and doesn't make any other discovery during the next ten years, he has still earned his salary and more. Industry has awakened to the advantages of mathematical research.

Richard V. Andree, *The Need for Modern Mathematics*

Boolean Algebra was originated by the English mathematician George Boole (1815–1864) who, in 1854, published the book *An Investigation into the Laws of Thought, on Which Are Founded the Mathematical Theories of Logic and Probability.* This was one of the first successful attempts to establish propositional logic on a purely algebraic basis.

BASIC THEORY OF THE BOOLEAN ALGEBRA

For our purposes it will be convenient to use a definition which is slightly different from the definition of a Boolean Algebra which was given on page 107. Instead of $\circ$, $*$, $\sim$, and $\oplus$ we shall use the corresponding set notation. In the exercises which accompany this section the student is asked to prove that this definition is equivalent to the one given previously.

Definition. *A **Boolean Algebra** is a set B of at least two distinct elements with two binary operations $\cup$ (read "cup") and $\cap$ (read "cap"), and one unary operation $'$ (read "prime") such that B is closed with respect to each of these three operations, and for all a, b, and c belonging to B the following axioms are satisfied.*

A1. $a \cup b = b \cup a.$
A2. $a \cap b = b \cap a.$
A3. $a \cup (b \cup c) = (a \cup b) \cup c.$

A4. $a \cap (b \cap c) = (a \cap b) \cap c$.
A5. $a \cup (b \cap c) = (a \cup b) \cap (a \cup c)$.
A6. $a \cap (b \cup c) = (a \cap b) \cup (a \cap c)$.
A7. There exists an element Φ belonging to B such that $a \cup \Phi = a$.
A8. There exists an element I belonging to B such that $a \cap I = a$.
A9. $a \cup a' = I$.
A10. $a \cap a' = \Phi$.

In this axiomatic system, the operations $\cup$, $\cap$, and $'$, and the elements of the set B are undefined. In an application, these undefined terms may be interpreted in any manner whatsoever as long as they satisfy the axiomatic system.

Note the symmetry of the axioms. If one interchanges $\cap$ and $\cup$ and also interchanges Φ and I the same set of axioms results. This property is referred to as the duality of a set of axioms and is stated as our first theorem.

Theorem 1. (*Principle of Duality*) *Any theorem of Boolean Algebra remains valid if $\cap$ is interchanged with $\cup$, and Φ is interchanged with I systematically in the theorem.*

In some theorems that follow, it will be convenient to use a few definitions and symbols common in mathematics. These will be defined now in order to preserve the continuity of thought later. Let A and B represent statements.

Definition. $A \Rightarrow B$ *means "if A then B", or "A implies B".*

Definition. $A \Leftrightarrow B$ *means "$A \Rightarrow B$ and $B \Rightarrow A$", or "A and B are equivalent."*

Definition. $A \nRightarrow B$ *means "A does not imply B".*

Definition. *If a and b are elements of a set S, then $a = b$ means that a and b are identical; that is, a and b are different designations of the same element.*

There are an unlimited number of theorems that can be derived from the axioms; however, only a small number are needed for our purposes.

Theorem 2. $I \cap a = a$.

Proof. $a \cap I = a$ (By A8)
                    $a \cap I = I \cap a$ (By A2)
                    $I \cap a = a$.   ∎

Theorem 3. $\Phi \cup a = a$.

Proof.   Apply Theorem 1 to Theorem 2.

Theorem 4. $a' \cup a = I$.

Proof.   The proof is left to the reader.

Theorem 5. $a' \cap a = \Phi$.

Proof.   The proof is left to the reader.

Theorem 6. $a \cup I = I$.

Proof. $a \cup I = (a \cup I) \cap I$ (By A8)
                $= (a \cup I) \cap (a \cup a')$ (By A9)
                $= a \cup (I \cap a')$ (By A5)
                $= a \cup a'$ (Theorem 2)
                $= I$.   (By A9)   ∎

Theorem 7. $a \cap \Phi = \Phi$.

Proof.   Apply Theorem 1 to Theorem 6.

Theorem 8. $. [a \cap b = a] \Rightarrow [a \cap b' = \Phi]$.

Proof.   The proof is left to the reader.

Theorem 9. $[a \cap b' = \Phi] \Rightarrow [a \cup b = b]$.

Proof. $a \cup b = (a \cup b) \cap I$ (By A8)
                $= (b \cup a) \cap I$ (By A1)
                $= (b \cup a) \cap (b \cup b')$ (By A9)
                $= b \cup (a \cap b')$ (By A5)
                $= b \cup \Phi$ (By hypothesis)
                $= b$.   (By A7)   ∎

Theorem 10. $[a \cup b = b] \Rightarrow [a \cap b = a]$.

Proof. The proof is left to the reader. *Hint:* Use the duals of Theorems 8 and 9 after interchanging a and b.

Theorem 11. $[a \cap b = a] \Leftrightarrow [a \cap b' = \Phi] \Leftrightarrow [a \cup b = b]$.

Proof.

$$[a \cap b = a] \Rightarrow [a \cap b' = \Phi] \qquad \text{(By Theorem 8)}$$
$$[a \cap b' = \Phi] \Rightarrow [a \cup b = b] \qquad \text{(By Theorem 9)}$$
$$[a \cup b = b] \Rightarrow [a \cap b = a]. \qquad \text{(By Theorem 10)*}$$

∎

Theorem 12. $a \cup a = a$.

Proof.

$$a \cap a' = \Phi \qquad \text{(By A10)}$$
$$[a \cap a' = \Phi] \Leftrightarrow [a \cup a = a]. \quad \text{(By Theorem 11)} \quad ∎$$

Theorem 13. $a \cap a = a$.

Proof. Apply Theorem 1 to Theorem 12.

Theorem 14. $a \cup (a \cup b) = a \cup b$.

Proof.

$$a \cup (a \cup b) = (a \cup a) \cup b \quad \text{(By A3)}$$
$$= a \cup b. \qquad \text{(By Theorem 12)} \quad ∎$$

Theorem 15. $a \cap (a \cap b) = a \cap b$.

Proof. Apply Theorem 1 to Theorem 14.

Theorem 16. (Law of Absorption)

$$a \cap (a \cup b) = a \cup (a \cap b) = a.$$

---

* Observe the nature of this proof. Whenever three or more statements are to be proved equivalent the method used in this theorem saves a considerable amount of work. To prove $X \Leftrightarrow Y$ we must produce two arguments, one for $X \Rightarrow Y$ and another for $Y \Rightarrow X$. Therefore, if $X \Leftrightarrow Y \Leftrightarrow Z$ is proved as $X \Leftrightarrow Y$ and $Y \Leftrightarrow Z$, it involves four arguments: $X \Rightarrow Y$, $Y \Rightarrow X$, $Y \Rightarrow Z$ and $Z \Rightarrow Y$. On the other hand a chain proof of the type $X \Rightarrow Y \Rightarrow Z \Rightarrow X$ requires only three arguments and allows us to arrange the proofs in any convenient order. For example, if $Y \Rightarrow Z$ is difficult to prove, then some other chain such as $X \Rightarrow Z \Rightarrow Y \Rightarrow X$ may be used which avoids the necessity of proving $Y \Rightarrow Z$.

Proof. $a \cup (a \cup b) = a \cup b$ (By Theorem 14)
$[a \cup (a \cup b) = a \cup b] \Leftrightarrow [a \cap (a \cup b) = a]$ (By Theorem 11)
Apply Theorem 1 to $a \cap (a \cup b) = a$ to get $a \cup (a \cap b) = a$.   ∎

Theorem 17. $\Phi' = I$ and $I' = \Phi$.

Proof. $\Phi' = \Phi \cup \Phi'$ (By Theorem 3)
                     $= I$ (By A9)
Apply Theorem 1 to $\Phi' = I$ to get $I' = \Phi$.   ∎

Theorem 18.
$[b = c] \Leftrightarrow [a \cup b = a \cup c$, and $a \cap b = a \cap c$ for some $a]$.

Proof.
It is trivial that

$$[b = c] \Rightarrow [a \cup b = a \cup c, \text{ and } a \cap b = a \cap c].$$

We now show that

$$[a \cup b = a \cup c, \text{ and } a \cap b = a \cap c] \Rightarrow [b = c].$$

$$
\begin{aligned}
b &= b \cap (b \cup a) & &\text{(By Theorem 16)}\\
&= b \cap (c \cup a) & &\text{(By hypothesis)}\\
&= (b \cap c) \cup (b \cap a) & &\text{(By A6)}\\
&= (b \cap c) \cup (c \cap a) & &\text{(By hyp. and A2)}\\
&= (c \cap b) \cup (c \cap a) & &\text{(By A2)}\\
&= c \cap (b \cup a) & &\text{(By A6)}\\
&= c \cap (c \cup a) & &\text{(By hyp. and A2)}\\
&= c. & &\text{(By Theorem 16)} ∎
\end{aligned}
$$

Note that in Boolean Algebra the Cancellation Laws do not hold; that is, $[a \cup b = a \cup c] \not\Rightarrow [b = c]$ and $[a \cap b = a \cap c] \not\Rightarrow [b = c]$. This means that from $a \cup b = a \cup c$ it does not follow that $b = c$; and from $a \cap b = a \cap c$ it does not follow that $b = c$.

Theorem 19. Φ and I are unique.

Proof.   Suppose there exist Φ and Φ_1 both satisfying A7, then for every a, $a \cup \Phi = a$ and $a \cup \Phi_1 = a$. In particular, $\Phi_1 \cup \Phi = \Phi_1$ and $\Phi \cup \Phi_1 = \Phi$. Combining the last two equations produces

$$\Phi_1 = \Phi_1 \cup \Phi = \Phi \cup \Phi_1 = \Phi.$$

Therefore Φ is unique. Now apply Theorem 1 to the above proof to show that I is unique.   ∎

Theorem 20. $(a')' = a$.

Proof.   The proof is left to the reader. *Hint:* Apply Theorem 18 to a, $(a')'$ and a'. We shall often write a'' instead of $(a')'$.

Theorem 21.   (DeMorgan's Laws)
$$(a \cup b)' = a' \cap b' \quad \text{and} \quad (a \cap b)' = a' \cup b'.$$

Proof.   The proof is left to the reader. *Hint:* Apply Theorem 18 to $(a \cup b)'$, $a' \cap b'$ and $a \cup b$ to obtain the first statement.

Theorem 22. $[a \cup b = b,$ and $b \cup c = c] \Rightarrow [a \cup c = c]$.

Proof.   The proof is left to the reader.

We shall now introduce another binary relation denoted by $\subseteq$ and read "is included in".

Definition. $[a \subseteq b] \Leftrightarrow [a \cap b' = \Phi]$.

This relation is reflexive, antisymmetric, and transitive.

Reflexive:	$a \subseteq a$, for all a.
Antisymmetric:	$[a \subseteq b$ and $b \subseteq a] \Rightarrow [a = b]$.
Transitive:	$[a \subseteq b$ and $b \subseteq c] \Rightarrow [a \subseteq c]$.

The proof of the first two properties will be left to the reader. Note that the binary relation $\leq$ (less than or equal to) between real numbers has these same properties.

Theorem 23. $a \subseteq I$.

Proof.

$a \cap I' = a \cap \Phi$	(By Theorem 17)
$\quad = \Phi$.	(By Theorem 7)
$[a \cap I' = \Phi] \Rightarrow [a \subseteq I]$.	(By definition) ∎

Theorem 24. $\Phi \subseteq a$.

Proof.

$\Phi \cap a' = \Phi$	(By Th. 7 and A2)
$[\Phi \cap a' = \Phi] \Rightarrow [\Phi \subseteq a]$.	(By definition) ∎

If Theorems 23 and 24 are combined, the following statement is produced.

Corollary. $\Phi \subseteq a \subseteq I$.

This corollary shows why Φ and I are sometimes referred to as *universal bounds*.

Theorem 25. $[a \subseteq b \text{ and } b \subseteq c] \Rightarrow [a \subseteq c]$.

Proof. The proof is left to the reader.

Theorem 26. $[a \subseteq b \text{ and } b \subseteq a] \Leftrightarrow [a = b]$.

Proof. We first show that $[a \subseteq b \text{ and } b \subseteq a] \Rightarrow [a = b]$.

$[a \subseteq b \quad \text{and} \quad b \subseteq a] \Rightarrow [a \cap b' = \Phi \quad \text{and} \quad b \cap a' = \Phi]$
$$\text{(By definition)}$$

$[a \cap b' = \Phi \quad \text{and} \quad b \cap a' = \Phi] \Rightarrow [a \cup b = b \quad \text{and} \quad b \cup a = a]$
$$\text{(By Theorem 11)}$$

Therefore $a = b \cup a = a \cup b = b$. $\qquad$ (By A1)

This proof is reversible, that is, we can start with the conclusion and work backwards, using the same reasons for each step and arrive at the hypothesis. Reversing the proof given produces the other half of the argument and the theorem is thus completed. $\qquad$ ∎

Theorem 27. $[a \subseteq \Phi] \Leftrightarrow [a = \Phi]$.

Proof. The proof is left to the reader.

Theorem 28. $[a \subseteq b] \Leftrightarrow [b' \subseteq a']$.

Proof. The proof is left to the reader.

This is a sufficient number of proofs to illustrate the method of proof and to establish some of the most important theorems needed in the applications.

EXERCISES

1. Prove Theorems 4, 5, 8, 10, 20, 21, 22, 25, 27, and 28.

2. Show that the binary relation $\subseteq$ is reflexive and antisymmetric.

3. Show that $(a \cup b \cup c \cup d) \cap (a \cup b \cup d) \cap (a \cup c) = a \cup [c \cap (b \cup d)]$.

4. Show that $(x \cap y') \cup [z \cap (x' \cup y \cup w)] = z \cup (x \cap z')$.

APPLICATION TO SWITCHING NETWORKS

A correspondence will be set up between the undefined elements and operations of a Boolean Algebra and a switching network. It will then be shown that the network satisfies the ten axioms of the algebra. Before the correspondence is set up we shall give a brief explanation of the terminology of switching networks and some of the conventional ways of diagraming them.

A switch is a device for opening or closing an electric circuit and it will be idealized as an element that has only two stable states, either open or closed. An electric circuit may contain many electrical elements, such as switches, resistances, and electromotive forces; however, in the application under consideration, the only elements of importance are the switches. For this reason, in what follows, a switching network will sometimes be referred to simply as a network, and all elements of our electric network will be switches. In the usual schematic diagram of a circuit, a switch is indicated as in Figure 69a but we shall indicate a switch as in Figure 69b.

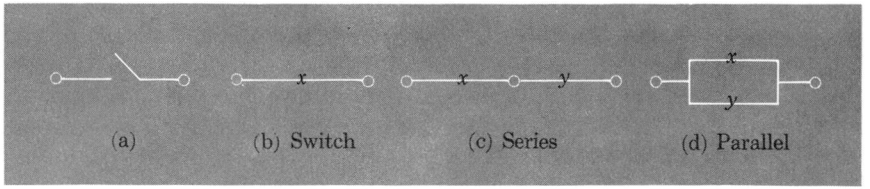

(a)   (b) Switch   (c) Series   (d) Parallel

FIG. 69

Two switches are *connected in series* if and only if the circuit is closed when both switches are closed but open if either switch is open. A series connection is schematically indicated in Figure 69c. Two switches are *connected in parallel* if and only if the circuit is closed

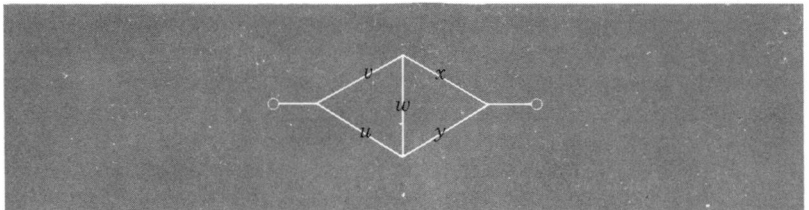

FIG. 70

when either or both switches are closed, and open when both switches are open. A parallel connection is schematically indicated in Figure 69*d*. A combination of switches that is neither connected in series nor in parallel will be called a *bridge network*; however, a bridge network can be described by equivalent series-parallel connections. (See Exercise 6.) An example of a bridge network is given in Figure 70.

To get some idea of the connection between switching networks and Boolean Algebra, let us first consider two switches connected in parallel. The switches will be indicated by the letters x and y in the diagram. Each switch has two stable states, either open or closed. Electricity will flow, or fail to flow, from one terminal to the other depending on the *states* of the switches. Designate the state of an open switch by the symbol 0 and the state of a closed switch by 1. Since the state of a switch is variable, that is, either open or closed, let us designate the state of the switch x by X and the state of the switch y by Y. If x is closed $X = 1$ and if x is open $X = 0$. These are the only two values that X, or Y, can assume. Let F represent the state of the parallel network. Then $F = 0$ if the network is open and $F = 1$ if the network is closed. Since the state of this network is completely determined by the states of the two switches, F must be a function of two variables X and Y, therefore $F = F(X, Y)$. When x and y are both open the network is open, and when either or both x and y are closed the network is closed as indicated in the following table.

TABLE I

Switches	State of Switches	State of Switching Network
x open, y open	$X = 0, Y = 0$	$F(X, Y) = F(0, 0) = 0$
x open, y closed	$X = 0, Y = 1$	$F(X, Y) = F(0, 1) = 1$
x closed, y open	$X = 1, Y = 0$	$F(X, Y) = F(1, 0) = 1$
x closed, y closed	$X - 1, Y - 1$	$F(X, Y) - F(1, 1) - 1$

The function $F(X, Y)$ is called the *switching function* of the network, and it completely characterizes the state of the network in terms of the states of the switches involved in the network. The notation $F(X, Y)$ indicates only that the state F of a network depends on the states X and Y of the switches, and does not indicate that the switches are connected in parallel. To indicate symbolically that the switches are connected in parallel let us write

$$F(X, Y) = X + Y.$$

Then $F(X, Y) = X + Y$ is the switching function of two switches x and y connected in parallel. Observe that the symbols 0 and 1 are not the numbers zero and one, and that the symbol $+$ does not indicate ordinary addition.

It is common practice not to differentiate between the switch x and the state X of the switch x, but rather to designate both by the same letter x. This does not cause any confusion, since one can determine the meaning of the symbol x by its use. In a schematic drawing of a network x represents a switch but in the switching function of the network x represents the state of the switch. *Henceforth we shall use only small letters to represent either the switches or their states.*

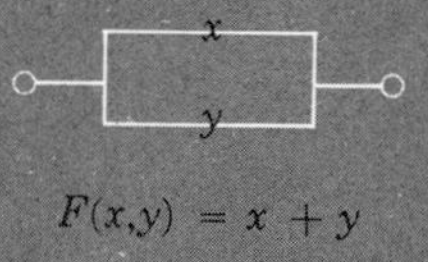

(a) $F(x,y) = x + y$

x	y	$F(x,y)$
0	0	0
0	1	1
1	0	1
1	1	1

(b)

$+$	0	1
0	0	1
1	1	1

(c)

$\cup$	Φ	I
Φ	Φ	I
I	I	I

(d)

FIG. 71

In Figure 71b the results of Table 1 are used to indicate the switching function $F(x, y) = x + y$. This figure suggests the "addition" table given in Figure 71c. Note that $0 + 0 = 0$, $0 + 1 = 1 + 0 = 1$ and $1 + 1 = 1$. The last expression is the only one different from the addition of the numbers zero and one.

Now let Φ and I be the special elements which always exist in a Boolean Algebra and make a table for the binary operation $\cup$ on these elements as indicated in Figure 71d. This table can be constructed by using Axiom A7 and Theorem 6. Observe the similarity between the tables in 71c and 71d. Notice further that we can obtain table 71d from table 71c by systematically replacing $+$ by $\cup$, 0 by Φ, and 1 by I; and by reversing the substitutions we can obtain 71c from 71d.

Next let us consider a network consisting of two switches connected in series as indicated in Figure 72a. Let $F(x, y) = x \cdot y$, or $F(x, y) = xy$, be the switching function of two switches connected in series and, as before, construct table 72b. Observe that the network is closed only when both x and y are closed. This suggests the "multiplication" table given in Figure 72c. Note that $0 \cdot 0 = 0 \cdot 1 = 1 \cdot 0 = 0$, $1 \cdot 1 = 1$, and that the symbols 0 and 1 behave like the numbers zero and one under ordinary multiplication. If we now make a table for the binary operation $\cap$ on the special elements Φ and I of the Boolean Algebra, as in 72d, we observe that the table is similar to the one in 72c. Again it is possible to change from one of these tables to the other by systematically interchanging $\cdot$ and $\cap$, 0 and Φ, and 1 and I.

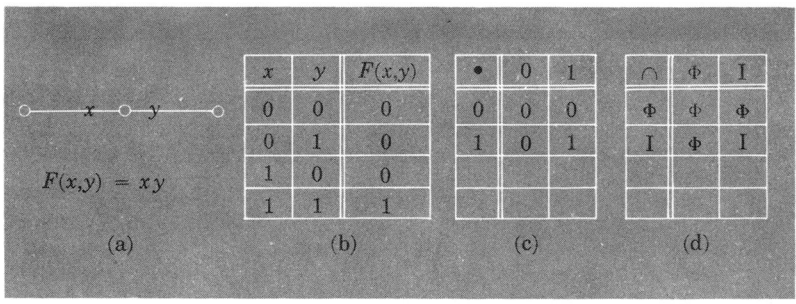

FIG. 72

Another similarity between a switching network and the elements of a Boolean Algebra will be observed if we denote switches having opposite states by x and x'. Thus, if x is open, x' is closed and if x is closed, x' is open. This behavior presented in tabular form in Figure 73a can be compared with the table in Figure 73b giving the result of the prime operation on Φ and I in Boolean Algebra.

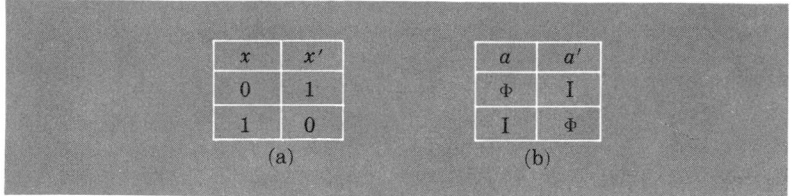

x	x'
0	1
1	0

(a)

a	a'
Φ	I
I	Φ

(b)

FIG. 73

The reader can show that each of the axioms A1 through A10 is satisfied by the set $\{\Phi, I\}$ with operations $\cup$, $\cap$, and $'$ as given in tables 71d, 72d, and 73b. It is therefore a Boolean Algebra of two elements. It also can be shown that the set $\{0, 1\}$, with the operations $+$, $\cdot$, and $'$ as defined in tables 71c, 72c, and 73a forms a Boolean Algebra of two elements.

We are now ready to set up a correspondence between a switching network and our mathematical model, Boolean Algebra.

$$
\begin{array}{ccccccc}
\text{Boolean Algebra:} & x & x' & \cup & \cap & \Phi & I \\
& \updownarrow & \updownarrow & \updownarrow & \updownarrow & \updownarrow & \updownarrow \\
\text{Switching Network:} & x & x' & + & \cdot & 0 & 1
\end{array}
$$

With this correspondence we are able to transcribe the axioms and theorems of Boolean Algebra into statements about switching networks. Before we do this let us emphasize a few points and agree on some further notation.

1. Observe that the letter x plays a dual role since it both indicates the switch in a network and also the state of the switch; that is, in addition to indicating a switch, x represents a variable of the algebra that can assume the value 0 or 1.

2. When we write $x + yz$ this will mean $x + (y \cdot z)$; that is, the same conventions govern the order of the operations $+$ and $\cdot$ for switching networks as govern the order of addition and multiplication of ordinary numbers.

3. Instead of having x denote the state of a single switch, it is sometimes useful to let x denote the state of an entire network.

4. Two switching networks S_1 and S_2 are equivalent if both are open or both are closed for the same state of the switches in S_1 and S_2, and this equivalence is denoted by $S_1 \sim S_2$.

Now we can show that a switching network does satisfy the ten axioms of Boolean Algebra. The first axiom is A1, $a \cup b = b \cup a$. By applying the correspondence that we have set up, we obtain $a + b = b + a$, which can be interpreted as the statement that the two parallel networks ⊶$\boxed{{}^{a}_{b}}$⊷ and ⊶$\boxed{{}^{b}_{a}}$⊷ are equivalent. This is certainly true. The remaining axioms are interpreted in a similar manner.

TABLE II

Boolean Algebra or Switching Function	*Switching Network*

A1. $a + b = b + a$.

A2. $ab = ba$.

A3. $a + (b + c)$ $= (a + b) + c$.

A4. $a(bc)$ $= (ab)c$.

A5. $a(b + c)$ $= ab + ac$.

A6. $a + b \cdot c$ $= (a + b)(a + c)$.

A7. $a + 0 = a$.

A8. $a \cdot 1 = a$.

A9. $a + a' = 1$.

A10. $a \cdot a' = 0$.

All the theorems of Boolean Algebra can be applied to switching functions without further justification. However, it will be instructive to check some of the theorems as applied to a switching network.

Theorem	*Switching Network*

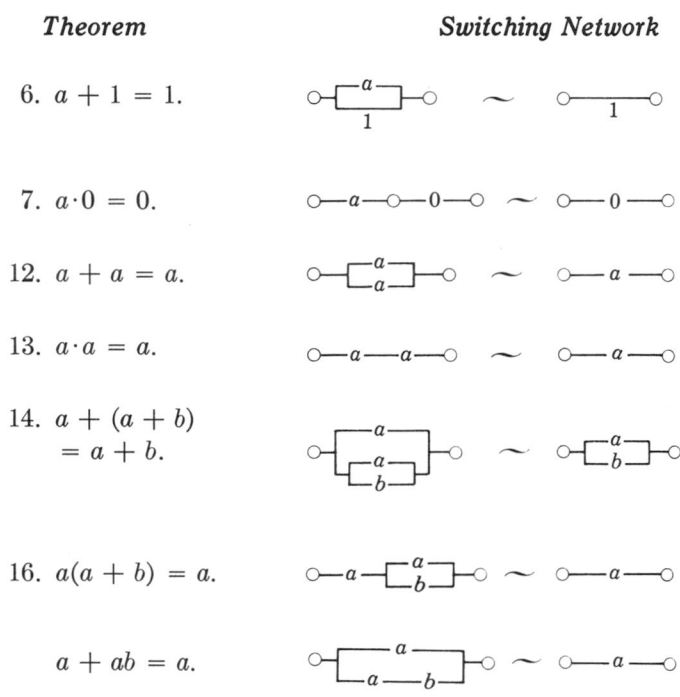

6. $a + 1 = 1$.

7. $a \cdot 0 = 0$.

12. $a + a = a$.

13. $a \cdot a = a$.

14. $a + (a + b)$
$\quad = a + b$.

16. $a(a + b) = a$.

$\quad a + ab = a$.

Let us apply our mathematical model to the simplification of switching networks. A given network, under the correspondence set up, will be represented by its switching function, which may be simplified using Boolean Algebra. Then this simplified expression can be reinterpreted as a switching network. If there are fewer switches in the resulting network, then we shall say that the network has been simplified. Under some circumstances the elimination of one or two switches may not be significant. However, if a company produces many products using the same switching network, then a considerable saving may be realized. Furthermore, in applications where reliability is of prime importance, the elimination of one or two switches may be very significant.

In some of the examples that follow, the network could be simplified without recourse to Boolean Algebra; however, it is the procedure that we are interested in showing.

Example 1. $F(x, y) = x + xy$
$$= (x \cdot 1) + xy$$
$$= x(1 + y)$$
$$= x \cdot 1$$
$$= x.$$

Theorem 16 could have been used, but for practice, only the axioms were used. In the switching network two switches are indicated by the same letter x. This does not necessarily mean that they are the same switch, only that they are always opened or closed together.

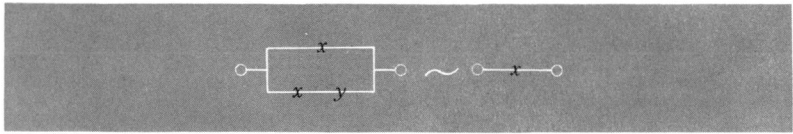

FIG. 74

Example 2. $F(x, y) = xy' + xy$
$$= x(y' + y)$$
$$= x \cdot 1$$
$$= x.$$

Here y and y' may be different switches, so that the network of four switches may be replaced by one switch.

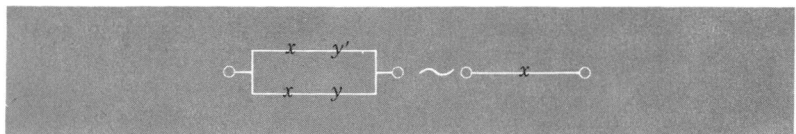

FIG. 75

Example **3.**

$$F(a, b, c) = abc + ab'c + a'b'c$$
$$= c[ab + ab' + a'b']$$
$$= c[a(b + b') + a'b']$$
$$= c[a \cdot 1 + a'b'] = c[a + a'b']$$
$$= c[(a + a')(a + b')] = c[1(a + b')] = c(a + b').$$

Since only one of the two switches b and b' remains in the simplified diagram it can be designated either by b' or by b.

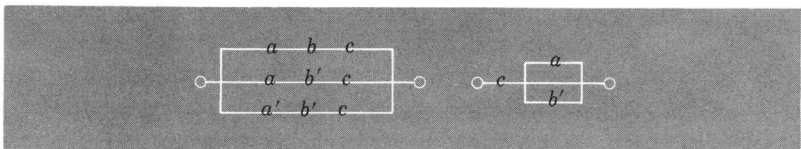

FIG. 76

Example **4.** Determine a switching function for the bridge network in Figure 77a.

Solution. Since the bridge network does not consist of series-parallel connections, we cannot write the switching function by just inspecting the network. What we shall do is to determine when the bridge network is open or closed. There are four distinct paths through the network as indicated in Figure 77b. If the switches in any path are closed, the network will be closed; otherwise the network will be open. Therefore, the network is closed when xy or yz or xwz or ywy are closed, and open otherwise. Hence, the switching function f is

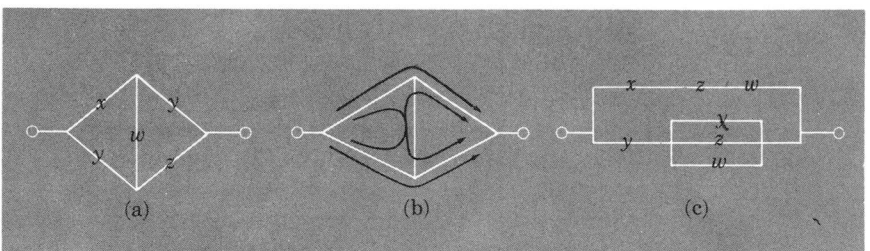

FIG. 77

$f(x, y, z, w) = xy + yz + xwz + ywy = xzw + xy + yz + yw = xzw + y(x + z + w)$ as shown in Figure 77c.

Many switching networks are verbally specified and must be converted into switching networks. This transition can sometimes be accomplished very nicely by introducing Boolean functions of several variables.

Definition. *A **Boolean function** or a **Boolean polynomial** is an expression derived from a finite number of applications of the operations* $\cup$, $\cap$, *and* $'$ *to the elements of a Boolean Algebra.*

Since we are at present interested in the application of Boolean Algebra to switching networks, the Boolean Algebra consisting of the set $\{0, 1\}$ and the operations $+$, $\cdot$, and $'$ will be used in what follows. We shall let $2a = a + a$, $3a = a + a + a$ and, in general, if k is a positive integer let $ka = a + a + \cdots + a$ be the "sum" of k "summands". We shall also let $a^2 = a \cdot a$, $a^3 = a \cdot a \cdot a$ and, in general, let $a^k = a \cdot a \cdot a \cdots \cdot a$ be the "product" of k "factors". Then by Theorems 12 and 13, $ka = a$ and $a^k = a$. Therefore, no multiples or powers appear in the Boolean polynomials. In one variable, there are only four Boolean polynomials; namely,

$$a, \quad a', \quad 0 = a \cdot a', \quad \text{and} \quad 1 = a + a'.$$

We shall now briefly state some definitions and theorems on Boolean functions that are useful in switching networks.

Definition. *A **minimal Boolean polynomial** in n variables* $x_1, x_2, \cdots,$ x_n *is the "product" of n letters in which the i-th letter is either* x_i *or* x_i'.

For example, the minimal polynomials in two variables x_1 and x_2 are:

$$x_1 \cdot x_2, \quad x_1' \cdot x_2, \quad x_1 \cdot x_2', \quad x_1' \cdot x_2'.$$

In three variables x_1, x_2, and x_3 the minimal polynomials are:

$$x_1 \cdot x_2 \cdot x_3, \quad x_1 \cdot x_2 \cdot x_3', \quad x_1 \cdot x_2' \cdot x_3, \quad x_1' \cdot x_2 \cdot x_3,$$

$$x_1 \cdot x_2' \cdot x_3', \quad x_1' \cdot x_2' \cdot x_3, \quad x_1' \cdot x_2 \cdot x_3', \quad x_1' \cdot x_2' \cdot x_3'.$$

For a minimal polynomial in n variables there are two ways of selecting the first variable x_1 or x_1', two ways of selecting the second variable x_2 or x_2', $\cdots$, two ways of selecting the n-th variable x_n or x_n'; hence there are 2^n minimal polynomials in n variables.

Theorem 29.   *There is one and only one way to write a given Boolean polynomial as 0 or as the "sum" of minimal polynomials.*

We shall not present a formal proof of this theorem but shall illustrate it by the following example. Let F be a Boolean polynomial:

$$F = F(x, y, z) = [(x' + y)' \cdot z] + [x' \cdot (x + z)].$$

The primes can be removed from this expression by using Theorem 21 and the double primes can be removed by using Theorem 20. The result is an expression in primed and unprimed letters connected by $\cdot$ and $+$.

$$F = [(x'' \cdot y') \cdot z] + [x' \cdot (x + z)] = [(x \cdot y') \cdot z] + [x' \cdot (x + z)]$$

Next, any $\cdot$ outside a grouping containing a $+$ can be expanded by Axiom 4. The result is an expression of letters in which the $\cdot$ operations are performed before the $+$ operations. In our example

$$F = [(x \cdot y') \cdot z] + [(x' \cdot x) + (x' \cdot z)].$$

Because of the associativity indicated in Axioms A3 and A4

$$F = (x \cdot y' \cdot z) + (x' \cdot x) + (x' \cdot z).$$

Now F is written as groups of primed and unprimed letters connected by $\cdot$, and the groups are connected by $+$. Furthermore, it may be possible to simplify each group. For example, if any group has the same letter occurring more than once, all but one occurrence may be dropped since $a \cdot a = a$. If a letter and its prime both occur in a group the whole group can be dropped since $x \cdot x' = 0$ and $0 + x = x$. Hence

$$F = (x \cdot y' \cdot z) + 0 + (x' \cdot z) = (x \cdot y' \cdot z) + (x' \cdot z).$$

Finally, if a group Y does not contain a letter, say x or x', this letter can be introduced into the group by replacing Y by $1 \cdot Y$, using A8, and then replacing 1 by $x + x'$, using A9, as follows:

$$Y = 1 \cdot Y = (x + x') \cdot Y = (x \cdot Y) + (x' \cdot Y).$$

Therefore, F can be written as follows:

$$F = (x \cdot y' \cdot z) + [(x' \cdot z) \cdot 1] = (x \cdot y' \cdot z) + [(x' \cdot z) \cdot (y + y')]$$
$$= (x \cdot y' \cdot z) + (x' \cdot z \cdot y) + (x' \cdot z \cdot y')$$
$$= (x \cdot y' \cdot z) + (x' \cdot y \cdot z) + (x' \cdot y' \cdot z).$$

Now each group of the Boolean function F consists of all the letters, primed or unprimed, appearing only once connected by $\cdot$, and the groups connected by $+$.

Definition. *A Boolean polynomial is in* **canonical form** *when it is expressed as the "sum" of minimal polynomials.*

The question of the equality of two Boolean polynomials can be settled by simply expressing the two functions in canonical form and seeing if they are the same.

The final theorem, which will be left to the reader to prove, concerns canonical forms. Before presenting this theorem, let us recall what it means to define a function f, say, of two variables x and y. A function $f(x, y)$ is defined when the values of the function are known for all possible values that the variables x and y can assume. In our present case the variables of the function, as well as the function itself, can assume only two values, 0 and 1. Therefore $f(x, y)$ is completely specified when the values of $f(1, 1)$, $f(1, 0)$, $f(0, 1)$ and $f(0, 0)$ are known.

Theorem 30. *The Boolean functions $F(x, y)$ and $G(x, y, z)$ have the following canonical forms.*

$$F(x, y) = F(1, 1)xy + F(1, 0)xy' + F(0, 1)x'y + F(0, 0)x'y'.$$
$$G(x, y, z) = G(1, 1, 1)xyz + G(1, 1, 0)xyz' + G(1, 0, 1)xy'z$$
$$+ G(0, 1, 1)x'yz + G(1, 0, 0)xy'z' + G(0, 1, 0)x'yz'$$
$$+ G(0, 0, 1)x'y'z + G(0, 0, 0)x'y'z'.$$

Using Theorem 30 we can solve the following problem.

Example **5.** Find a switching network that can control one light from two different locations.

Solution. Assume that both switches are open and that the light is off so that we can fill in the first row of Figure 78a. If either switch is closed, the light goes on. This is indicated in the second and third rows. When both switches are in states opposite from the original states the light is off. This is indicated in the last row. Therefore,

$$f(x, y) = f(1, 1)xy + f(1, 0)xy' + f(0, 1)x'y + f(0, 0)x'y',$$
$$f(x, y) = 0 \cdot xy + 1 \cdot xy' + 1 \cdot x'y + 0 \cdot x'y',$$
$$f(x, y) = xy' + x'y.$$

This network is shown in Figure 78b and in practice is accomplished by two single-pole double-throw switches as shown in Figure 78c.

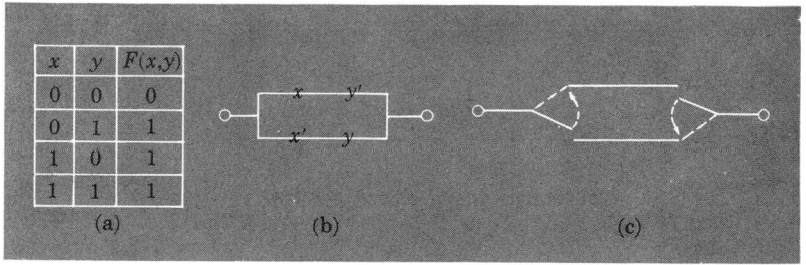

(a)   (b)   (c)

FIG. 78

Example 6. Design the following network using three switches x, y, and z. The network is closed when x is open unless y and z are both open or both closed, in which case the circuit is open. It is also closed when x is closed unless y or z (but not both) are closed, in which case the circuit is open.

x	y	z	$g(x, y, z)$
0	0	0	0
0	1	1	0
0	1	0	1
0	0	1	1
1	0	1	0
1	1	0	0
1	0	0	1
1	1	1	1

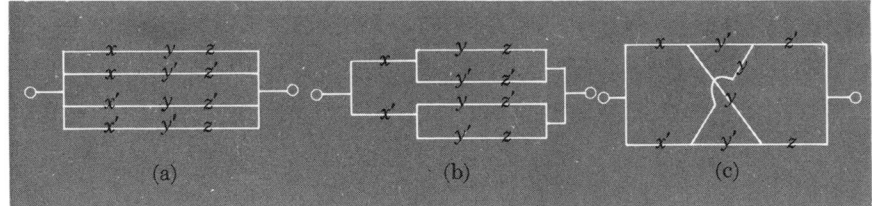

FIG. 79

Solution. The first two lines of the table indicate that the circuit is open when x is open and y and z are both open or closed, that is, in the same state. Lines 3 and 4 indicate that the circuit is closed when x is open and y and z have opposite states. Continuing in this manner, we can complete the table. Using Theorem 30, we get

$$
\begin{aligned}
g(x, y, z) = {} & g(1, 1, 1)xyz + g(1, 1, 0)xyz' + g(1, 0, 1)xy'z \\
& + g(0, 1, 1)x'yz + g(1, 0, 0)xy'z' + g(0, 1, 0)x'yz' \\
& + g(0, 0, 1)x'y'z + g(0, 0, 0)x'y'z'.
\end{aligned}
$$

$$
g(x, y, z) = xyz + xy'z' + x'yz' + x'y'z.
$$

The network indicated by $g(x, y, z)$ is given in Figure 79a.

This function can be simplified as follows:

$$
g(x, y, z) = x(yz + y'z') + x'(yz' + y'z),
$$

with a saving of two switches as indicated in Figure 79b. This network can be further simplified by employing a bridge network as shown in Figure 79c. Unfortunately, no systematic procedure seems to be available for determining from the switching function whether a bridge network will use fewer switches.

CONCLUDING REMARKS

We have investigated two problems of switching networks that sometimes can be solved by Boolean Algebra. The first problem is to determine an equivalent network with fewer switches for a given switching network. This is accomplished by first characterizing the network by an algebraic function, called the switching function, transforming the function using Boolean Algebra, and then reinterpreting the function as a network. If the resulting network has fewer switches we say that it has been simplified. The other problem is to determine a network that possesses certain specified properties. This is done by determining the state of each switch and then, using the canonical form of a Boolean function, finding the switching function and hence the network.

The application of Boolean Algebra to switching networks was first investigated by C. E. Shannon and was published in 1938. With the advent of the digital computer and the increasing complexity of the telephone switching networks the subject has been extensively developed in recent years. Boolean Algebra is also useful in the study of propositional logic and the subsets of a set. For the reader interested in pursuing the subject further, the first reference contains both applications and a rather extensive bibliography.

EXERCISES

1. Show that there is a Boolean Algebra of exactly two elements by showing that two specific elements satisfy A1 through A10.

2. Write the switching function, f, for each of the following networks.

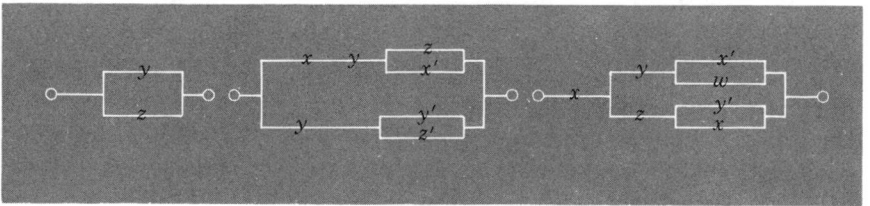

FIG. 80

3. Draw a switching network that represents each of the following switching functions.
(a) $f(x, y) = x(x + y') + x'y$.
(b) $f(x, y, z, w) = xy(z + w') + (x + z)(x + w)$.
(c) $f(x, y, z) = (x' + y)'(xz + y)$.

4. Establish the equivalence of the following networks.
(a)

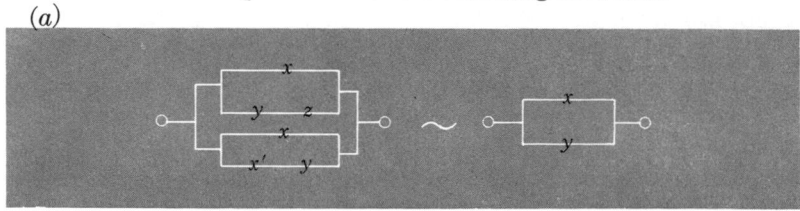

FIG. 81

(b)

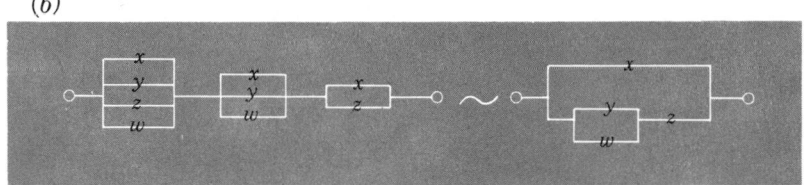

FIG. 82

5. Prove Theorem 30 by showing that the equation for $F(x, y)$ is satisfied for all values of x and y.

6. Show the equivalence of the bridge circuit and the series-parallel circuit indicated here.

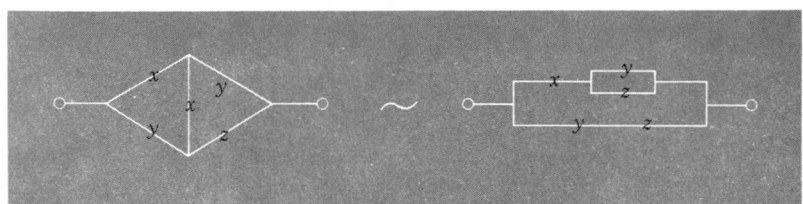

FIG. 83

7. Change the following Boolean functions to canonical form.
(a) $f(x, y, z) = [(xy')' + z'][z + x']'$.
(b) $f(x, y, z) = (x' + y)'(x + z)' + (yz)'$.

8. (a) Show that any non-empty set S, considered as a universal set, along with the empty set forms a Boolean Algebra of two elements under the operations of set union, intersection, and complementation.

(b) Show that the set of all subsets of a given set is a Boolean Algebra under the same set operations.

9. Show that the two definitions of a Boolean Algebra given in this section and on page 107 are equivalent.

*10. Consider the following logical problem.

A farmer is taking a fox, a goose, and a bag of corn to market. On his way, he must cross a river in a small boat that will hold only the farmer and one of the items that he plans to sell; that is, either the fox, the goose, or the corn. In the absence of the farmer, the fox would eat the goose, and the goose would eat the corn.

(a) Determine how the farmer can cross the river without losing the goose or the corn. (Two solutions)

(b) Set up an electric switching network using four double-pole double-throw switches which will simulate electrically the above problem in the following sense. The four switches, S_1, S_2, S_3, and S_4, are mounted and labeled as shown here.

S_1	S_2	S_3	S_4
FARMER	FOX	GOOSE	CORN

All the switches in the same relative position would represent the farmer, the fox, the goose, and the corn on the same side of the river. Throwing switches S_1 and S_2 would represent the farmer rowing the fox across the river. This switching network should turn on a red light if the incorrect sequence of switches is thrown, otherwise the light should remain off. The reader will better appreciate the power of the methods of Boolean Algebra if he first tries to determine the switching network by trial and error.

REFERENCES

1. F. E. HOHN, *Applied Boolean Algrebra, An Elementary Introduction*, New York, Macmillan, 1960.
2. G. BIRKHOFF and S. MACLANE, *A Survey of Modern Algebra*, Revised Edition, New York, Macmillan, 1953, Chapter XI.
3. C. E. SHANNON, *A Symbolic Analysis of Relay and Switching Circuits*, Trans. Amer. Inst. Elec. Eng., Vol. 57, 1938, pp. 713–723.
4. H. EVES and C. V. NEWSOM, *An Introduction to the Foundations and Fundamental Concepts of Mathematics*, New York, Holt, Rinehart & Winston, Inc., 1958.

Answers to Selected Exercises

1. (a) 3, 13, 23, 33, 43.
   (b) Washington, Lincoln, Jefferson, T. Roosevelt, Wilson,····.
   (c) 3, −3.
   (d) Catcher, pitcher, first baseman, center fielder, right fielder,····.
   (e) 0, 5, −5, 10, −10,····.
   (f) 1.
   (g) Julius Caesar, Romeo and Juliet, Hamlet, As You Like It, Macbeth,····.
   (h) There are no elements in this set, therefore none can be listed.
   (i) 3/8, 7, −2/3, 3.14, 0,····.
   (j) 0.
   (k) −4, −2, 0, 2, 4, 6.
   (l) 31, 37, 41, 43, 47.

2. There are many possible universal sets. A few such sets are given. Many other correct answers exist. Here S, J, and $\overline{R}$ represent the given set, the set of integers, and the set of rational numbers, respectively.
   (a) S; J; or $\overline{R}$.
   (b) S; the set of leaders of all nations of the world; or the set of all people who have lived in the United States.
   (c) S; the odd integers; J; or $\overline{R}$.
   (d) S; or all playing positions in basketball, baseball, or hockey.
   (e) S; J; or $\overline{R}$.
   (f) S; J; all $r \,\epsilon\, \overline{R}$ such that $-3 < r < 2$; or all integers between -5 and 5.

209

(*g*) *S*; all English plays; all English and American plays; or all pieces of English literature produced since 500 A.D.

(*h*) *S*; the set of positive integers; *J*; or $\overline{R}$.

(*i*) *S*; or the set which contains all rational numbers and all square roots of rational numbers.

(*j*) *S*; all even integers; *J*; or $\overline{R}$.

(*k*) *S*; all even integers; *J*; or $\overline{R}$.

(*l*) *S*; the set of prime numbers; the set of odd prime numbers; *J*; or $\overline{R}$.

3. (*a*) $-26, -21, -16, -11, -6, -1, 4, 9, 14$.

   (*b*) $-9, -7, -5, -3, -1, 1, 3, 5, 7$.

   (*c*) $-11/3, -3, -7/3, -5/3, -1, -1/3, 1/3, 1, 5/3$.

   (*d*) $14, 12, 10, 8, 6, 4, 2, 0, -2$.

4. (*b*), (*c*), (*e*), (*f*).

5. (*a*) The set of positive integers.   (*b*) $\{6\}$.   (*c*) The set which has as its only element the first president of the United States.

   (*d*) The set of names of states in the United States which begin with the letter *z*.   (*e*) $\{$Kentucky, Kansas$\}$.

6. (*a*) The set of even integers, or $\{0, 2, -2, 4, -4, 6, -6, \cdots\}$.

   (*b*) $\{x \mid x = 3n,$ where $n \,\epsilon\, J\}$, $\{3n \mid n \,\epsilon\, J\}$, or $\{0, 3, -3, 6, -6, \cdots\}$.

   (*c*) $\{x \mid x \,\epsilon\, J$ and $-6 < x < 3\}$, $\{x \mid x \,\epsilon\, J$ and $-5 \leqq x \leqq 2\}$; the set of all integers which are between -6 and 3; or the set of integers between -5 and 2, inclusive.

   (*d*) $\{1, 2, 3, 4, 5, 6, 10, 12, 15, 20, 30, 60\}$, or the set of positive integral divisors of 60.

7. (*a*) $2, 3, 4, 6$.   (*b*) $2, 3, 5, 6, 10, 15$.   (*c*) $2, 4, 8, 16, 32, 64$.   (*d*) $2, 5,$ $10, 19, 38, 95$.   (*e*) $2, 3, 4, 5, 6, 9, 10, 12, 15, 18, 20, 30, 36, 45, 60, 90$.

8. A prime integer is an integer $n > 1$ which has no proper integral divisors.

Page 11

1. $B \subset A,\ C \subset A,\ D \subset A,\ B \subset D,\ B \subset E,\ C \subset E,\ D \subset E$.

2. $L \subseteq B$.

3. (*a*) The salad is not all citrus fruit.   (*b*) The salad consists entirely of citrus fruit.

4. (*a*) $A \subseteq D$.   (*b*) $A \subset B$.   (*c*) $B \subset C$.

Page 19

1. (*a*) *B*.   (*b*) *A*.   (*c*) *C*.   (*d*) *A*.   (*e*) $\varnothing$.   (*f*) *A*.   (*g*) *C*.   (*h*) *B*.

   (*i*) *B'*.

2. (a) $\emptyset$. (b) A. (c) U. (d) U. (e) $\emptyset$. (f) A. (g) $\emptyset$. (h) U.

3. (a) A. (b) A. (c) $\emptyset$. (d) U.

4. (a) $\emptyset$. (b) U. (c) C. (d) B.

5.

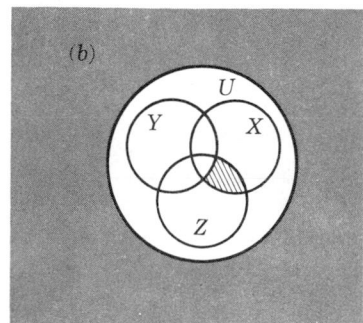

(c) $X' \cap Y \cap Z$.

(d) $(X \cup Y \cup Z)' = X' \cap Y' \cap Z'$.

(e) $Y' \cup X \cup Z$.

6.

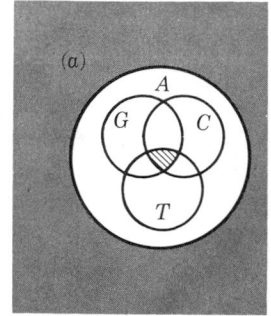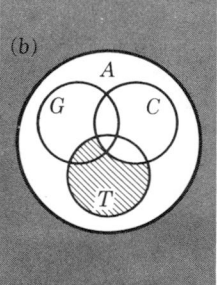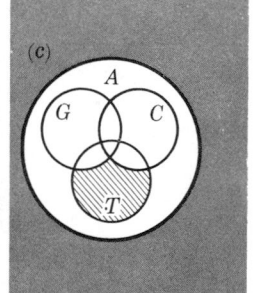

7. (a) $A \cap B$ = set of all integral multiples of 6.

(b) $A \cup B$ = set of all integers divisible by 2 or by 3.

(c) $B \cap C$ = set of all integral multiples of 12.

(d) J.   (e) A.

(f) $A - C$ = set of all odd multiples of $2 = \{4n + 2 \mid n \in J\}$.

(g) $J - C$ = set of all integers which are not multiples of 4, or $\{x \mid x \text{ is } 4n + 1, 4n + 2, \text{ or } 4n + 3, \text{ where } n \in J\}$.

8. (a) T. (b) R. (c) The set of points in the line segment AE.

(d) R. (e) No. (f) No.

9. (*a*) A.   (*b*) $B' = C$ and $C' = B$.

10. (*a*) A'.   (*b*) $\varnothing$.   (*c*) A.   (*d*) $\varnothing$.   (*e*) $\varnothing$.

11.

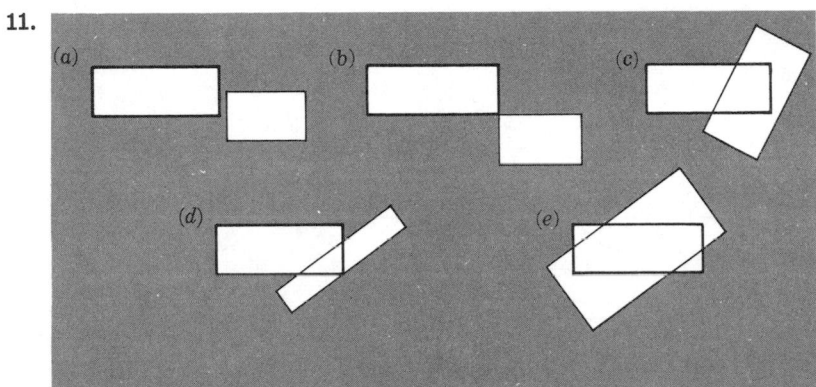

12.

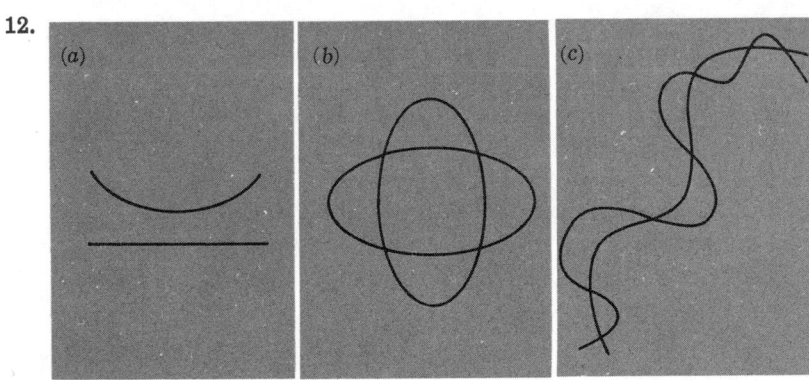

13.

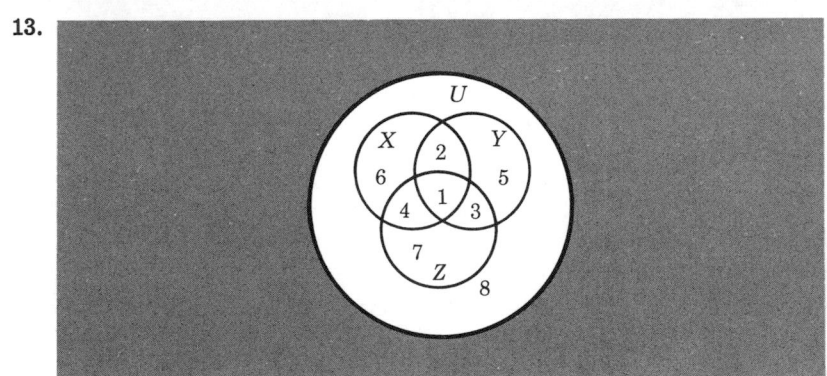

14. (*a*) $S \cap T$.   (*b*) $T \cap W$.   (*c*) $S \cap W$.   (*d*) $(T \cup S)' = T' \cap S'$.
(*e*) $T' \cap S' \cap W'$.   (*f*) $W \cap T'$.   (*g*) $T \cap S \cap W$.
(*h*) $W \cap (S \cap T)'$.

Page 25
1. (*a*) $P = \{\varnothing, \{a\}, \{b\}, \{c\}, \{a, b\}, \{a, c\}, \{b, c\}, D\}$.

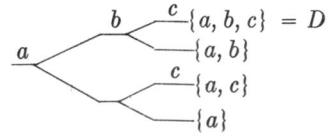

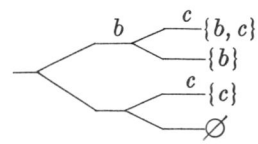

2. (*a*) 1.   (*b*) 2.   (*c*) 4.   (*d*) 8.   (*e*) 16.   (*f*) 32.   (*g*) 2^n.

3. (*a*) 1.   (*b*) 3.   (*c*) 7.   (*d*) 15.   (*e*) 31.   (*f*) $2^n - 1$.

Page 42
2. First establish the following independent statements.
Statement P.   If $A \cap B = B$, then $A \supseteq B$.
Discussion. Given $A \cap B = B$. If $x \in B$, then since $B = A \cap B$, $x \in A \cap B$. Since $x \in A \cap B$, then $x \in A$ and $x \in B$. Therefore, whenever $x \in B$, then $x \in A$ and, by definition, B is a subset of A.
Statement Q.   If $A \supseteq B$, then $A \cup B = A$.
Discussion. By definition, $A \cup B \supseteq A$. To show the inclusion in the opposite direction we observe that if $y \in A \cup B$, then $y \in A$ or $y \in B$. Since $A \supseteq B$, every element of B is an element of A, therefore when $y \in B$ then $y \in A$. Thus every element y of $A \cup B$ is in A and $A \cup B \subseteq A$. Therefore $A \cup B = A$.
Statement R.   If $A \cup B = A$, then $A \cap B = B$.
Discussion. Given $A \cup B = A$. If $x \in B$, then $x \in A \cup B$. Since $A \cup B = A$, then $x \in A$. Therefore, whenever $x \in B$, then $x \in A$ and $x \in A \cap B$. Therefore $A \cap B \supseteq B$. By Statement 3, $A \cap B \subseteq B$. Therefore $A \cap B = B$.
(*a*) Statements P and Q.   (*b*) Statements Q and R.
(*c*) Statements R and P.

4. $A \cup B = B \cup A$ (Commutative Law for Set
                                                             Union)

              $A \cap B = B \cap A$ (Commutative Law for Set
                                                             Intersection)

       $(A \cup B) \cup C = A \cup (B \cup C)$ (Associative Law for Set
                                                             Union)

       $(A \cap B) \cap C = A \cap (B \cap C)$ (Associative Law for Set
                                                             Intersection)

$A \cap (B \cup C) = (A \cap B) \cup (A \cap C)$ (Distributive Law for Set Intersection with Respect to Set Union)

All of these statements are true.

5. In Exercise 1, all are true. In Exercise 2, all are false, unless the inclusion symbol is reversed. In Exercise 3, the statement is true.

6. $a(b + c) = ab + ac$ is true, but $a + bc = (a + b)(a + c)$ is false. For example $2(3 + 4) = 2 \cdot 3 + 2 \cdot 4$, but $2 + 3 \cdot 4 \neq (2 + 3)(2 + 4)$.

7. (a) $(R \cap S) \cup (R \cap T)$.   (b) $(S \cup R) \cap (S \cup T)$.
   (c) $(Z \cap X) \cup (Y \cap X)$.   (d) $(M \cup P) \cap (N \cup P)$.
   (e) $B \cap (A \cup C)$.   (f) $T \cup (R \cap S)$.   (g) $(W \cup H) \cap P$.
   (h) $(B \cap C) \cup D$.

8. (a) U.   (b) U.   (c) B'.   (d) C'.   (e) A'.   (f) $\varnothing$.
   (g) W'.   (h) $A \cup B'$.   (i) K.

9. (a) U.   (b) $A \cup T$.   (c) W.   (d) $\varnothing$.   (e) S.   (f) $\varnothing$.   (g) U.
   (h) B.   (i) U.   (j) B'.   (k) D.   (l) U.   (m) C'.   (n) $B \cup A'$.
   (o) $D \cap C'$.   (p) U.   (q) $\varnothing$.   (r) $A \cup B \cup C$.   (s) K'.
   (t) $T \cup R$.   (u) Y.   (v) $A \cup B$.

11. If $A \subseteq B$, then by the Law of Consistency $A \cap B = A$. Therefore $A \cap B' = (A \cap B) \cap B' = \varnothing$.

12. $B \epsilon P$.

13. (a) $P = \{\varnothing, X\}$.   (b) $Q = \{\varnothing, \{\varnothing\}, \{X\}, P\}$.

14. $P = \{S_n \mid S_n$ is a set of n points of intersection of the given lines, where $n = 0, 1, 2, 3, 4, 5,$ or $6\}$. P has $2^6 = 64$ elements.

15. (a) $\varnothing$.   (b) C.   (c) B.   (d) The set of integers between 1 and 50, inclusive, which are not multiples of 3; that is, $D' = \{x \mid x = 3n + 1$ or $x = 3n + 2$, where $n \epsilon J$ and $1 \le x \le 50\}$.
   (e) The set of odd integral multiples of 3 between 1 and 50, inclusive.
   (f) The set of even integral multiples of 3 between 1 and 50, inclusive.
   (g) $\{x \mid x = 2n + 1$ or $x = 3n$, where $1 \le x \le 50$ and $n \epsilon J\}$.
   (h) $\{x \mid x = 2n$ and $x \neq 3m$, where $1 \le x \le 50$ and $n, m \epsilon J\}$.
   (i) Same as (h).
   (j) $\{x \mid x = 2n$ or $x \neq 3m$, where $1 \le x \le 50$ and $n, m \epsilon J\}$.
   (k) Same as (j).

16. $t = 2$, $B = \{2, 3\}$, $C = \{B, 2\}$. In general, the relationship expressed by ϵ is not transitive.

18. (a) $(A - B) - C = (A - B) \cap C' = A \cap B' \cap C' = A \cap (B \cup C)'$
$= A - (B \cup C)$.

19. (a) $A \triangle B = (A \cup B) - (A \cap B)$. $A \triangle B = (A \cup B) \cap (A \cap B)'$.

(b)

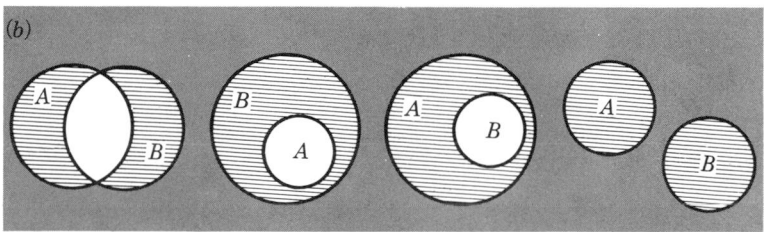

When $A = B$, the symmetric difference is $\varnothing$.

(c) First show $A \triangle B = (A \cap B') \cup (B \cap A')$, then by interchanging B and A, show that $A \triangle B = B \triangle A$. Then

$$(A \triangle B) \triangle C = [(A \triangle B) \cap C'] \cup [C \cap (A \triangle B)'].$$

Show that $(A \triangle B) \cap C' = (B \cap A' \cap C') \cup (A \cap B' \cap C')$ and that $C \cap (A \triangle B)' = (C \cap B' \cap A') \cup (A \cap B \cap C)$.

Thus $(A \triangle B) \triangle C = (B \cap A' \cap C') \cup (A \cap B' \cap C') \cup (C \cap B' \cap A')$ $\cup (A \cap B \cap C)$. Since $A \triangle (B \triangle C) = (B \triangle C) \triangle A = (C \triangle B) \triangle A$, the expression for $(C \triangle B) \triangle A$ can be obtained from the expression for $(A \triangle B) \triangle C$ by interchanging A and C.

Page 53

1. (a) $\{(-2, 4), (1, 4), (0, 4)\}$. (b) $\{(7, 7)\}$.

(c) $\{(1/2, a), (1/2, x), (1/2, z), (1/2, t), (-1, a), (-1, x), (-1, z), (-1, t), (8, a), (8, x), (8, z), (8, t), (-3/8, a), (-3/8, x), (-3/8, z), (-3/8, t)\}$.

2. (a) $n(A \times B) = n(A) \cdot n(B)$,
$n(A \times A) = [n(A)]^2$.

3. (a)

m	$(m, +)$	$(m, 0)$	$(m, *)$	$(m, -)$
t	$(t, +)$	$(t, 0)$	$(t, *)$	$(t, -)$
p	$(p, +)$	$(p, 0)$	$(p, *)$	$(p, -)$
q	$(q, +)$	$(q, 0)$	$(q, *)$	$(q, -)$
r	$(r, +)$	$(r, 0)$	$(r, *)$	$(r, -)$
	$+$	0	$*$	$-$

4. $\{(1, 4, 6), (2, 4, 6), (3, 4, 6), (1, 5, 6), (2, 5, 6), (3, 5, 6), (1, 4, 7), (2, 4, 7), (3, 4, 7), (1, 5, 7), (2, 5, 7), (3, 5, 7), (1, 4, 8), (2, 4, 8), (3, 4, 8), (1, 5, 8), (2, 5, 8), (3, 5, 8), (1, 4, 9), (2, 4, 9), (3, 4, 9), (1, 5, 9), (2, 5, 9), (3, 5, 9)\}$.

5. (a) $n(A \times B \times C) = n(A) \cdot n(B) \cdot n(C)$.
   (b) $n(A \times A \times A) = [n(A)]^3$.

6. 30.

7. 16.

8. 9.

10. 12, 6.

11. (a) 775.   (b) 1275.   (c) 2775.

12. (i) L can be obtained by adding Z, T, and E.
   (ii) $L = Z + T + E$, $119 = 10 + 77 + 32$.

13. (a) No.   (b) 2037.   (c) 3742.

Page 59
1. (a) 10, 10.   (b) 11, 10.   (c) 33, 33.   (d) 98, $n + 1$.

2. (a) No.   (b) Yes.   (c) Yes.   (d) No.   (e) Yes.   (f) Yes.

5. (b) Except when D and E both coincide with C.

6. (a) 1.   (b) 2.   (c) 6.   (d) 24.   (e) 120.

7. The product of the first n positive integers is $1 \cdot 2 \cdot 3 \cdot \ldots \cdot n$ and this product is denoted by $n!$ The number of ways is $n(n - 1)(n - 2) \cdot \ldots \cdot 3 \cdot 2 \cdot 1 = n!$

8. (a) $5! = 120$.   (b) $7! = 5040$.   (c) $9! = 362,880$.   (d) $8! = 40,320$.

Page 66
1. To indicate the 1–1 correspondences let the first number listed here correspond to 1, the second to 2, and, in general, the nth one correspond to the positive integer n.
   (a) $0, 1, -1, 2, -2, \cdots$.   (b) $0, 3, -3, 6, -6, \cdots$.
   (c) $1, -1, 3, -3, 5, -5, \cdots$.   (d) $2, 7, -3, 12, -8, 17, -13, \cdots$.
   (e) $-7, 5, -19, 17, -31, 29, -43, \cdots$.
   (f) $0, 1/7, -1/7, 2/7, -2/7, 3/7, -3/7, \cdots$.

2. Since H is a subset of K, disregard H, for $H \cup K = K$. Those elements in T which are not in K are $-10, -15, -20, -25, \cdots$. Thus
   $K = \{-7, -6, -5, -4, -3, -2, -1, 0, 1, 2, \cdots\}$
   $T - K = \{-10, -15, -20, -25, \cdots\}$ and
   $H \cup K \cup T = \{-7, -10, -6, -15, -5, -20, -4, -25, \cdots\}$. Since all elements of the union can be listed in such a way that there is a first one, a second one, and, in general, an nth one, this set is a countable set.

3. Let S_n denote the nth set. The following sets are disjoint and each is countable: S_1, $S_2 - S_1$, $S_3 - (S_1 \cup S_2)$, $S_4 - (S_1 \cup S_2 \cup S_3)$, $\cdots$, $S_n - (S_1 \cup \cdots \cup S_{n-1})$, $\cdots$. Slice these sets diagonally.

4. $A_{jk} \leftrightarrow \frac{1}{2} (j + k - 1)(j + k - 2) + k$.

5. (a) Yes. (b) A straight line bisecting the angle between the given lines extended. (c) No. (d) Yes. Draw AC and BD. If these lines are parallel set up the correspondence by using lines parallel to them. If AC and BD intersect draw straight lines through their point of intersection.

6. (a) 0. (b) 2. (c) -1. (d) 1. (e) -2. (f) 3. (g) 3. (h) 1.

Page 71

1. (a) Under the second correspondence a real number q corresponds to a point twice as far from the origin. (b) Yes. Let an order-preserving correspondence be given. By interchanging the points on L which correspond to two numbers, such as 0 and 1 in Q, we have $0 < 1 < 2$ but the point corresponding to 1 will not be between the points corresponding to 0 and 2.

2. (a) None. Only the points 0 and 1 will coincide.
(b) Same as (a).
(c) Same as (a).
(d) 3, if $j = 1$; 11, if $j = 2$; 33, if $j = 3$.

3. (a) $k = 1$: Between 1 and 2. In general, between k and $k + 1$.
(b) Equal. (c) When k is rational. (d) The rational numbers are dense in the interval T from 0 to 1. Let a and b be two points in the interval H, then $a - k$ and $b - k$ are two points in T. If x is a rational number such that $a - k < x < b - k$, then adding k shows that $a < x + k < b$.

Page 90

1. The power set is closed with respect to each of these operations.

2.

Set	$+$	$-$	$\times$	$\div$
(a)	No. $3 + 5 = 8$	No. $5 - 7 = -2$	Yes.	No. $3 \div 5 = 3/5$
(b)	No. $4 + 5 = 9$	No. $5 - 7 = -2$	No. $2(3) = 6$	No. $3 \div 5 = 3/5$
(c)	Yes.	Yes.	Yes.	No. $3 \div 0$ is undefined.
(d)	Yes.	Yes.	Yes.	No. $3 \div 5 = 3/5$

3. Subtraction, division, $x \bigcirc y = 3x - y$, $x \bigcirc y = \sqrt{x} + y$.

4. Subtraction, division, $x \bigcirc y = 2x + y$, $x \bigcirc y = (x + y)^2$.

5. $\{\emptyset, F, F', U\}$.

6. $\{\emptyset, \{d\}, \{c, d\}, \{a, b, c\}, \{a, b\}, \{c\}, \{a, b, d\}, U\}$.

Page 132

1. (a) (Shakespeare, Newton), (Newton, Shakespeare), (Descartes, Fermat), (Fermat, Descartes),····.
    (b) (Babe Ruth, Gehrig), (Gehrig, Babe Ruth), (John L. Sullivan, Corbett), (Corbett, John L. Sullivan),····.

2. (a) $(12, 3)$, $(21, 7)$, $(10, 5)$,····.   (b) $(6, 20)$, $(2, 9)$, $(5, 40)$,····.
    (c) $(10, 4)$, $(11, 7)$, $(5, 5)$,····.   (d) $(5, 3)$, $(-5, -3)$, $(0, 0)$,····.

3.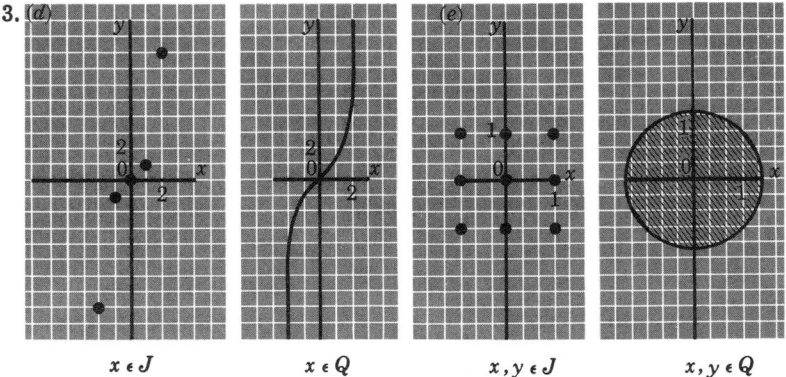

$x \in J$ $\qquad$ $x \in Q$ $\qquad$ $x, y \in J$ $\qquad$ $x, y \in Q$

(d) $d(R) = J$, $r(R) = \{n^3 \mid n \in J\} = \{0, 1, -1, 8, -8, 27, -27, \cdots\}$; $d(R) = r(R) = Q$.

(e) $d(R) = r(R) = \{-1, 0, 1\}$; $d(R) = r(R) = \{t \mid -\sqrt{2} \leqq t \leqq \sqrt{2}, t \in Q\}$.

4.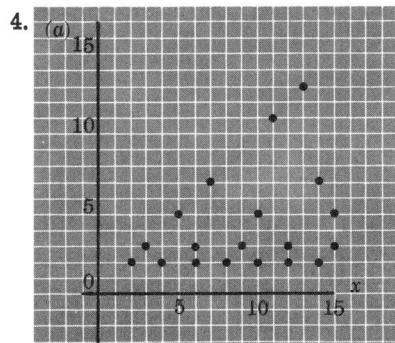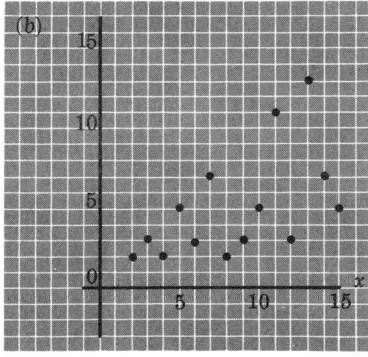

(a) $d(R) = \{x \mid x \in J \text{ and } x > 1\}$, $r(R) = $ set of prime integers.

(b) $d(R)$ and $r(R)$ are the same as in (a).

5.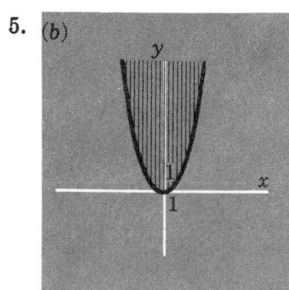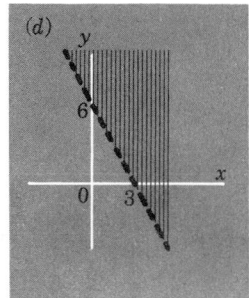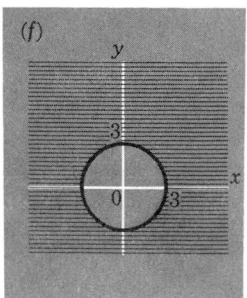

(b) $d(R) = Q$. $r(R) = \{y \mid y \geqq 0, y \in Q\}$.

(d) $d(R) = r(R) = Q$.

(f) $d(R) = r(R) = Q$.

6.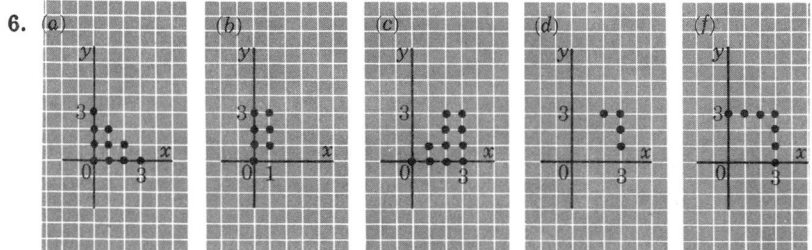

(a) $d(R) = r(R) = S$.   (b) $d(R) = \{0, 1\}$, $r(R) = S$.

(c) $d(R) = r(R) = S$.   (d) $d(R) = \{2, 3\}$, $r(R) = \{1, 2, 3\}$.

(e) $d(R) = r(R) = \varnothing$.   (f) $d(R) = r(R) = S$.

8.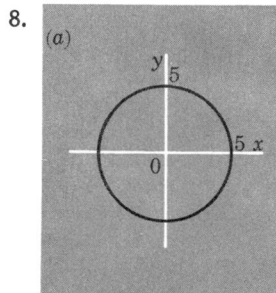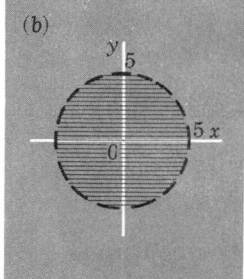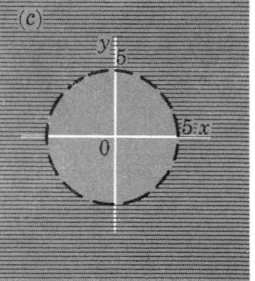

Each is a relation.

(d) The entire xy-plane.

9. Let A, B, and C be the sets of points in Exercise 8(*a*), (*b*), and (*c*), respectively.

 (*a*) $A \cup B$. (*b*) $A \cup C$.

10.

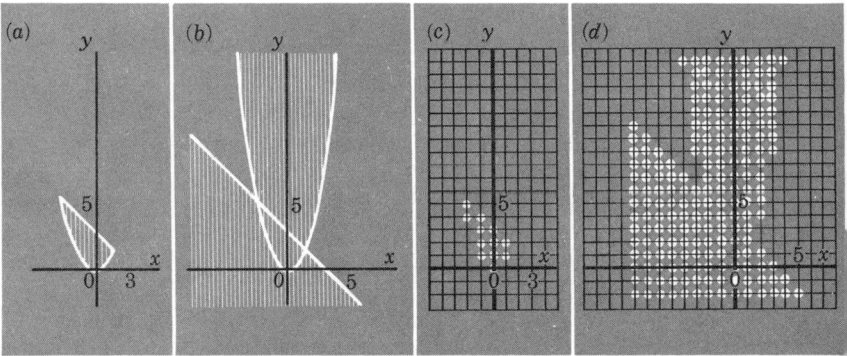

Each is a relation.

11.

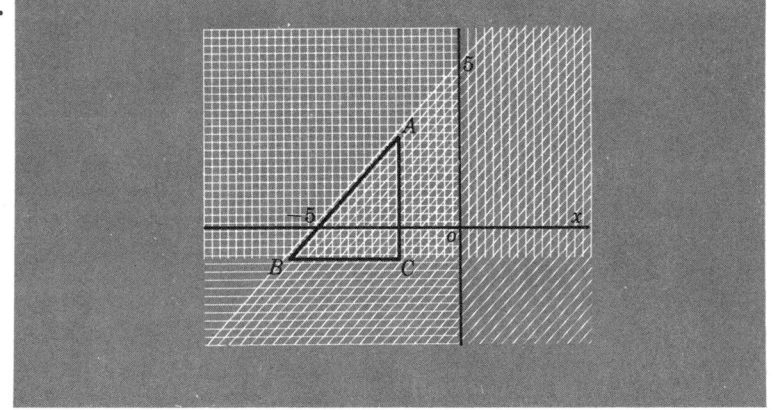

$R \cap S \cap T$ is triangle ABC plus its interior. It is a relation.

12. (*a*) Yes. The even integers, and the odd integers.

  (*b*) Yes. $\{0, 5, -5, 10, -10, 15, -15, \cdots\}$,
   $\{1, 6, -4, 11, -9, 16, -14, \cdots\}$,
   $\{2, 7, -3, 12, -8, 17, -13, \cdots\}$,
   $\{3, 8, -2, 13, -7, 18, -12, \cdots\}$, and
   $\{4, 9, -1, 14, -6, 19, -11, \cdots\}$.

(c) Yes. The books having one page, those having two pages, those having three pages,···, those having n pages,···, where n is a positive integer.

(d) No.   (e) No.   (f) Yes. All chairs in the furniture store, all tables, all beds,···.

14. (b) and (f).

16. (a) $y = x + 3$, $x \epsilon J$, $-1 \leqq x \leqq 2$; $d(R) = \{-1, 0, 1, 2\}$, $r(R) = \{2, 3, 4, 5\}$.

(b) $y = x^2$, $x = -3$, $\sqrt{2}$, or 2; $d(R) = \{-3, \sqrt{2}, 2\}$, $r(R) = \{2, 4, 9\}$.

(c) $y = \sqrt{x^2 + 1}$, $x \epsilon J$, $-2 \leqq x \leqq 2$; $d(R) = \{-2, -1, 0, 1, 2\}$, $r(R) = \{1, \sqrt{2}, \sqrt{5}\}$.

17. (a) Domain of R.   (b) Range of R.

18. Relations in D: $\{(a, a)\}$; $\{(a, b)\}$; $\{(b, a)\}$; $\{(b, b)\}$; $\{(a, a), (a, b)\}$; $\{(a, a), (b, a)\}$; $\{(a, a), (b, b)\}$; $\{(a, b), (b, a)\}$; $\{(a, b), (b, b)\}$; $\{(b, a) (b, b)\}$; $\{(a, a), (a, b), (b, a)\}$; $\{(a, a), (a, b), (b, b)\}$; $\{(a, a)(b, a)(b, b)\}$; $\{(a, b), (b, a), (b, b)\}$; $\{(a, a), (a, b), (b, a), (b, b)\}$.

(a) $\{(a, a)\}$; $\{(b, b)\}$; $\{(a, a), (b, b)\}$; $\{(a, a), (a, b), (b, b)\}$; $\{(a, a), (b, a), (b, b)\}$; $\{(a, a), (a, b), (b, a), (b, b)\}$.

(b) $\{(a, a)\}$; $\{(b, b)\}$; $\{(a, a), (b, b)\}$; $\{(a, b), (b, a)\}$; $\{(a, a), (a, b), (b, a)\}$; $\{(a, b), (b, a), (b, b)\}$; $\{(a, a), (a, b), (b, a), (b, b)\}$.

(c) $\{(a, a)\}$; $\{(b, b)\}$; $\{(a, a), (b, b)\}$; $\{(a, a), (a, b), (b, a), (b, b)\}$.

(d) $\{(a, a)\}$; $\{(b, b)\}$; $\{(a, a), (b, b)\}$; $\{(a, a), (a, b), (b, a), (b, b)\}$.

19. The reverse image of D under R denoted by $R_r(D)$.

Page 150

1. (b), (c), (d), (f), (h), and (i) are functions.

(a), (e), (g), and (j) are relations which are not functions.

(d), (f), and (h) have inverses.

2. (b), (e), and (f) are functions.

4. (a) $d(F) = r(F) = Q$.

(b) $d(F) = r(F) = \{t \mid t \geqq 0, t \epsilon Q\}$.

(c) $d(F) = \{x \mid x \leqq -3 \text{ or } x \geqq 3, x \epsilon Q\}$, $r(F) = \{y \mid y \geqq 0, y \epsilon Q\}$.

(d) $d(F) = \{x \mid -3 \leqq x \leqq 3, x \epsilon Q\}$, $r(F) = \{y \mid 0 \leqq y \leqq 3, y \epsilon Q\}$.

(e) $d(F) = Q$, $r(F) = \{y \mid y \geqq -3, y \epsilon Q\}$.

(f) $d(F) = r(F) = Q - \{1\}$.

5. (a) $d(F) = \{-3, -2, -1, 0, 1, 2, 3\}$, $r(F) = \{-13, -11, -9, -7, -5, -3, -1\}$.

(b) $d(F) = \{-2, 3, 5, 8\}$, $r(F) = \{7, -2, -1, 2\}$.

(c) $d(F) = J$, $r(F) = \{x \mid x \epsilon J, x \geqq 0\}$.

(d) $d(F) = \{0, 1, 2, 3, 4, 5, 6\}$, $r(F) = \{0, -1, -2, -3, -4, -5, -6\}$.

(e) $d(F) = J$, $r(F) = \{2, 3\} \cup \{n^2 - 3 \mid n \epsilon J \text{ and } n \geqq 2\}$.

6.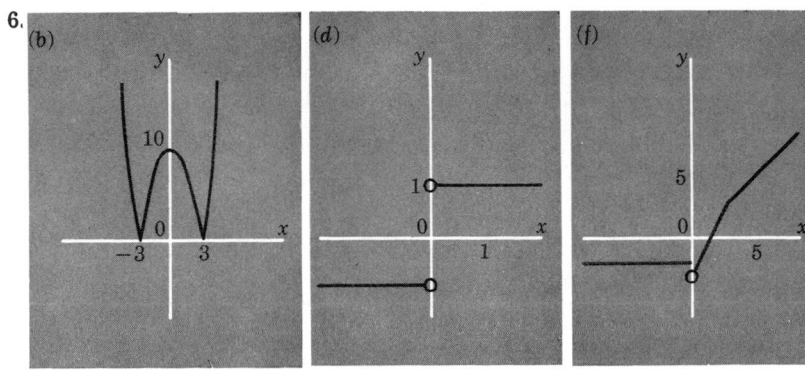

7. (a) $3x^2$.   (b) $10x$.   (c) $-21x^6$.   (d) 0.   (e) $30x^4$.

8. (a) -3.   (b) 30.   (c) 3.   (d) 2.   (e) 0.   (f) 11.   (g) -1.
   (h) $2a^2 - b^2 + 7abc$.   (i) -1.   (j) $ac^2 - b^2t$.   (k) $3 - a^2 - 2ab - b^2$.
   (l) $(3a^2 - 1)/a^2$.   (m) $3x^2 + 6hx + 3h^2 - 2h - 2x - 3$.
   (n) $6hx + 3h^2 - 2h$.   (o) $\dfrac{3a^2 - 2a - 3}{3 - a^2}$.   (p) $4x + 10y + x^2 - y^2$.
   (q) $-2x - h$.   (r) a.

9. (a) $-3x^4 + 2x^3 + 12x^2 - 6x - 9$.   (b) $\{(-1, 2), (3/2, 3/4)\}$.
   (c) $2x^2 - 2x$.   (d) $2x^2 - y^2 + 7xyz - 7x + 3y - xy$.
   (e) $3x^4 - 16x^2 + 18$.   (f) $-9x^4 + 12x^3 + 14x^2 - 12x - 6$.
   (g) $\dfrac{2x^2 - 6x + 3}{x^2 - 2x + 1}$.   (h) $(3 - x^2)/(2 - x^2)$.

11. Let f and g denote the first and second functions, respectively. Then
   $(2, 4) \, \epsilon \, g$ but $(2, 4) \, {\not\epsilon} \, f$. However, all other pairs in g are in f, therefore
   $f \neq g$ but $f \subset g$.

12. (a) $\{(-1, 0), (0, 5)\}$.   (b) $\{(0, 3), (1, 5)\}$.

13. The degree of each polynomial is given.   (a) 3.   (d) 1.   (e) 6.
   (g) 0.

14. (a) $y = (x - 2)/3$.   (b) The given function.
   (c) $y = (6 - x)/2$, $x \geqq 6$.   (d) $y = -\sqrt{x}$.

15.

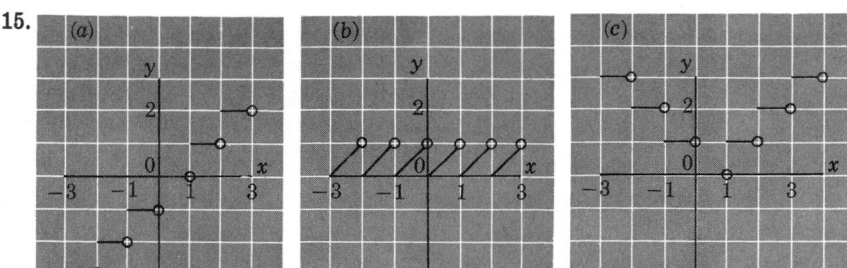

16. (a) $(2, 1)$.   (b) $x = 2$.   (c) $y = 1$.

(d) The circle with center at $(2, 1)$ and radius 2.

17. (a) $\{1/2, 0, 3/2\}$.   (b) $\{\sqrt{5}, -\sqrt{5}\}$.   (c) $\{1\}$.   (d) $\{0, 3, -3\}$.

The relation f_r is a function for (a) and (c) only.

18. (a) $r \rightarrow u,\ s \rightarrow v;\ r \rightarrow v,\ s \rightarrow u;\ r \rightarrow u,\ s \rightarrow u;\ r \rightarrow v,\ s \rightarrow v$. The first two have inverses.

(b) There are 27 functions. Those which have inverses are: $r \rightarrow u$, $s \rightarrow v,\ t \rightarrow w;\ r \rightarrow u,\ s \rightarrow w,\ t \rightarrow v;\ r \rightarrow v,\ s \rightarrow u,\ t \rightarrow w;\ r \rightarrow v$, $s \rightarrow w,\ t \rightarrow u;\ r \rightarrow w, s \rightarrow u, t \rightarrow v;\ r \rightarrow w, s \rightarrow v, t \rightarrow u$. The remaining 21 functions map two or more elements into the same image.

19. All.

20. Theorem 1 follows easily from the definition.

Proof of Theorem 2. One of the numbers a or $-a$ is $|a|$, therefore, if z is greater than or equal to each of them, it must be greater than or equal to $|a|$.

Proof of first half of Theorem 3. If $a \geq 0$, then $|a| = a$. If $a \leq 0$, then $|a| = -a > 0$. Since $-a$ is positive, and a is negative $a \leq -a = |a|$. Therefore in either case $|a| \geq a$. The proof of the last half is left to the reader.

Hint for Theorem 4. Apply Theorem 3 to both a and b and add the resulting statements to obtain $|a| + |b| \geq a + b$ and $|a| + |b| \geq -(a + b)$. Then apply Theorem 2.

Hint for Theorem 6. Use Theorem 5 to obtain $|a|\,|b| = \sqrt{(ab)^2} = |ab|$.

Page 162

1. We shall use the abbreviations c.e., i., c.i., and a.i. for conditional equation, identity, conditional inequality, and absolute inequality, respectively.

(a) i.	(b) c.i.	(c) a.i.	(d) c.e.	(e) c.i.	(f) c.e.
(g) c.i.	(h) c.e.	(i) c.i.	(j) a.i.	(k) c.i.	(l) c.e.
(m) c.i.	(n) c.e.	(o) c.e.	(p) i.	(q) c.e.	(r) a.i.
(s) i.	(t) c.i.	(u) c.e.	(v) c.e.	(w) i.	(x) i.
(y) c.i.	(z) c.e.				

3. (a) The square of a real number is never negative. If x and y are real numbers then $x - y$ is a real number. Therefore its square is non-negative. Thus $(x - y)^2 \geq 0$; $x^2 - 2xy + y^2 \geq 0$; and $x^2 + y^2 \geq 2xy$.

   (b) *Hint.* Start with the real numbers $|x|$ and $|y|$.

   (c) *Hint.* Add statements like the one in (a).

Page 180

1.

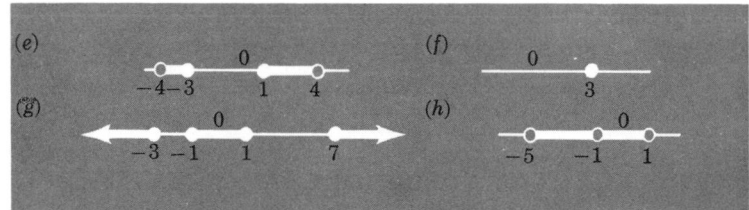

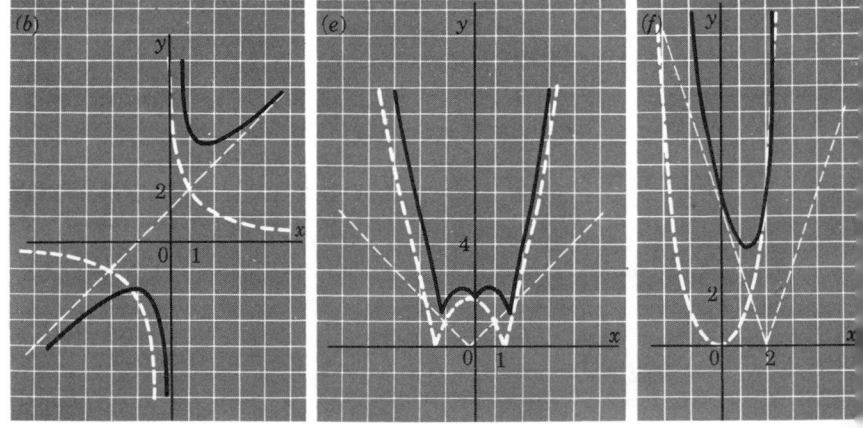

5.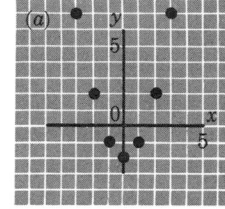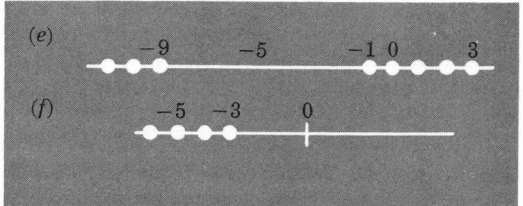

11. (a) $-1, -3, 1/2$.
(c) $2, -4, 5/7$.
(e) $5/2, 1/5, 4, -3$.

(b) $1, -7/5, -3/2$.
(d) $\sqrt{7}, -\sqrt{7}, 1, 1/3$.
(f) $\sqrt{5}, -\sqrt{5}, 5/3, 1/4$.

Page 190

1. *Th.* 4. $a' \cup a = I$.

Proof.	$a \cup a' = I$	(A9)
	$a \cup a' = a' \cup a$	(A1)
	$a' \cup a = I$.	

Th. 5. $a' \cap a = \Phi$.
Proof.   Apply Th. 1 to Th. 4.

Th. 10. $[a \cup b = b] \Rightarrow [a \cap b = a]$.
Proof.   Interchange a and b and use the duals of Th. 8 and 9.
    $[b \cup a \Rightarrow b] \Rightarrow [b \cup a' = \Phi]$
    $[b \cup a' = \Phi] \Rightarrow [b \cap a = a]$
Combine the first and last statements and use A1 and A2.
    $[a \cup b = b] \Rightarrow [a \cap b = a]$.

Th. 8. $[a \cap b = a] \Rightarrow [a \cap b' = \Phi]$.

Proof.	$a \cap b' = (a \cap b) \cap b'$	(Sub.)
	$= a \cap (b \cap b')$	(A4)
	$= a \cap \Phi$	(A10)
	$= \Phi$.	(Th. 7)

Th. 20. $(a')' = a$.

Proof.	$a' \cup (a')' = I$	(A9)
	$a' \cap (a')' = \Phi$	(A10)
	$a' \cup a = I$	(Th. 4)
	$a' \cap a = \Phi$	(Th. 5)

Combine these statements.
    $a' \cup (a')' = a' \cup a$ and $a' \cap (a')' = a' \cap a$
Therefore $(a')' = a$.   (Th. 18)

Th. 21. $(a \cup b)' = a' \cap b'$ and $(a \cap b) = a' \cup b'$.
Proof.   First we show that $(a \cup b)' = a' \cap b'$.
  $(a \cup b) \cup (a \cup b)' = I$
  $(a \cup b) \cap (a \cup b)' = \Phi$

$(a \cup b) \cup (a' \cap b') = [(a \cup b) \cup a'] \cap [(a \cup b) \cup b']$	(A5)
$= [(a \cup a') \cup b] \cap [a \cup (b \cup b')]$	(A1, A3)
$= [I \cup b] \cap [a \cup I]$	(A9)
$= I \cap I$	(Th. 6)
$= I.$	(A8)
$(a \cup b) \cap (a' \cap b') = [a \cap (a' \cap b')] \cup [b \cap (a' \cap b')]$	(A2, A6)
$= [(a \cap a') \cap b'] \cup [(b \cap b') \cap a']$	(A4, A2)
$= [\Phi \cap b'] \cup [\Phi \cap a']$	(A10)
$= \Phi \cup \Phi$	(A8)
$= \Phi.$	(A7)

Therefore, $(a \cup b) \cup (a \cup b)' = (a \cup b) \cup (a' \cap b')$
          $(a \cup b) \cap (a \cup b)' = (a \cup b) \cap (a' \cap b')$, and
                $(a \cup b)' = a' \cap b'$.   (Th. 18)
To show that $(a \cap b)' = a' \cup b'$ apply Th. 1 to $(a \cup b)' = a' \cap b'$.

Th. 22. $[a \cup b = b,$ and $b \cup c = c] \Rightarrow [a \cup c = c]$.
Proof.

$b \cup c = c$	(Hyp.)
$(a \cup b) \cup c = c$	(Sub.)
$a \cup (b \cup c) = c$	(A3)
$a \cup c = c.$	(Sub.)

Th. 25. $[a \subseteq b$ and $b \subseteq c] \Rightarrow [a \subseteq c]$.
Proof.

$b \subseteq c \Rightarrow b \cap c' = \Phi$	(Def.)
$\Rightarrow b \cap c = b.$	(Th. 11)
$a \subseteq b \Rightarrow a \cap b' = \Phi$	(Def.)
$\Rightarrow a \cap b = a.$	(Th. 11)
Now $a = a \cap b$	(Sub.)
$= a \cap (b \cap c)$	(Sub.)
$= (a \cap b) \cap c$	(A4)
$= a \cap c.$	(Sub.)
$[a = a \cap c] \Rightarrow a \cap c' = \Phi$	(Th. 11)
$\Rightarrow a \subseteq c.$	(Def.)

Th. 27. $[a \subseteq \Phi] \Leftrightarrow [a = \Phi]$.
Proof.   We first show that
$a \subseteq \Phi \Rightarrow a = \Phi$.

$a \subseteq \Phi$	(Hyp.)
$\Phi \subseteq a$	(Th. 24)

Therefore $a = \Phi$.   (Th. 26)
Next we show that $[a = \Phi] \Rightarrow [a \subseteq \Phi]$
  $a = \Phi \rightarrow a \subseteq \Phi$ and $\Phi \subseteq a$ (Th. 26)

Th. 28. $[a \subseteq b] \Leftrightarrow [b' \subseteq a']$.

Proof. $[a \subseteq b] \Leftrightarrow [a \cap b' = \Phi]$ (Def.)

$[b' \subseteq a'] \Leftrightarrow [b' \cap (a')' = \Phi]$ (Def.)

$\Leftrightarrow [b' \cap a = \Phi]$ (Th. 20)

$\Leftrightarrow [a \cap b' = \Phi]$ (A2)

Therefore

$[a \subseteq b] \Leftrightarrow [b' \subseteq a']$.

2. *Reflexive:* $a \subseteq a$.

Proof. $a \cap a' = \Phi$ (A10)

Therefore $a \subseteq a$.   (Def.)

For the proof of the antisymmetric property see Theorem 26.

3. $(a \cup b \cup c \cup d) \cap (a \cup b \cup d) \cap (a \cup c)$

$= [(a \cup b \cup d) \cup c] \cap (a \cup b \cup d) \cap (a \cup c)$ (A3)

$= (a \cup b \cup d) \cap (a \cup c)$ (A4, Th. 16)

$= a \cup [(b \cup d) \cap c]$ (A5)

$= a \cup [c \cap (b \cup d)]$.   (A2)

4. Let $a = x \cap y'$, then $a' = (x \cap y')' = x' \cup y$, and   (Th. 21)

$(x \cap y') \cup [z \cap (x' \cup y \cup w)] = a \cup [z \cap (a' \cup w)]$

$= (a \cup z) \cap [(a \cup a') \cup w]$ (A5, A3)

$= (a \cup z) \cap (I \cup w)$ (A9)

$= (a \cup z) \cap I$ (Th. 2)

$= a \cup z$ (A8)

$= (x \cap y') \cup z$ (Sub.)

$= z \cup (x \cap y')$.   (A1)

Page 205

2. (a) $f(x, y, z) = x(y + z)$.

(b) $f(x, y, z) = xy(x' + z) + y(y' + z')$.

(c) $f(x, y, z, w) = x[y(x' + w) + z(x + y')]$.

3.

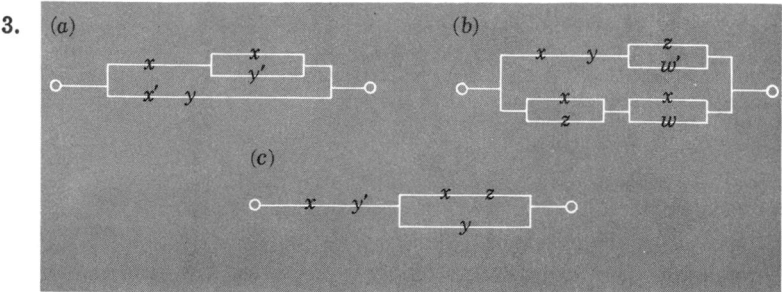

4. (*a*) Let $F(x, y, z)$ be the switching function of the first network.
$$
\begin{aligned}
F(x, y, z) &= (x + yz) + (x + x'y) \\
&= x + yz + x + x'y & \text{(A3)} \\
&= (x + x) + yz + x'y & \text{(A1, A3)} \\
&= x + yz + x'y & \text{(Th. 13)} \\
&= (x + x'y) + yz & \text{(A1, A3)} \\
&= (x + x')(x + y) + yz & \text{(A5)} \\
&= 1(x + y) + yz & \text{(A9)} \\
&= x + (y + yz) & \text{(A8, A3)} \\
&= x + y. & \text{(Th. 16)}
\end{aligned}
$$

(*b*) Let $f(x, y, z, w)$ be the switching function of the first network, then
$f(x, y, z, w) - (x + y + z + w) \cdot (x + y + z) \cdot (x + z)$. This is the same function as the one in Exercise 3, page 190, which was shown to be equal to $x + [z(y + w)]$. This is the switching function of the simplified network.

5. Theorem 30 is proved by substituting specific values of x and y into the formula. For example, consider
$f(x, y) = f(1, 1)xy + f(1, 0)xy' + f(0, 1)x'y + f(0, 0)x'y'$. Then
$$
\begin{aligned}
f(1, 1) &= f(1, 1) \cdot 1 \cdot 1 + f(1, 0) \cdot 1 \cdot 1' + f(0, 1) \cdot 1' \cdot 1 + f(0, 0) \cdot 1' \cdot 1' \\
&= f(1, 1) + f(1, 0) \cdot 1 \cdot 0 + f(0, 1) \cdot 0 \cdot 1 + f(0, 0) \cdot 0 \cdot 0 \\
&= f(1, 1) + f(1, 0) \cdot 0 + f(0, 1) \cdot 0 + f(0, 0) \cdot 0 \\
&= f(1, 1).
\end{aligned}
$$
The reader can show that this part of the theorem is true for all other specific replacements of x and y.

6. The bridge network is closed if xy, or yz, or xxz, or yxy is closed. Otherwise it is open. Therefore, the switching function is
$$
\begin{aligned}
f(x, y, z) &= xy + yz + xxz + yxy = xy + yz + xz + yz \\
&= xy + yz + xz = x(y + z) + yz.
\end{aligned}
$$

7. (*a*)
$$
\begin{aligned}
f(x, y, z) &= [(xy')' + z'][z + x']' \\
&= [(x' + y'') + z'][z' \cdot x''] \\
&= [x' + y + z'][z'x] \\
&= xx'z' + xyz' + xz'z' \\
&= 0 \cdot z + xyz' + xz' \\
&= xyz' + xz' \\
&= xyz' + x(y + y')z' \\
&= xyz' + xyz' + xy'z' \\
&= xyz' + xy'z'
\end{aligned}
$$

(*b*)
$$
\begin{aligned}
f(x, y, z) &= (x' + y)'(x + z)' + (yz)' \\
&= (x''y')(x'z') + (y' + z') \\
&= xx'y'z' + (y' + z') = 0 \cdot y'z' + y' + z' \\
&= y' + z' = (x + x')y'(z + z') + (x + x')(y + y')z'
\end{aligned}
$$

$$= (xy' + x'y')(z + z') + (x + x')(yz' + y'z')$$
$$= xy'z + x'y'z + xy'z' + x'y'z' + xyz' + xy'z' + x'yz'$$
$$\quad + x'y'z'$$
$$= xyz' + xy'z + xy'z' + xy'z' + x'yz' + x'y'z + x'y'z$$
$$\quad + x'y'z'$$
$$= xyz' + xy'z + xy'z' + x'yz' + x'y'z + x'y'z'.$$

10. (a) The farmer rows the goose across, returns and rows the fox across then brings back the goose. He then leaves the goose, rows the corn across, returns and rows the goose across. Another answer is: The farmer rows the goose across, returns and rows the corn across then brings back the goose. He then leaves the goose, rows the fox across, returns and rows the goose across.

(b) Let $F, f, g,$ and c represent the farmer, fox, goose, and corn, respectively. Construct the accompanying table using the condition that the switching network should be closed whenever the fox and goose or the goose and corn are together in the absence of the farmer. For example, the first row of the table represents the $F, f, g,$ and c

F	f	g	c	$h(F, f, g, c)$
1	1	1	1	0
1	1	1	0	0
1	1	0	1	0
1	0	1	1	0
0	1	1	1	1
1	1	0	0	1
1	0	1	0	0
0	1	1	0	1
0	1	0	1	0
0	0	1	1	1
1	0	0	1	1
0	0	0	1	0
0	0	1	0	0
0	1	0	0	0
1	0	0	0	1
0	0	0	0	0

together on the same side of the river and $h(F, f, g, c) = 0$ means the network is open since the fox will not eat the goose and the goose will not eat the corn in the presence of the farmer. The fifth row represents the farmer on one side of the river and the fox, goose, and corn together on the other side, and therefore the switching network should be closed; thus $h(F, f, g, c) = 1$. In like manner, the rest of the table can be completed. Note that the 1's and 0's under the columns headings F, f, g, and c represent only the relative positions of the farmer, fox, goose, and corn with respect to the river, not the elements of a Boolean Algebra. Physically, the first row of the table could be represented by the four double-pole double-throw switches in the same relative position. Using the canonical form of the switching function $h(F, f, g, c)$ we have

$$h(F, f, g, c) = F'fgc + Ffg'c' + F'fgc' + F'f'gc + Ff'g'c + F'f'g'c'$$
$$= F'gc(f + f') + Ffg'c' + F'fgc' + Ff'g'(c + c')$$
$$= F'g(c + c'f) + Fg'(f' + c'f).$$

The switching network is given below.

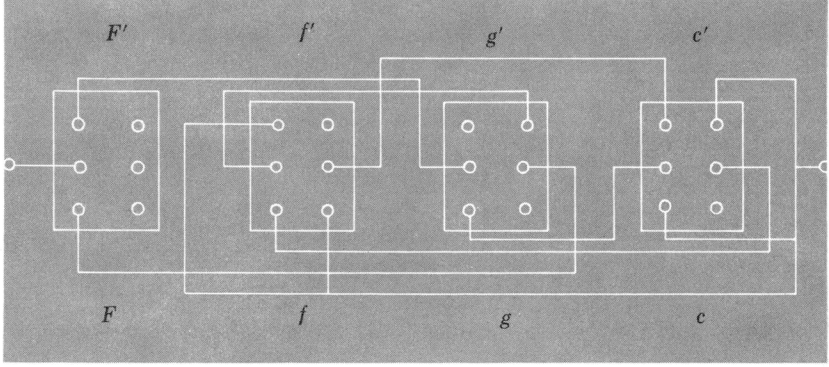

Index of Special Symbols

Part II

Introduction to
Mathematical
Logic

The Statement Calculus

The fundamental principles of logic which are used in mathematical reasoning are of sufficient importance to warrant consideration.

This treatment is divided into two main parts: the statement calculus and the restricted predicate calculus. Here, as in many other places in mathematics, the word "calculus" means "a method of calculation, especially one using a special system of algebraic notation". The *statement calculus*—sometimes referred to as the *sentential calculus*—shows how to represent statements by letters and how to obtain the truth-value of a complex statement by using only the truth-values of the component parts. The restricted predicate calculus deals with the specific content of the statement.

First, we shall consider the special type of statement which is of primary importance in scientific discourse.

1. TF-STATEMENTS

Sentences are usually classified as declarative, exclamatory, interrogative, and imperative. In our discussion of logic we shall confine ourselves to a special type of declarative sentence, the type to which it is meaningful to assign one and only one of the truth-values "true" or "false" at a given time, regardless of which is assigned. We *shall not* attempt to apply the principles of logic to such sentences as the following:

> Drive safely.
>
> What is your favorite sport?
>
> Stop, in the name of the law!

Can you explain why each of these sentences is excluded?

The type of sentence which we *shall* consider is represented by the following examples:

1. The popularity of Spanish music has gained immensely in recent years.
2. The biggest problem facing the founders was acquiring a physical plant.
3. The integer 3 is greater than the integer 7.
4. All triangles are isosceles.
5. Space ships will travel to the moon before 1975.

To these declarative sentences it is meaningful to assign one of the truth-values "true" or "false", but not both simultaneously. For instance, statement (1) has truth value "true" according to a recent article in "Coronet Magazine". Statement (2) might be either true or false depending on what physical plant is under consideration. Statements (3) and (4) have truth-value "false" if we base our conclusions on the usual elementary definitions of the terms involved, such as, "integer", "triangle", and "isosceles". We do not know the truth-value of (5) but for the sake of argument we might assume that it is either "true" or "false" for a given discussion.

We conclude this discussion of types of sentences by defining the special type that we shall be using in logic.*

Definition. *A **tf-statement** is a declarative sentence to which it is meaningful to assign a truth-value of "true" or "false", but not both simultaneously.*

By agreeing that we will not use declarative sentences that can be simultaneously true and false we are ruling out certain semantical

---

* Some authors use the word "proposition" or the word "statement" instead of the word "tf-statement". Both "statement" and "proposition" have long been used to denote concepts other than the specific one defined here.

paradoxes. One of the oldest and best known of these is a statement attributed to Epimenides, a Cretan philosopher of the sixth century B.C. He said, "Cretans always lie." If we consider the statement true, then Epimenides, being a Cretan himself is lying. Therefore what he says is not true but false. Therefore if the statement is true it is false.

Consider also the statement: "This statement is false." If we consider it true, then it is false. If we consider it false, then it is true. It is therefore a self-contradictory statement, and cannot be a tf-statement.*

EXERCISES

1. Which of the following are tf-statements?

(a) George Washington fought in the battle of Waterloo.

(b) When will the work on the house be completed?

(c) Time is on the side of right.

(d) Watch for the opening date.

(e) You need to be careful.

(f) When the windows are raised.

(g) What a noble work!

(h) Children play.

(i) A mixture of yellow and blue will produce green.

(j) Be as impartial as a traffic light.

(k) Our nation cannot afford to waste its best young minds.

(l) It seems to me that the purpose of law is to achieve justice.

(m) Where does your charity dollar go?

(n) One of the grossest errors that we can make is to assume that we have exhausted our intelligence and imagination.

(o) You should obey orders.

(p) Bring on the mountains!

(q) Curves don't come too sharp or hills too steep for this nimble car.

(r) Six shrines dedicated last summer.

(s) The hours that I walked among our lost legions were among the most poignant of my life.

---

* We shall frequently use "statement" instead of "tf-statement" when the meaning is clear.

(*t*) Memorials are not enough.

(*u*) From the shores of Tripoli.

(*v*) A blaze of fireworks lights the medieval face of Heidelberg, Germany.

(*w*) Travel by air and you will see many wondrous sights.

2. Give three tf-statements to which you can assign the truth-value "true", three to which you can assign the truth-value "false", and three which may be either "true" or "false".

2. CONNECTIVES, MODIFIERS, AND COMPOSITE STATEMENTS

Tf-statements are combined by means of such connectives as "and", "or", "if . . . then", and "if and only if"; and they are modified by the word "not". The five main types of statements obtained from connecting or modifying given statements are now illustrated and defined.

Conjunction

The process of joining two tf-statements by "and" produces a new statement known as the conjunction of the two tf-statements. For example, if the statements

Going to college is an interesting and profitable experience,

and

Visiting foreign countries brings a greater understanding of people of other lands,

are combined by the connective "and" we have the conjunction:

Going to college is an interesting and profitable experience, and visiting foreign countries brings a greater understanding of people of other lands.

The conjunction of the statements

James is clever,

and

Clara is clever,

produces

James is clever and Clara is clever,

or simply

James and Clara are clever.

Definition. *A **conjunction** is a statement obtained by joining two tf-statements by "and", or it is a statement which has the same meaning as two tf-statements joined by "and".*

Disjunction

The process of joining two tf-statements by "or" produces a new statement known as the disjunction, or alternation, of the two tf-statements. For example, if the statements

Carl will move into a smaller house,

and

James will start a new correspondence course Friday,

are combined by the connective "or" we have the disjunction:

Carl will move into a smaller house, or James will start a new correspondence course Friday.

The disjunction of

John will go,

and

Tom will go,

is

John will go or Tom will go,

or simply,

John or Tom will go.

Definition. *A **disjunction** is a statement obtained by joining two tf-statements by "or", or it is a statement which has the same meaning as two tf-statements joined by "or".*

Conditional

Similarly, the combination of two tf-statements by using the words "if . . . then" produces a conditional.* Thus the statements

> You have a factory job,

and

> You will work a maximum of four days a week,

combined in this fashion produces the conditional:

> If you have a factory job, then you will work a maximum of four days a week.

The two statements

> He will be disappointed,

and

> He is not invited,

can be combined in this order to form the conditional:

> If he is not invited then he will be disappointed,

or simply,

> He will be disappointed if he is not invited.

Definition. *A **conditional** is a statement obtained by combining two tf-statements by using the words "if . . . then", or it is a statement which has the same meaning as two tf-statements joined by "if . . . then".*

Biconditional

Two tf-statements may be connected by "if and only if". This produces a biconditional as illustrated in the following example.†

> A triangle is equilateral if and only if it is equiangular.

This single statement contains two conditionals; namely,

> If a triangle is equilateral, then it is equiangular,

and

> If a triangle is equiangular, then it is equilateral.

---

* Some authors use the word "implication" instead of the word "conditional". We shall reserve the word "implication" for another concept.

† Some authors use the word "equivalence" instead of the word "biconditional". We shall reserve the word "equivalence" for another concept.

Definition. *A **biconditional** is a statement obtained by combining two tf-statements by using the words "if and only if", or it is a statement which has the same meaning as two tf-statements joined by "if and only if".*

Negation

A tf-statement may be negated by preceding it by the words "it is not true that". For example, the negation, or denial, of the statement

Frozen foods of practically all kinds are in widespread use,

is the statement

It is not true that frozen foods of practically all kinds are in widespread use.

For many statements, equivalent forms of the negated statement are used. For example, the negation of

John is humorous,

is the statement

It is not true that John is humorous,

or

It is false that John is humorous,

or simply

John is not humorous.

When the words "it is not true that" (or "it is false that") are not used, caution should be exercised to obtain a statement which has *exactly* the same meaning as the statement obtained by prefixing these words.

Definition. *The **negation** of a tf-statement is a statement obtained by prefixing the words "it is not true that" to the tf-statement, or it is a statement which has the same meaning as the tf-statement preceded by the words "it is not true that".*

Since negating statements is important in mathematics, further discussion of this topic will be given in later sections.

All statements produced by conjunction, disjunction, implication, equivalence, and negation will be referred to as *composite statements* and the statements which were used to produce them will be referred to as the *elementary tf-statements* of the composite statements. Up to this point we have not discussed the nature of such composite statements. Are they *tf-statements*? This depends upon whether or not each statement has a truth-value. Logicians assign truth-values to these composite statements by means of truth-tables, which we shall discuss in a later section.

3. SYMBOLS AND SENTENTIAL STATEMENT PATTERNS

Modern logicians frequently use the letters p, q, r, and s to represent tf-statements, the letters T and F for true and false, respectively, and the following symbols for the connectives and the modifier:

$\wedge$ and,
$\vee$ or,
$\rightarrow$ if $\cdots$ then,
$\leftrightarrow$ if and only if,
$\sim$ not.

It is customary, as well as convenient, to refer to the symbols $\wedge$, $\vee$, $\rightarrow$, $\leftrightarrow$, and $\sim$ as *sentential connectives* even though one is a modifier.

If the letter p denotes the statement "Skippy saw an elephant", and the letter q denotes the statement "Skippy ate fifty cookies", then the *conjunction* "Skippy saw an elephant *and* he ate fifty cookies", is denoted by $p \wedge q$ (read "p and q"); the *disjunction* "Skippy saw an elephant *or* he ate fifty cookies", is denoted by $p \vee q$ (read "p or q"). The *conditional* "If Skippy saw an elephant, *then* he ate fifty cookies", is denoted by $p \rightarrow q$ (read "if p then q", or "p conditions q"); the *biconditional* "Skippy saw an elephant *if and only if* he ate fifty cookies", is denoted by $p \leftrightarrow q$ (read "p if and only if q", or "p bi-conditions q"); and the *negation* "*It is not true that* Skippy saw an. elephant", is denoted by $\sim p$ (read "not p").

Whenever a letter, such as p, represents a statement, such as "The sun is shining", it is frequently convenient to denote this by writing the letter p followed by a colon and the statement, as indicated below.

$$p: \text{The sun is shining.}$$

(Read "p represents 'The sun is shining' ".)
Similarly,

$$q: \text{This is Chicago,}$$

means that the letter q represents the statement "This is Chicago", and this notation can be read "q represents 'This is Chicago' ". Then $p \wedge q$ represents "The sun is shining and this is Chicago," and this can be indicated by

$$p \wedge q: \text{The sun is shining and this is Chicago.}$$

An example will show how this notation can be used to write statements in symbolic form. Given the statement

If tomorrow is Friday or Saturday, then Tom is late for his appointment,

we let

$$p: \text{Tomorrow is Friday,}$$
$$q: \text{Tomorrow is Saturday,}$$
and $\qquad r: \text{Tom is late for his appointment.}$

Then the symbolic form is $(p \vee q) \rightarrow r$. This form is a *sentential statement pattern* of which the given statement is an *instance*. It shows the structure of the statement without indicating the specific meaning of the letters.

Definition.   *A **sentential statement pattern** is a symbolic expression consisting of letters and sentential connectives which produces a tf-statement when the letters are replaced by tf-statements.*

Definition.   *An **instance** of a sentential statement pattern is a tf-statement obtained from it by replacing each of the letters by a specific tf-statement.*

"Skippy saw an elephant and he ate fifty cookies" is an instance of the sentential statement pattern $p \wedge q$. "The sun is shining and this is Chicago" is an instance of this same pattern.

The same sentence may be considered as an instance of two or more different sentential statement patterns. For example, if

p: Tomorrow is Friday or Saturday,

and r: Tom is late for his appointment,

then the sentence which we considered before has the sentential statement pattern $p \rightarrow r$, instead of $(p \vee q) \rightarrow r$.

For brevity, we shall use "statement pattern" or even "pattern" to mean "sentential statement pattern".

If p and q represent specified statements then $p \wedge q$ represents a statement and we often say that $p \wedge q$ *is* a statement. If, however, p and q do not represent specific statements then $p \wedge q$ is a sentential statement pattern each instance of which is a conjunction. For this reason $p \wedge q$ is a conjunctive sentential statement pattern which we shall call a conjunction when the meaning is clear. Similarly $p \vee q$, $p \rightarrow q$, $p \leftrightarrow q$, and $\sim p$ will be called a disjunction, a conditional, a biconditional, and a negation rather than a disjunction pattern, a conditional pattern, a biconditional pattern, and a negation pattern, respectively. If every instance of a statement pattern has truth-value "true" we may say that the pattern is always true, rather than say that it has only true instances.

EXERCISES

1. Classify each of the following statements as a simple tf-statement, a conjunction, a disjunction, a conditional, a biconditional, or a negation.

(a) He is hurt or he is pretending.

(b) Golf is the only sport, and this course is one of the finest in the East.

(c) He is safe if and only if he swam the river.

(d) No one saw the water begin to trickle down the landward side.

(e) If Huck Finn and Tom Sawyer had grown up to be rich and important, they might have started a club like Buring Tree.

(f) In men's faces, elements of strength express the mood.

(g) This is no wild prognostication.

(h) His muscle tone had been restored and he could look forward to a longer life.

(i) Nelson wants to look handsome and keep cool.

(j) Boys do not have to be alike.

(k) A fine public library and a museum contribute to the life of the city.

(l) If there is a prevention campaign he is expected to play a major role.

(m) Either his lack of energy or his lack of funds may keep him from succeeding.

(n) The plants will grow if you water them properly.

(o) The secrets of harnessing the hydrogen bomb and of conquering the frigid vastness of space are hidden in this strange world.

(p) The ceiling is unlimited.

(q) You can be a good American citizen if and only if you feel a strong loyalty to freedom.

(r) A rebeveled axe may not work well.

(s) Children can be taught the habit of success.

(t) Frankie had lost his footing on the treacherous mountain or some other danger had beset him.

(u) If you succeed you fail and if you fail you succeed.

(v) Alaska should be entered slowly by ship from Vancouver to Juneau, between the inland shores of the Inside Passage, through thick growing timber, or by car over the Alaska Highway, once called the Alcan, with its almost breathtaking, beautiful scenery.

2. Separate each of the statements in the preceding exercise into tf-statements p, q, etc. and write the statement in symbolic form using the logical symbols $\vee$, $\wedge$, $\rightarrow$, $\leftrightarrow$, and $\sim$, thus indicating a sentential statement pattern for each statement.

3. Negate the following statements:

(a) The best thing to give to your enemy is forgiveness.

(b) California is rich with the romance of the past.

(c) County health officers try to combat dirt and infection.

(d) The Arabian Nights atmosphere held many terrors for Lotta.

(e) In Bombay and Calcutta peddlers and tradesmen are numerous.

(f) Everyone can increase his creative abilities.

4. TRUTH-TABLES

This section indicates the truth-values that logicians assign to the statement patterns $p \wedge q$, $p \vee q$, $p \to q$, $p \leftrightarrow q$, and $\sim p$.

Let us consider what truth-values should be assigned to $p \wedge q$. We first make a table containing all the possible combinations of "true" and "false" for p and q, and ask when $p \wedge q$ is true. If p is true and q is true then certainly $p \wedge q$ is true. If, however, either p or q is false, or both are false, then $p \wedge q$ would be false, hence the entry under $p \wedge q$ will be "T" only when both p and q are true as indicated in Table 1.

CONJUNCTION

p	q	$p \wedge q$
T	T	T
T	F	F
F	T	F
F	F	F

Table 1

When is $p \vee q$ true? It will be true if p is true and q is false, or if p is false and q is true; and it will be false if both p and q are false. What truth-value does it have when both p and q are true?

Before we answer this question we observe that there are two types of disjunction; namely, *inclusive disjunction* and *exclusive disjunction*. Inclusive disjunction means "*p* or *q*, *or both*", while exclusive disjunction means "*p* or *q*, *but not both*". Mathematical logic uses inclusive disjunction as one of its basic tools. We therefore say that $p \vee q$ is true even if both p and q are true, as indicated in Table 2. Observe that in everyday speech the exclusive disjunction is usually used.

DISJUNCTION

p	q	$p \vee q$
T	T	T
T	F	T
F	T	T
F	F	F

Table 2

CONDITIONAL

p	q	$p \to q$
T	T	T
T	F	F
F	T	T
F	F	T

Table 3

The conditional $p \rightarrow q$ (read "p conditions q", "p only if q", or "if p then q") may be treated similarly. When will the conditional $p \rightarrow q$ be true? Many logicians and practically all mathematicians say that the conditional $p \rightarrow q$ is false *only when* p is true and q is false. In all other cases the conditional is true. Thus we have Table 3.

A specific example of a conditional statement from everyday life may give us a better understanding of Table 3.

Frank told his friend, "If Harold was paid today, then he purchased food for the outing." Under what conditions would we consider Frank's statement incorrect or untruthful? In order to analyze the situation we separate the statement into two parts p and q.

p: Harold was paid today.
q: Harold purchased food for the outing.

The first case considered in Table 3 is the case where p and q are both true. In terms of the example this would mean that Harold was paid today and he purchased food for the outing. Certainly we would agree that Frank's conditional statement was true. This corresponds to saying that $p \rightarrow q$ is true if both p and q are true.

In the second case p is true but q is false. This means that Harold was paid but he did not buy food for the outing. In this case Frank's statement is not true; that is, $p \rightarrow q$ is false.

The third case corresponds to the statement that Harold was not paid today but he bought food for the outing. This does not prove that Frank was wrong, and we would not feel that he was untruthful. He merely stated what Harold would do *if* he were paid. He made no prediction as to what would happen if he were not paid. Therefore we consider his conditional statement as true. Thus $p \rightarrow q$ is considered true if p is false and q is true.

Would Frank be proved incorrect if Harold did not get paid and he did not buy food for the outing? Obviously not, for Frank told what Harold would do *if* he were paid. There was no condition that had to be satisfied if he were not paid. Thus if p and q are both false the conditional statement is not incorrect or false. It must therefore be true. If then, p and q are both false, $p \rightarrow q$ is true.

In summary, we see that the statement "If Harold was paid today, then he purchased food for the outing" can be false statement if and only if Harold is paid but fails to purchase food for the outing. In all other cases this statement is true.

In the conditional $p \rightarrow q$, p is the *antecedent* (or the hypothesis) and q is the *consequent* (or the conclusion).

As a second example consider the following statement about geometrical objects. "If two angles of a triangle are equal, then the triangle is a right triangle." This statement, like many others that occur in geometry and elsewhere in mathematics, is a conditional statement. The antecedent and the consequent are, respectively,

p: Two angles of a triangle are equal,
q: The triangle is a right triangle.

According to our understanding of the English language this statement seems to predict that whenever two angles of a triangle are equal then the triangle must have a right angle. We consider specific cases corresponding to the rows of the conditional truth-table, Table 3, to see whether this prediction is always correct; that is, always true.

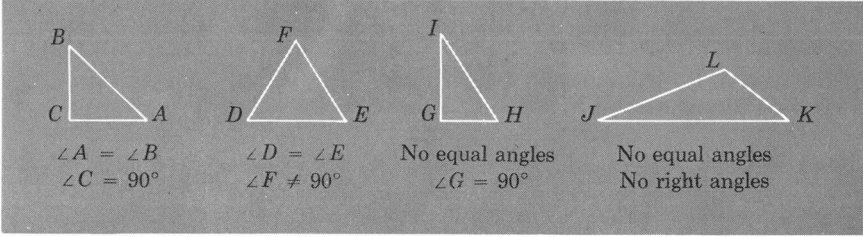

$\angle A = \angle B$ $\angle D = \angle E$ No equal angles   No equal angles
$\angle C = 90°$ $\angle F \neq 90°$ $\angle G = 90°$ No right angles

FIG. 1

If in triangle ABC, $\angle A = \angle B$, and $\angle C = 90°$, then the prediction that a right angle would accompany two equal angles is correct. In this case p is true, and q is true, and $p \rightarrow q$ is true. Our results agree with those of the truth-table.

If in triangle DEF, $\angle D = \angle E$, and $\angle F \neq 90°$, then the prediction that a right angle would accompany two equal angles is not correct. In this case p is true, but q is false, and according to the truth-table the implication is false. This agrees with our conclusion that the prediction is false.

If in triangle GHI there are no equal angles, but $\angle G = 90°$, is the prediction correct? The prediction did not tell us what would happen when no angles were equal, therefore such an example could not prove that the prediction is incorrect. This statement in no way affects the correctness of the prediction; therefore, we shall say that the prediction is correct in this case. For this example p is false, q is true, and $p \rightarrow q$ is true, and our results agree with the truth-table.

If JKL is not a right triangle and it has no equal angles then what can be said of the prediction? As in the preceding case, the prediction did not indicate what would happen if no angles were equal, and therefore is considered correct. Here p is false, q is false, and $p \rightarrow q$ is true. As a result of the two examples of the conditional that have been discussed in detail we should observe two things. First, *when the antecedent is false the conditional is always true*, regardless of the truth or falsity of the consequent. Second, *when the consequent is true, the conditional is always true*, regardless of the truth or falsity of the antecedent.

When a conditional—such as the geometrical statement that we have just discussed—is considered in mathematics it is usually for the purpose of finding out whether it is *always* true. Let us approach this particular statement from this point of view. Is the following statement always true?

If two angles of a triangle are equal, then the triangle is a right triangle.

If the reader suspects that this statement could be false, he should try to give an example which would show that the statement is false in that case. Since a conditional can be false only when the antecedent is true and the consequent is false, he should look for a triangle with two equal angles which is not a right triangle. This type of example is easy to find. An equilateral triangle is one of the simplest examples; furthermore, *only one* such example is needed to show that the statement is not *always* true.

Given two tf-statements, even though they seem unrelated, such as

p: John weighs 200 pounds,
q: The sum of 5 and 2 is 6,

very few people would object to the statement

$p \wedge q$: John weighs 200 pounds, and the sum of 5 and 2 is 6,

or to

$p \vee q$: John weighs 200 pounds, or the sum of 5 and 2 is 6.

They would also find it easy enough to decide what truth-values to attach to $p \wedge q$ and $p \vee q$. However,

$p \rightarrow q$: If John weighs 200 pounds, then the sum of 5 and 2 is 6,

sounds rather unusual. One might ask whether such a combination should be allowed, and if it is allowed what truth-value it should have.

If such combinations are not allowed then some rule must be given which will determine what tf-statements can be combined to form conditionals. Mathematicians have found that it is more difficult to set up such a rule than it is to allow the unusual combinations along with the agreement that the truth-value of $p \rightarrow q$ is that given in Table 3, regardless of what statements p and q represent. A similar type of agreement is made for $p \leftrightarrow q$. As a result mathematicians do not hesitate to combine any two tf-statements by using any one of the connectives.

When two statements are joined by "if $\cdots$ then" one must be careful not to confuse the truth or falsity of either of the statements with the *truth or falsity of the conditional* or to expect any cause and effect relationship between the antecedent and the consequent. In the specific example at hand,

$p \rightarrow q$: If John weighs 200 pounds, then the sum of 5 and 2 is 6,

the consequent is false. By the agreement that $p \rightarrow q$ is false if and only if p is true and q is false, we observe that the *conditional* is false if p is true, and is true if p is false. That is, the *conditional* will be false if John weighs 200 pounds and will be true if John does not weigh 200 pounds.

Fortunately, such unusual combinations do not occur frequently in mathematical arguments.

Definition.   *The **converse*** of the conditional $p \rightarrow q$ is the conditional $q \rightarrow p$.

Thus to obtain the converse of a conditional, interchange its antecedent and its consequent.

---

* For a more detailed discussion of converses, see Exner and Rosskopf, *Logic in Elementary Mathematics* (New York, McGraw-Hill, 1959), pp. 71–73.

The truth-table for $p \leftrightarrow q$ is given by Table 4. Since the biconditional is a double conditional it is evident that the biconditional will be true if and only if p and q are both true or both false.

BICONDITIONAL

NEGATION

p	q	$p \leftrightarrow q$
T	T	T
T	F	F
F	T	F
F	F	T

p	$\sim p$
T	F
F	T

Table 4

Table 5

The truth-table for negation is quite simple for we have agreed that "p" and "not p" cannot occur simultaneously. The results are in Table 5.

For future reference the preceding truth-tables can be combined into Table 6 given below.

p	q	$p \wedge q$	$p \vee q$	$p \rightarrow q$	$p \leftrightarrow q$	$\sim p$	$\sim q$
T	T	T	T	T	T	F	F
T	F	F	T	F	F	F	T
F	T	F	T	T	F	T	F
F	F	F	F	T	T	T	T

Table 6

Our question concerning the nature of composite statements is now answered. Since the truth-tables assign to each composite statement a truth-value, each composite statement is a tf-statement.

Two examples will give some practice in determining truth-values of composite statements.

Example 1.   Given p: It is raining.

q: A triangle has three sides.

We investigate the statements $p \wedge q$; $p \vee q$; $p \rightarrow q$; $p \leftrightarrow q$; $\sim p$; and $\sim q$.

Let us consider the case when it is raining. Then p is true, and q is always true. Therefore p and q are both true and by the conjunction table $p \wedge q$ is true. By the disjunction table $p \vee q$ is true when both p and q are true; by the conditional table $p \to q$ is true when both are true; and by the biconditional table $p \leftrightarrow q$ is true if both are true. Since p and q are both true $\sim p$ is false, and so is $\sim q$. (These results can be read quickly from the top line of Table 6.)

Consider now the case when it is not raining; then p is false. Also $p \wedge q$ is false, $p \vee q$ is true, $p \to q$ is true, $p \leftrightarrow q$ is false, $\sim p$ is true, and $\sim q$ is false.

Example 2.   Given p: It is raining.

q: A triangle has only two sides.

If it is raining, p is true; and since q is false, it follows that $p \wedge q$ is false, $p \vee q$ is true, $p \to q$ is false, $p \leftrightarrow q$ is false, $\sim p$ is false, and $\sim q$ is true.

If, however, it is not raining, then p is false, and since q is false, it follows that $p \wedge q$ is false, $p \vee q$ is false, $p \to q$ is true, $p \leftrightarrow q$ is true, $\sim p$ is true, and $\sim q$ is true. Of these, perhaps the composite statement which is hardest to understand is the conditional $p \to q$; that is, "If it is raining then a triangle has only two sides." The truth or falsity of the *conditional* is not the same as the truth or falsity of q which states that a triangle has only two sides; for, as we have observed before, $p \to q$ is false if it is raining and true if it is not raining. This is a result of our agreeing that *the conditional* $p \to q$ *is false only when* p *is true and* q *is false*.

EXERCISES

1. The symbol "$\vee$" denotes *inclusive* disjunction, and $p \vee q$ means "p or q, *or both*". The symbol "$\underline{\vee}$" denotes *exclusive* disjunction, and $p \underline{\vee} q$ means "either p or q, *but not both*". Make a truth-table for exclusive disjunction.

2. Formulate in English the statement which corresponds to each of the following symbolic statements and determine its truth-value, given that

p: The diameter of the earth is 3,000 miles.

w: Three-eighths of sixteen is six.

r: Jupiter revolves about the sun.

$s: 2 + 4 = 7.$
$q:$ The earth is a planet.
$t: 0.75$ is a whole number.

(a) $p \lor w.$	(e) $s \to q.$	(i) $\sim q \lor t.$
(b) $p \to s.$	(f) $q \land p.$	(j) $w \to p.$
(c) $q \leftrightarrow r.$	(g) $\sim p \land \sim w.$	(k) $(q \land r) \to s.^*$
(d) $w \to s.$	(h) $\sim p.$	(l) $(q \land r) \lor (q \land s).$

3. (a) What is the truth-value of $p \land q$ if q is false?
   (b) What is the truth-value of $p \lor q$ if q is true?
   (c) What is the truth-value of $p \to q$ if q is true?
   (d) What is the truth-value of $(p \land q) \to (p \lor q)$ if q is false?

5. LOGICALLY VALID STATEMENT PATTERNS

Composite tf-statements may be combined to produce more complex tf-statements such as those represented by

$$[(p \to q) \land (q \to r)] \to (p \to r),$$
$$[p \to (q \land r)] \leftrightarrow [(p \to q) \land (p \to r)].\dagger$$

Some of these statement patterns are true regardless of what statements p, q, and r represent, and are therefore completely independent of the truth-values of the elementary tf-statements involved. They are logically valid statement patterns, or *tautologies*. Some tautologies are used so frequently that they are referred to as laws of logic.‡ Many tautologies can be separated into logically equivalent parts which are very useful in constructing proofs.

---

* Parentheses are necessary since $(q \land r) \to s$ is different from $q \land (r \to s)$. For example, if q, r, and s are all false, then $q \land r$ is false, and therefore $(q \land r) \to s$ is *true* because of a false antecedent. On the other hand, $r \to s$ is true, because r is false and $q \land (r \to s)$ is *false* because q is false.

† The first of these two statements can be read "if p conditions q, and q conditions r, then p conditions r"; and the second one can be read "p conditions q and r, if and only if, p conditions q, and q conditions r".

‡ If the author uses the word "proposition" when referring to tf-statements he may refer to the laws of logic as the laws of propositional algebra.

Definition. *A sentential statement pattern is a* **logically valid sentential statement pattern,** *or a* **tautology,** *if and only if every instance of this pattern is true.*

This definition makes no distinction between a logically valid sentential statement pattern and a tautology; however, in practice we usually refer to those logically valid sentential statement patterns which are frequently used, as tautologies, or laws of logic. For brevity, in the remaining sections of the statement calculus we shall often use "valid statement pattern" or "valid pattern" for "logically valid sentential statement pattern". We shall also use the single word "pattern" for "statement pattern" whether it is logically valid or not.

How do we prove that a statement pattern is logically valid? Merely by showing that every statement obtained from it is true, regardless of the truth-value of its elementary tf-statements. The following examples will illustrate the procedure.

Theorem 1.   (The Law of Contradiction): $\sim (p \wedge \sim p)$ *is a tautology.*

Proof. We must consider all possibilities. There are only two, since p is either true or false; hence only two rows are needed in the proof-table.

p	$\sim p$	$p \wedge \sim p$	$\sim (p \wedge \sim p)$
T	F	F	T
F	T	F	T

Explanation. If p is true, then by the negation table $\sim p$ is false; if p is false, then $\sim p$ is true. In both cases $p \wedge \sim p$ is false, since one of the statements p or $\sim p$ is false. Hence the negation of $p \wedge \sim p$, which is denoted by $\sim (p \wedge \sim p)$, must be true in both cases. Thus every instance is *true*, and the pattern is a tautology.

To emphasize the nature of a logically valid statement pattern we point out that there is no elementary tf-statement p which will make the truth-value of the composite statement $\sim (p \wedge \sim p)$ false.

If the tautology involves two statements p and q, four rows are needed in the proof-table, just as in the truth-tables, to consider all possibilities. If it involves p, q, and r, eight rows are needed. How many would be needed if the tautology involved four statements? Five statements? N statements, where N is a whole number?

The pattern $\sim q \to \sim p$ is the *contrapositive* of $p \to q$. The contrapositive is frequently used in mathematical proofs.

Theorem 2.   (**Law of Contraposition**): $(p \to q) \leftrightarrow (\sim q \to \sim p)$

Proof.

p	q	$\sim p$	$\sim q$	$p \to q$	$\sim q \to \sim p$	$(p \to q) \leftrightarrow (\sim q \to \sim p)$
T	T	F	F	T	T	T
T	F	F	T	F	F	T
F	T	T	F	T	T	T
F	F	T	T	T	T	T

Explanation of the first row of the proof. If p and q are both true, then $\sim p$ and $\sim q$ are both false. By the conditional table $p \to q$ is true when both p and q are true, and by the same table $\sim q \to \sim p$ is true when both $\sim q$ and $\sim p$ are false. Since $p \to q$ and $\sim q \to \sim p$ are both true, the biconditional formed from them is true. Similar arguments are used on the remaining rows. Since the biconditional is true for every instance this is a tautology.

Theorem 3.   (**Law of Syllogism**): $[(p \to q) \land (q \to r)] \to (p \to r)$

Proof.

p	q	r	$p \to q$	$q \to r$	$(p \to q) \land (q \to r)$	$p \to r$	$[(p \to q) \land (q \to r)] \to (p \to r)$
T	T	T	T	T	T	T	T
T	F	T	F	T	F	T	T
F	T	T	T	T	T	T	T
F	F	T	T	T	T	T	T
T	T	F	T	F	F	F	T
T	F	F	F	T	F	F	T
F	T	F	T	F	F	T	T
F	F	F	T	T	T	T	T

The last column in each of the three preceding proofs can be omitted since the truth of the pattern in the column heading can be verified by inspection of one or two of the preceding columns. In Theorem 1, the truth of the theorem can be verified by noticing that each entry in the third column is false, thus each negation is true. In Theorem 2, the truth of the theorem can be readily established by comparing columns 5 and 6, in which the entries always agree. In Theorem 3, the final results can be obtained by applying Table 3 to columns 6 and 7. In no case is the entry in column 6 true when the entry in column 7 is false. Therefore the conditional has no false instances.

It is possible to reduce the amount of writing involved in a proof-table merely by writing the letters "T" and "F" under the letters p, q, and r, and also under the connectives and the modified statement. For example, the proof-table in Theorem 1 can be condensed to

$$
\begin{array}{c|ccc}
\sim & (p \wedge & \sim p) \\
\hline
T & T\ F & F \\
T & F\ F & T.
\end{array}
$$

To obtain this condensed form first fill in the truth values for p, then those for $\sim p$, then those for $p \wedge \sim p$ by writing under the "and" sign. Finally, under the negation sign write the truth values for $\sim(p \wedge \sim p)$. Observe that this order of filling in columns is the one used in the original proof; that is, p, $\sim p$, $p \wedge \sim p$, and finally $\sim(p \wedge \sim p)$. The proof-table for Theorem 2 can be condensed to

$$
\begin{array}{ccc|c|ccc}
(p & \rightarrow & q) & \leftrightarrow & (\sim q & \rightarrow & \sim p) \\
T & T & T & T & F & T & F \\
T & F & F & T & T & F & F \\
F & T & T & T & F & T & T \\
F & T & F & T & T & T & T.
\end{array}
$$

The student can readily obtain this by filling in the columns following the method set up in the proof of Theorem 2.

The proof of Theorem 4 is given in this more compact form.*

Theorem 4. $(p \rightarrow q) \leftrightarrow (\sim p \vee q)$.

Proof.
$$
\begin{array}{ccc|c|ccc}
(p & \rightarrow & q) & \leftrightarrow & (\sim p & \vee & q) \\
T & T & T & T & F & T & T \\
T & F & F & T & F & F & F \\
F & T & T & T & T & T & T \\
F & T & F & T & T & T & F
\end{array}
$$

---

* For further examples see *Concepts and Structure of Mathematics*, College Mathematics Staff, University of Chicago press, pp. 40–47.

Remarks. The proof-tables that we have just used are a mechanical means for finding out whether complex patterns have only true instances; hence they establish the fact that certain patterns are tautologies. *This mechanical procedure should not prevent thoughtful consideration of the meaning of the patterns involved.*

The student should try to develop some feeling for the plausibility of these patterns and try to see their relationship to other patterns, for this will integrate his thinking and his knowledge in such a fashion as to make the recall of the facts much easier than if he tried the impossible task of remembering meaningless symbols or manipulations.

For example, in Theorem 1 the pattern $\sim(p \wedge \sim p)$ [Read "not, (p and not p)"] merely indicates that p and $\sim p$ cannot occur simultaneously. This was the assumption upon which the negation table was established. Basically, it says that a statement cannot simultaneously be true and false, though it may be true at one time and false at another.

Let us now look at the pattern $p \vee \sim p$, a pattern called the *Law of the Excluded Middle*, the proof of which is left as an exercise. What does it mean? It expresses the fact that either p or $\sim p$ will be true in all cases. We know that even though the symbol " $\vee$ " would allow both p and $\sim p$ to be true, Theorem 1 says that only one of these can occur at a time. This tells us that we are dealing with statements that fall into one and only one of the two classes labeled "true" and "false", and that no other classes are needed for the classification of all statements being used. This is in keeping with the basic definition of a tf-statement as a declarative sentence to which it is meaningful to assign a truth-value of "true" or "false", but not both at the same time. Since there are only two truth-values possible for each statement, the logic which we are studying is a two-value logic.*

The double negation $\sim(\sim p) \leftrightarrow p$ says essentially that when $\sim p$

---

* Many-valued logics have been developed. They are usually referred to as non-Aristotelian logics since they deny Aristotle's law of the excluded middle. They have proved useful in probability and the quantum theory of modern physics. Additional information on many-valued logics can be found in Eves and Newsom, *An Introduction to the Foundations and Fundamental Concepts of Mathematics* (New York, Holt, 1958), pp. 277–280; and in R. L. Wilder, *Foundations of Mathematics* (New York, Wiley, 1952), p. 263.

is not true, then p is true; and if p is true, then $\sim p$ is not true.* Both statement patterns are consistent with the statement pattern $p \lor \sim p$ and $\sim (p \land \sim p)$.

In order to fix firmly in mind the relationship between $p \to q$ and $\sim p \lor q$ we reason as follows:

The pattern $\sim p \lor p$ has only true instances. We shall attempt to alter this pattern so that the truth-value of the altered pattern will agree with the truth-value of $p \to q$.

The conditional means "if p then q" which we may interpret as "if p is true, then q must be true in order that the conditional be true". We therefore replace $\sim p \lor p$ by the pattern $\sim p \lor q$, merely thinking in terms of what will happen when p is true and the conditional is true. Does this procedure produce a pattern which always agrees with $p \to q$ in truth-value?

A quick check will show that if p is true, then $\sim p \lor q$ will be true if q is true, and false if q is false. This is exactly what happens to $p \to q$. Thus when p is true, $p \to q$ and $\sim p \lor q$ have the same truth-value. If p is false, $p \to q$ is true regardless of the truth-value of q; and if p is false, then $\sim p$ is true, and $\sim p \lor q$ is true regardless of the truth-value of q. Thus when p is false $p \to q$ and $\sim p \lor q$ have the same truth value. This check establishes the fact that $p \to q$ and $\sim p \lor q$ are equivalent patterns.

Observe that we altered the pattern $\sim p \lor p$ by considering only one case; namely, the case where p is true and $p \to q$ is true, reasoning that the truth of p forces the truth of q *if* the conditional is true. Thus we decided to replace p by q to obtain $\sim p \lor q$ as a possible equivalent of $p \to q$. We then checked all other cases to be sure that the truth-value of $\sim p \lor q$ always agrees with that of $p \to q$. This is a method of establishing an equivalence without using a proof table. With practice the reader may be able to check such patterns mentally.

The Law of Contraposition can now be obtained quickly from the relationship just discussed, which we write as $(r \to s) \leftrightarrow (\sim r \lor s)$. This is just $(p \to q) \leftrightarrow (\sim p \lor q)$ written by using different letters. If now, we replace r by $\sim q$ and s by $\sim p$ we obtain

$$(\sim q \to \sim p) \leftrightarrow [\sim (\sim q) \lor \sim p]$$

or simply $$(\sim q \to \sim p) \leftrightarrow (q \lor \sim p).$$

---

* The proof that this is a tautology is left for the exercises, but the reader can readily verify this before going further. He can also show that $p \lor \sim p$ is always true.

Since $(\sim p \lor q) \leftrightarrow (q \lor \sim p)$ then $(p \rightarrow q) \leftrightarrow (\sim q \rightarrow \sim p)$.

The pattern $[p \rightarrow (q \land r)] \leftrightarrow [(p \rightarrow q) \land (p \rightarrow r)]$ says that if p conditions q and r, then p conditions q, and p conditions r. Conversely, if p conditions q, and p conditions r, then p conditions q and r.

Tautologies Frequently Used

We list here, for future reference, some tautologies that are frequently used in proofs.

T1.   Law of Excluded Middle, $p \lor \sim p$.
T2.   Law of Contradiction, $\sim(p \land \sim p)$.
T3.   Law of Detachment, $[p \land (p \rightarrow q)] \rightarrow q$.
T4.   Law of Syllogism, $[(p \rightarrow q) \land (q \rightarrow r)] \rightarrow (p \rightarrow r)$.
T5.   Law of Double Negation, $\sim(\sim p) \leftrightarrow p$.
T6.   Law of Contraposition, $(p \rightarrow q) \leftrightarrow (\sim q \rightarrow \sim p)$.
T7. $[(p \rightarrow q) \land \sim q] \rightarrow \sim p$.
T8. $[(p \lor q) \land \sim p] \rightarrow q$.
T9. $[(p \rightarrow r) \land (q \rightarrow s) \land (p \lor q)] \rightarrow (r \lor s)$.
T10. $(p \land q) \rightarrow p$.
T11. $[p \rightarrow (q \land r)] \leftrightarrow [(p \rightarrow q) \land (p \rightarrow r)]$.
T12. $[(p \lor q) \rightarrow r] \leftrightarrow [(p \rightarrow r) \land (q \rightarrow r)]$.
T13. $(p \leftrightarrow q) \leftrightarrow [(p \rightarrow q) \land (q \rightarrow p)]$.
T14. $[(p \land q) \rightarrow r] \leftrightarrow [p \rightarrow (q \rightarrow r)]$.
T15. $[p \land (q \lor r)] \leftrightarrow [(p \land q) \lor (p \land r)]$.
T16. $[p \lor (q \land r)] \leftrightarrow [(p \lor q) \land (p \lor r)]$.
T17. $\sim(p \land q) \leftrightarrow [\sim p \lor \sim q]$.
T18. $\sim(p \lor q) \leftrightarrow [\sim p \land \sim q]$.
T19. $\sim(p \rightarrow q) \leftrightarrow [p \land \sim q]$.
T20. $\sim(p \leftrightarrow q) \leftrightarrow [(p \land \sim q) \lor (\sim p \land q)] \leftrightarrow (p \leftrightarrow \sim q)$.
T21. $p \rightarrow (p \lor q)$.

6. IMPLICATION AND EQUIVALENCE

Both in logic and in mathematics there are conditionals for which the truth-value is never false. The tautology T8 is an example from logic, and the statement from plane geometry that two triangles are similar whenever they are congruent is an example from mathematics. Similarly, there are biconditionals for which the truth-value is never false.

Definition. *An **implication** is a conditional which never has a false truth-value.*

When we need to emphasize that the conditional $r \rightarrow s$ is an implication we shall write $r \Rightarrow s$, which is read "r implies s".

Definition. *An **equivalence** is a biconditional which never has a false truth-value.*

When we need to emphasize that the biconditional $r \leftrightarrow s$ is an equivalence we shall write $r \Leftrightarrow s$, which is read "r is equivalent to s", or "r and s are equivalent".

Theorems 2 and 3 show that the Law of Contraposition is an equivalence and that the Law of Syllogism is an implication. Since Theorem 4 is an equivalence it can be written $(p \rightarrow q) \Leftrightarrow (\sim p \lor q)$ and read "p conditions q is equivalent to $\sim p$ or q". Among the tautologies listed on page 259 the reader can find other examples of implications and equivalences, since every tautology which has the form of a conditional is an implication, and every tautology which has the form of a biconditional is an equivalence.

The conditional *If the sun shines at noon today, then 2 = 5*, is not an implication since it is false if the sun shines at noon today.

Can we find a short way to prove that a statement of the form $p \rightarrow q$ is an implication? The conditional table shows that a conditional is true except when p is true and q is false. Therefore we must show that it is impossible for p to be true and q to be false. There are two ways of doing this: (1) show that whenever p is true then q is true, or (2) show that whenever q is false then p is false. If either (1) or (2) can be established then the conditional will be an implication.

To emphasize these two ways of proving that certain conditional statements are implications we state them as follows:

To show that a conditional statement is an implication show that whenever the antecedent is true then the consequent is true.

To show that a conditional statement is an implication show that whenever the consequent is false then the antecedent is false.

Since an equivalence is a double implication, to establish the equivalence $p \leftrightarrow q$ we must show that p implies q and q implies p. Therefore we have the following method of establishing an equivalence which is frequently used in mathematical proofs.

If it can be shown that whenever p is true then q is true, and whenever q is true then p is true, then $p \leftrightarrow q$ is an equivalence; that is, $p \Leftrightarrow q$.

If it can be shown that whenever q is false then p is false, and whenever p is false then q is false, then $p \leftrightarrow q$ is an equivalence; that is, $p \Leftrightarrow q$.

If two statement patterns are equivalent they have the same truth-value; that is, they are simultaneously true or simultaneously false. Since, in the sentential calculus, the truth-value is all that is important, we may as well use one of the two equivalent statement patterns as the other. This will be convenient when we negate $p \rightarrow q$ in Section 9. To find the negation of this conditional we shall merely negate its equivalent statement $\sim p \vee q$ by using T18.

EXERCISES

1. Prove that the following statements are tautologies.

(a) $\sim(\sim p) \leftrightarrow p$.   [Law of Double Negation]

(b) $p \vee (\sim p)$.   [Law of Excluded Middle]

(c) $[p \wedge (p \rightarrow q)] \rightarrow q$.   [Law of Detachment]

(d) $\sim(p \wedge q) \leftrightarrow (\sim p \vee \sim q)$.

(e) $\sim(p \vee q) \leftrightarrow (\sim p \wedge \sim q)$.

(f) $[p \rightarrow (q \wedge r)] \leftrightarrow [(p \rightarrow q) \wedge (p \rightarrow r)]$.

(g) $[(p \vee q) \rightarrow r] \leftrightarrow [(p \rightarrow r) \wedge (q \rightarrow r)]$.

(h) $[p \rightarrow (q \vee r)] \leftrightarrow [\sim r \rightarrow (p \rightarrow q)]$.

2. Determine whether or not the following statements are tautologies.

(a) $[(p \rightarrow q) \vee (p \rightarrow r)] \leftrightarrow [p \rightarrow (q \vee r)]$.

(b) $\sim(p \rightarrow q) \rightarrow (p \vee q)$.

3. Prove three of the tautologies listed at the end of the preceding section for which the truth of the statement is not readily apparent to you.

4. Write the proof-table of Theorem 3 in condensed form.

5. (a) The inverse of the conditional $p \to q$ is the statement $\sim p \to \sim q$. Show that the inverse of a conditional is the contrapositive of its converse conditional.

(b) Apply the law of contraposition to the inverse conditional given in part (a).

6. Use a proof-table to prove the following theorems. Also give examples.

(a) The converse of a true conditional is not always true.

(b) The inverse of a true conditional is not always true.

(c) Can the statement in (b) be established by combining the results of other exercises and theorems already given, rather than by proof-tables?

7. Show that

(a) $p \wedge q \leftrightarrow q \wedge p, (p \wedge q) \wedge r \leftrightarrow p \wedge (q \wedge r) \leftrightarrow (p \wedge r) \wedge q$.

(b) $p \vee q \leftrightarrow q \vee p, (p \vee q) \vee r \leftrightarrow p \vee (q \vee r) \leftrightarrow (p \vee r) \vee q$.

8. Show that

(a) $[(q \vee r) \wedge p] \leftrightarrow [(q \wedge p) \vee (r \wedge p)] \leftrightarrow [p \wedge (q \vee r)]$.

(b) $[(q \wedge r) \vee p] \leftrightarrow [(q \vee p) \wedge (r \vee p)] \leftrightarrow [p \vee (q \wedge r)]$.

7. SUBSTITUTIONS AND REPLACEMENTS

The task of establishing the fact that very complex statements are tautologies can be greatly simplified by substituting the symbol p or q, or their equivalents, for more complicated parts of the statement. Three examples will illustrate the process.

***Example* 1.** Show that $[\{p \vee \sim(r \wedge s)\} \wedge \sim p] \to \sim(r \wedge s)$ is a tautology.

Solution. Let q represent $\sim(r \wedge s)$. Then the statement becomes $[(p \vee q) \wedge \sim p)] \to q$, which is T8 and is therefore a tautology.

The reasoning here is that $\sim(r \wedge s)$ is a statement pattern which can be represented by a simpler notation such as q having the same truth value as $\sim(r \wedge s)$. Thus q will produce the same result in the proof-table as will the more complicated statement that it represents.

***Example* 2.**   Show   that $[\{p \vee \sim(r \wedge s)\} \wedge \sim p] \rightarrow [\sim r \vee \sim s]$
is a tautology.

Solution.   As before, let q represent $\sim(r \wedge s)$. By T17, $\sim(r \wedge s) \leftrightarrow$
$(\sim r \vee \sim s)$; therefore q also represents the equivalent statement
$\sim r \vee \sim s$. These replacements produce $[(p \vee q) \wedge \sim p] \rightarrow q$, which
is T8 again.

***Example* 3.**   Show   that $[p \rightarrow \sim(r \rightarrow s)] \leftrightarrow [(r \rightarrow s) \rightarrow \sim p]$ is a
tautology. Let q represent $\sim(r \rightarrow s)$, then the statement becomes
$(p \rightarrow q) \leftrightarrow (\sim q \rightarrow \sim p)$, which is the tautology known as the Law of
Contraposition.

EXERCISES

1. Use substitutions or replacements to show that the following
statements are tautologies.

    (*a*) $[r \wedge (s \vee t)] \vee \sim[r \wedge (s \vee t)]$.

    (*b*) $[(\sim t \rightarrow r) \wedge (\sim u \rightarrow s) \wedge (\sim t \vee \sim u)] \rightarrow (r \vee s)$.

    (*c*) $\{[p \rightarrow \sim(t \wedge s)] \wedge [(\sim t \vee \sim s) \rightarrow r]\} \rightarrow (p \rightarrow r)$.

    (*d*) $\{[(u \wedge w) \rightarrow t] \wedge (q \vee r)\} \leftrightarrow$
        $(\{[(u \wedge w) \rightarrow t] \wedge q\} \vee \{[u \rightarrow (w \rightarrow t)] \wedge r\})$.

    (*e*) $[(r \rightarrow s) \wedge (t \rightarrow w)] \rightarrow (\sim s \rightarrow \sim r)$.

    (*f*) $\{[(r \rightarrow s) \wedge (r \rightarrow t)] \wedge ([r \rightarrow (s \wedge t)] \rightarrow q)\} \rightarrow q$.

    (*g*) $[(\sim t \wedge \sim w) \wedge (q \vee r)]$
        $\leftrightarrow [\{\sim(t \vee w) \wedge q\} \vee \{\sim(t \vee w) \wedge r\}]$.

    (*h*) $\sim[(r \vee s) \rightarrow (t \wedge w)] \leftrightarrow [(r \vee s) \wedge (\sim t \vee \sim w)]$.

    (*i*) $[(p \rightarrow q) \wedge (\sim r \rightarrow \sim q) \wedge (\sim r)] \rightarrow \sim p$.

8. RELATIONS BETWEEN $\sim$, $\wedge$, $\vee$, $\rightarrow$, $\leftrightarrow$.

Theorem 4 shows that the conditional can be defined in terms of
disjunction and negation. Can the remaining logical connectives be
defined in terms of $\vee$ and $\sim$? If we replace p by $\sim r$ and q by $\sim s$ in
T18, we obtain $\sim(\sim r \vee \sim s) \leftrightarrow [\sim(\sim r) \wedge \sim(\sim s)] = r \wedge s$; there-

fore, conjunction can be obtained. Also, $p \leftrightarrow q$ can be defined as $(\sim p \vee q) \wedge (p \vee \sim q)$, since, by Theorem 4, this is equivalent to $(p \rightarrow q) \wedge (q \rightarrow p)$. Therefore, starting with $\vee$ and $\sim$ the three remaining connectives can be defined as follows:

$p \wedge q$ means $\sim(\sim p \vee \sim q)$;

$p \rightarrow q$ means $\sim p \vee q$;

$p \leftrightarrow q$ means $(\sim p \vee q) \wedge (p \vee \sim q)$

$\qquad\qquad$ or $\quad \sim[\sim(\sim p \vee q) \vee \sim(p \vee \sim q)]$.

The reader might be interested in trying to express the remaining connectives of logic (a) in terms of conjunction and negation, or (b) in terms of the conditional and negation.*

In 1913, H. M. Sheffer showed that the five fundamental symbols discussed here (frequently referred to as the sentential connectives, even though one is a modifier) can be defined by starting with one symbol called the Sheffer stroke, written p/q (read "p stroke q") which means "not p or not q". Thus p/p means "not p or not p" and therefore defines $\sim p$. Also $(p/p)/(q/q)$ means $\sim(p/p)$ or $\sim(q/q)$; which is $\sim(\sim p) \vee \sim(\sim q)$, and this reduces to $p \vee q$. Since we have just shown that the three remaining logical connectives can be defined in terms of disjunction and negation, it follows that all of these symbols can be defined in terms of the Sheffer stroke.

The relations pointed out in the preceding paragraphs indicate that the concepts of symbolic logic which have been presented up to this point could be presented by using fewer symbols for sentential connectives. However, the use of more symbols produces a simpler presentation.

9. FURTHER REMARKS ON NEGATION

It is important that we be able to negate statements. We consider here the negations of $\sim p$, $p \wedge q$, $p \vee q$, $p \rightarrow q$, and $p \leftrightarrow q$.

The negation of $\sim p$ is $\sim(\sim p)$, which is p.

The negation of $p \wedge q$ indicates that we do not have both p and q; therefore, we must fail to have one of them. Therefore, $\sim(p \wedge q)$

---

* *Op. cit.*, Eves and Newsom, pp. 266–267.

should be equivalent to $\sim p \vee \sim q$. This result agrees with T17, which we assume that the reader has verified.

The negation of $p \vee q$ indicates that we have neither p nor q, and therefore $\sim(p \vee q)$ should be equivalent to $\sim p \wedge \sim q$. This agrees with T18.

The negation of $p \rightarrow q$ is $\sim(p \rightarrow q)$. Since $p \rightarrow q$ is equivalent to $\sim p \vee q$, by Theorem 4, then $\sim(p \rightarrow q)$ is equivalent to $\sim(\sim p \vee q)$, which by T18 is $\sim(\sim p) \wedge \sim q$, or simply $p \wedge \sim q$. It should be observed that the negation of a conditional is not a conditional but rather a conjunction.

The negation of $p \leftrightarrow q$ can easily be obtained by negating its equivalent form, given by T11. Then $\sim[(p \rightarrow q) \wedge (q \rightarrow p)]$ is $\sim(p \rightarrow q)$ $\vee \sim(q \rightarrow p)$ which can be changed to $(p \wedge \sim q) \vee (q \vee \sim p)$.

For future reference we list these negations.

Statement	Negation
$\sim p$	p
$p \wedge q$	$\sim p \vee \sim q$
$p \vee q$	$\sim p \wedge \sim q$
$p \rightarrow q$	$p \wedge \sim q$
$p \leftrightarrow q$	$(p \wedge \sim q) \vee (q \wedge \sim p)$

Example 1.   The negation of

Jane flew or Tom went by boat,

is

Jane did not fly and Tom did not go by boat.

Example 2.   The negation of

Patty succeeds if and only if she has Sarah's help,

is

Patty succeeds and she does not have Sarah's help; or Patty does not succeed and she has Sarah's help,

which might be rephrased to read:

Patty succeeds without Sarah's help or Patty does not succeed with Sarah's help.

We shall now negate some statements which are more involved.

Example **3.**

> If his work is hard and his rewards are
> few then he should seek another position.

We observe that this is a conditional statement.

Let w: His work is hard,
                    r: His rewards are few,
                    a: He should seek another position,

We can represent it as $(w \wedge r) \to a$. The negation $\sim[(w \wedge r) \to a]$ is the negation of a conditional. From the negation chart we see that it should have the form $(w \wedge r) \wedge \sim a$, which would be the statement:

> His work is hard and his rewards are few, and he should
> not seek another position.

This would probably sound better if it were written as follows:

> His work is hard and his rewards are few but he
> should not seek another position.

Example **4.**

> Access is by invitation, and if you succeed you will see one
> of the greatest private collections of painting in Europe.

Let a: Access is by invitation,
      s: You succeed,
      c: You will see one of the greatest private collections of paint-
          ing in Europe.

The given statement is of the form $a \wedge (s \to c)$. Therefore, its negation $\sim[a \wedge (s \to c)]$ is, first of all, the negation of a conjunction, and is therefore $\sim a \vee \sim(s \to c)$. The second step is to negate the conditional. This produces $\sim a \vee (s \wedge \sim c)$.

> Access is not by invitation; or you succeed
> and you will not see one of the greatest private
> collections of painting in Europe.

Example 5.

The river overflows as the tide comes up, the swans merrily sail down the middle of the street, and kids proudly paddle kayaks.

Let r: The river overflows as the tide comes up,
       s: The swans merrily sail down the middle of the street,
       k: The kids proudly paddle kayaks.

This statement is of the form $(r \wedge s) \wedge k$. The negation of $\sim[(r \wedge s) \wedge k]$ is $\sim(r \wedge s) \vee \sim k$. Since negation of $\sim(r \wedge s)$ is $\sim r \vee \sim s$, the negation sought is $(\sim r \vee \sim s) \vee \sim k$. Thus we see that the negation of the composite statement $(r \wedge s) \wedge k$ necessitates the negation of one or more of the elementary statements. In terms of the original statement the negation is:

> The river does not overflow as the tide comes up, or the swans do not sail merrily down the street, or the kids do not proudly paddle kayaks.

Example 6.

> If the dike is broken, then the farmlands will be flooded and the crops will be destroyed.

Let d: The dike is broken,
                   f: The farmlands will be flooded,
                   c: The crops will be destroyed,

Then the statement can be represented as $d \rightarrow (f \wedge c)$ and the negation $\sim[d \rightarrow (f \wedge c)]$ is $d \wedge \sim(f \wedge c)$ which can be simplified to $d \wedge (\sim f \vee \sim c)$. By T15 this is equivalent to $(d \wedge \sim f) \vee (d \wedge \sim c)$. The negation follows:

> The dike may break and the farmlands not be flooded, or the dike may break and the crops not be destroyed.

In more compact form we might write:

> The breaking of the dike will not flood the farmlands; or the breaking of the dike will not destroy the crops.

Remember that the "or" used here is the inclusive "or"; therefore the negated statement includes the possibility that the dike may break, the farmlands not be flooded, and the crops not be destroyed.

10. STATEMENTS INVOLVING FIXED TRUTH-VALUES

The statement $p \lor \sim p$ is always true, and the statement $p \land \sim p$ is never true. What can be said of the statement $(p \lor \sim p) \land q$? Since $p \lor \sim p$ is always true, the given conjunction will be true when q is true and false when q is false. It therefore has the same truth-value as q and is thus equivalent to q. In simplifying a statement like $r \lor [(p \lor \sim p) \land q]$ we use the fact that $(p \lor \sim p) \land q$ is equivalent to q to obtain $r \lor q$ as the simplification.

Similarly if $(p \land \sim p) \lor q$ is given we observe that $p \land \sim p$ is never true; therefore, the given disjunction will be true if q is true and false if q is false. It is therefore equivalent to q. Using this information we can replace $(r \land s) \land [(p \lor \sim p) \lor q]$ by $(r \land s) \land q$.

Expressions involving other statements that are always true or always false can often be simplified in the same way. Thus

$$[(p \to q) \leftrightarrow (\sim q \to \sim p)] \land r$$

reduces to r, because $(p \to q) \leftrightarrow (\sim q \to \sim p)$ is always true. The truth-value of the conjunction therefore agrees with the truth-value of r. Observe that $[(p \to q) \leftrightarrow (\sim q \to \sim p)] \lor r$ is always true because the first of the statements in the disjunction is always true. The statement $[(p \land \sim p) \to q] \land r$ reduces to r because a conditional with a false antecedent is always true.

In simplifying statements we shall frequently replace a statement by an equivalent statement, as illustrated in the following example.

Example. Simplify

$$[\{[(q \land \sim t) \land p] \lor [(q \land \sim t) \land \sim p]\} \lor \sim q] \to r.$$

Simplification.

$$[\{[(q \wedge \sim t) \wedge p] \vee [(q \wedge \sim t) \wedge \sim p]\} \vee \sim q] \to r,$$
$$\{[(q \wedge \sim t) \wedge (p \vee \sim p)] \vee \sim q\} \to r, \quad \text{(T15)}$$
$$(q \wedge \sim t) \vee \sim q \to r,$$
$$\{(q \vee \sim q) \wedge (\sim t \vee \sim q)\} \to r, \quad \text{(T16)}$$
$$(\sim t \vee \sim q) \to r,$$
$$\sim (t \wedge q) \to r, \quad \text{(T17)}$$
$$(t \wedge q) \vee r. \quad \text{(Th. 4)}$$

EXERCISES

1. Negate each of the following sentences.

    (*a*) The search for truth is an important branch of human endeavor and in it, mathematics has played a major role.

    (*b*) If you've become completely covered with dirt from the rodeo arena, and you're panting with joy and excitement, then you have the symptoms of rodeo fever.

    (*c*) You will be able to earn money if you are properly trained.

    (*d*) To achieve success in our time a politician must become well known.

    (*e*) Today's turnpikes might last for generations without further maintenance, if they carried only air-supported vehicles.

    (*f*) The sky turns from atmospheric blue to vacuum black; the stars appear in the sky; the sun is a diamond glory; the rocket thrust is cut off; and there is a stark unbroken silence.

    (*g*) A first class traveler often considers himself snubbed if during the voyage he does not receive an invitation to the captain's party.

    (*h*) If we take a vacation, then you will enjoy it if you do not worry about finances.

    (*i*) If we take a vacation, then you will enjoy it if and only if you do not worry about finances.

    (*j*) If he receives a good commission then he will make a profit if he invests wisely, but he will not make a profit if he does not invest wisely.

2. Determine which of the following pairs of statement patterns are equivalent.

(a) $\begin{cases} p \leftrightarrow \sim q, \\ q \leftrightarrow \sim p. \end{cases}$ (b) $\begin{cases} \sim(r \rightarrow \sim s), \\ r \wedge s. \end{cases}$ (c) $\begin{cases} p \rightarrow q, \\ q \rightarrow p. \end{cases}$

(d) $\begin{cases} p \wedge (p \rightarrow q), \\ p \wedge q. \end{cases}$ (e) $\begin{cases} \sim(p \rightarrow \sim q), \\ p \wedge (p \rightarrow q). \end{cases}$

(f) $\begin{cases} (q \vee \sim p) \wedge r, \\ (q \wedge r) \vee (\sim p \wedge \sim r). \end{cases}$ (g) $\begin{cases} [p \rightarrow (q \vee \sim q)] \wedge w, \\ w. \end{cases}$

(h) $\begin{cases} (q \wedge \sim q) \wedge p, \\ p. \end{cases}$ (i) $\begin{cases} (p \wedge q) \rightarrow q, \\ p \vee \sim q. \end{cases}$

3. State a sentence logically equivalent to each of the following sentences.

(a) John is not correct or Frank is elected.

(b) Jane will be in danger if Jack will not notify her.

(c) It is not true that Jack is not guilty and that Frank lied.

(d) It may be raining and our food may be lost or stolen.

(e) If Jack does not have the correct number then he cannot win a prize.

(f) He is not the father of Paul or Frank.

4. Simplify the following statement patterns.

(a) $\sim[p \vee \sim (q \wedge r)].$ (b) $p \wedge (\sim p \vee q).$

(c) $p \vee [\sim p \vee (q \wedge \sim q)].$

(d) $[(\sim r \wedge \sim s) \vee \sim(r \vee s)] \rightarrow (\sim r \wedge \sim s).$

(e) $[p \wedge (q \wedge s)] \vee [\sim p \wedge (q \wedge s)].$

(f) $w \wedge s \wedge [\sim\{(p \rightarrow q) \leftrightarrow (\sim q \rightarrow \sim p)\} \rightarrow r].$

11. INFERENCE AND ARGUMENT*

When certain specific statements are assumed to be true there may be other statements which must also be true according to the laws of logic.

Example **1.** If we assume that the statements

---

* This section can be omitted and later combined with Inference and Argument Section 18.

The sun rises in the east,

and

If the sun rises in the east, then early morning shadows cannot point eastward,

are true then good common sense tells us that we should be able to conclude that the early morning shadows cannot point eastward. Let us examine this conclusion in the light of the logical concepts which we have been studying.

Let p: The sun rises in the east,
         q: Early morning shadows cannot point eastward.

Then we have true statements of the form p and $p \rightarrow q$, and the conclusion that we seek is q. That is, we ask whether or not q must be true whenever p and $p \rightarrow q$ are true. Starting with the fact that p is true we consider $p \rightarrow q$. Since p is true and this conditional is true, then q must also be true; for a conditional with a true antecedent can be true only when the consequent is also true. We therefore conclude that if p and $p \rightarrow q$ are true, then q must be true.

In terms of the original statements we conclude that if we accept the statements "The sun rises in the east" and "If the sun rises in the east, then the early morning shadows cannot point eastward" as true statements, then we must, according to the rules of logic, accept the statement "The early morning shadows cannot point eastward" as true.

In this type of reasoning the things that are *assumed* are referred to as the *premises*, the *assumptions*, or the *hypotheses*. Thus "p is true" and "$p \rightarrow q$ is true" are the premises, and "q is true" is the conclusion.

In many cases it is desirable to indicate the reason for each step that must be taken to establish the fact that a conclusion must be true if the premises are true. The following analysis illustrates this procedure.

Statement. If p and $p \rightarrow q$ are true, then q is true.

First Argument.

	p is true.	Premise (or hypothesis).
	$p \rightarrow q$ is true.	Premise (or hypothesis).
Therefore	q is true.	A true conditional with a true antecedent must have a true consequent. ∎

Though the following argument is somewhat longer it shows how a tautology can be used.

Second Argument.

p is true.	Premise.
$p \to q$ is true.	Premise.
$p \wedge (p \to q)$ is true.	Conjunction truth-table.
$[p \wedge (p \to q)] \to q$ is true.	Law of Detachment, T3.
Therefore q is true.	The antecedent of the tautology $[p \wedge (p \to q)] \to q$ is true, therefore its consequent must be true. ∎

Observe that in these two arguments we did not use the specific statements given at the beginning of the example which p and q were originally chosen to represent. The only property that was used was the truth of the statements p and $p \to q$. Therefore, these arguments show that *regardless of what true statement p represents and regardless of what true conditional of the form $p \to q$ is given we can conclude from them that q is a true statement.*

Since, by the usual dictionary definition, inference is the process of deriving the strict logical consequences of assumed premises, we frequently say that from the truth of p and $p \to q$ we validly *infer* the truth of q. We also say that the truth of q *follows logically* from the truth of p and $p \to q$, or that the truth of q is a *logical consequence* of the truth of p and $p \to q$.

Instead of the statement "If p and $p \to q$ are true, then q is true", mathematicians usually use the shorter statement "If p and $p \to q$, then q," and they assume that this shorter statement has the same meaning as the longer one. The argument usually given is a condensed form of the Second Argument. The letter *"P"* is used for "premise". (Observe that if p is not accompanied by a truth-value we assume that it is true.)

Statement.   If p and $p \to q$, then q.

Argument.

(1)	p	P
(2)	$p \to q$	P
(3)	q	(1), (2), and T3

∎

The steps in this argument are numbered. The third step is the result of statements (1) and (2) and the Law of Detachment as indicated on the right. Observe that regardless of the truth-values of p and $p \to q$ we know, by T3, that $[p \wedge (p \to q)] \to q$ is logically valid. We are trying to show that q must be true if p and $p \to q$ are true. The truth of q will follow if the Law of Detachment has a true antecedent, and the truth of the antecedent follows from the conjunction of true premises.

Remarks. Observe that this shorter argument does not include the third and fourth lines of the Second Argument; that is, (1) the conjunction of the true statements which form the antecedent, and (2) the statement of the tautology involved. We use instead the fact that *the consequent of an implication is true whenever the antecedent is true.*

In order to emphasize this shorter form a second example is given.

Statement. If $\sim r$ and $s \to r$, then $\sim s$.

Short Argument.

$$
\begin{array}{lll}
(1) & \sim r & P \\
(2) & s \to r & P \\
(3) & \sim s & (1),\ (2),\ \text{T7}.
\end{array}
$$

Long Argument.

$$
\begin{array}{lll}
(1) & \sim r & P \\
(2) & s \to r & P \\
(3) & (s \to r) \wedge \sim r & (1),\ (2) \\
(4) & [(s \to r) \wedge \sim r] \to \sim s & \text{T7} \\
(5) & \sim s & (4),\ (5),\ \text{T3}.
\end{array}
$$

In the arguments which follow we shall often *substitute an equivalent statement for a given pattern.*

Valid Inference

The word *inference* will be used to designate a set of premises accompanied by a suggested conclusion, regardless of whether or not the conclusion is a logical consequence of the premises. It is often convenient to state the premises and separate them from the conclusion by a horizontal line. Thus the inference of Example 1 could be summarized as follows.

The sun rises in the east. If the sun rises in the east,
then early morning shadows cannot point eastward.

Early morning shadows cannot point eastward.

It is a specific example of the general summarized form

$$p$$
$$p \rightarrow q$$
$$q.$$

Each time a specific set of premises and a conclusion are given
they can be expressed symbolically in terms of elementary tf-statements and sentential connectives. This produces an *inference pattern*.
For example, the inference pattern produced in Example 1 was

$$p$$
$$p \rightarrow q$$
$$q.$$

Replacing each of the letters p, q, r, $\cdots$, by a tf-statement produces
an *instance* of the inference pattern. For example, if in the inference
pattern of Example 1, p is replaced by "The clock has stopped" and
q is replaced by "The class has started", then the following instance
of that pattern is produced.

The clock has stopped. If the clock
has stopped, then the class has started.

The class has started.

If there is an instance of the inference pattern for which the premises
are true and the conclusion is false, this instance is a *counterexample*
of the inference pattern.

An inference pattern is *valid* if it has no counterexamples.

Each inference pattern can be written as a conditional of the following form:

(conjunction of premises) $\rightarrow$ (conclusion).

If the inference pattern is valid then this conditional which has the
conjunction of the premises as its antecedent and the conclusion as its
consequent must be a logically valid sentential statement pattern, for
it can never happen that the antecedent is true and the consequent

is false. Conversely, if this conditional is a logically valid statement pattern its consequent must be true when its antecedent is true and the inference pattern is valid. For example, the inference pattern of Example 1 is valid and $[p \wedge (p \to q)] \to q$ is a tautology.

The fact that a specific inference pattern is valid can be expressed in each of the following ways:

(a) The inference from premises to conclusion is *valid*.

(b) The conclusion is a *logical consequence* of the premises.

(c) The conclusion *follows logically* from the premises.

(d) The premises *imply* the conclusion.

The preceding discussion provides the basis of two rules for testing the validity of inference patterns.

Rule I.

To show that an inference pattern is invalid produce a counterexample to the inference pattern.

Rule II.

To show that an inference pattern is valid show that the conditional (conjunction of premises) $\to$ (conclusion) is a logically valid sentential statement pattern.

In actual practice proof-tables may prove unwieldy in establishing a logically valid statement pattern; therefore it is often better to produce an argument which consists of a sequence of logical steps and shows that the conjunction of true premises produces a true conclusion. In the last half of this chapter we shall be working with open statements and quantified statements for which no practical proof-table method is available; therefore, a chain of justified statements is the best general approach.

It should be stressed here that mathematical reasoning places no emphasis on whether the premises of an inference express "true-to-life" situations. An inference states what may logically follow *if the premises are accepted as true*. What we are able to conclude depends upon what we assume, and it is possible to *reason correctly* from some strange sounding premises to some strange sounding conclusions. Using the pattern just established we observe that the following inference is valid.

> If wishes are horses, then beggars
> can ride. Wishes are horses.
> _____
> Beggars can ride.

It is not our prerogative to question the premises, but we are given the right to decide whether or not the conclusion is a logical result of accepting the premises as true. If this seems strange to one unfamiliar with the ways of mathematical thinking let it suffice for the present to know that very valuable and far-reaching results have been obtained with this type of reasoning on which deductive systems and modern abstract thinking are based. More information is given in the section on deductive systems.

Direct Argument

The purpose of each of the following examples is to determine whether the inference pattern is valid or invalid.

Example 2.

> Burns took the turnpike or Mr. Jenkins missed
> the train. Mr. Jenkins caught the train.
> _____
> Burns took the turnpike.

Let r: Burns took the turnpike,

and s: Mr. Jenkins caught the train.

Then we have the inference pattern

$$r \lor \sim s$$
$$\underline{s \quad\quad\quad}$$
$$r.$$

Statement. If $r \lor \sim s$ and s, then r.

Argument.

	(1)	$r \lor \sim s$	P
	(2)	s	P
	(3)	r	(1), (2), and T8

This is a valid inference.   ■

Example **3.**

If there was a blizzard then traveling was difficult.
If they arrived on time, then traveling was not
difficult. They arrived on time.

There was no blizzard.

Let p: There was a blizzard,
                        q: Traveling was difficult,

and r: They arrived on time.

Statement. If $p \rightarrow q$, $. \rightarrow \sim q$, and r, then $\sim p$.

Argument.

(1)	r	P
(2)	$r \rightarrow \sim q$	P
(3)	$\sim q$	(1), (2), and T3
(4)	$p \rightarrow q$	P
(5)	$\sim q \rightarrow \sim p$	(4) and T6
(6)	$\sim p$	(3), (5) and T3

This is a valid inference.

Second Argument. Observe that we could produce a proof by showing that $[(p \rightarrow q) \wedge (r \rightarrow \sim q) \wedge r] \rightarrow \sim p$ is a logically valid statement pattern, and then using the fact that the truth of the antecedent insures the truth of the consequent. This would involve an entire proof-table with eight rows unless we used only those rows for which the premises are true.

Third Argument. Start with the premise that r is true. If r and $r \rightarrow \sim q$ are both true, then $\sim q$ must be true. If $\sim q$ is true, then q is false. Since $p \rightarrow q$ must be true, and q must be false, then p must be false. Therefore $\sim p$ is true. This is the desired conclusion.

Example **4.**

If Kate is late Mary is unhappy.

Mary is unhappy.

This example has the form

$p \rightarrow q$

q.

This does not appear to be a valid inference. If we cannot immediately produce a counterexample, the quickest way out is to test $(p \to q) \to q$ for logical validity by using a proof table.

$(p \to q)$			$\to$	q
T	T	T	T	T
T	F	F	T	F
F	T	T	T	T
F	T	F	F	F

This statement pattern is false when p and q are both false, even though $p \to q$ is true. Therefore, a counterexample is

> If 7 is less than 3, then 9 is less than 5.
> _____
> 9 is less than 5.

Therefore, we cannot logically draw the conclusion that Mary is unhappy from the statement "If Kate is late Mary is unhappy". It may happen that Kate is not late and Mary is happy. In this case the premise is true but the conclusion is false; therefore, this is also a counterexample.

In Example 1, we learned that given p and $p \to q$ we can conclude q; but from this example we learn that from $p \to q$ alone we cannot conclude q. Observe that $(p \to q) \to q$ is *not* a logically valid statement pattern. Example 5 may be somewhat more confusing.

Example 5.

> If Los Angeles is in California then
> golf balls are sold in Chicago.
> _____
> Golf balls are sold in Chicago.

We should remind ourselves that we are not asking whether it is true that golf balls are sold in Chicago, but we are asking whether the truth of the statement "Golf balls are sold in Chicago" is a *logical consequence* of the given conditional statement "If Los Angeles is in California then golf balls are sold in Chicago". Here it is difficult not to use what we might believe is true; namely "Los Angeles is in California" and "Golf balls are sold in Chicago". Nevertheless, these statements were not given as true; that is, they were not stated as premises. Only the truth of the conditional was given. Observe that this inference is of the form "If $p \to q$, then q". We have already shown that q cannot be logically detached from $p \to q$. If we insist on declaring that q is true then we are considering a different example; namely, one of the form

$$\frac{\begin{array}{c} q \\ p \to q \end{array}}{q.}$$

which is trivially valid because the conclusion is one of the premises.

Example 6. Is the following inference pattern valid?

$$\frac{\begin{array}{c} p \lor q \\ {\sim}p \end{array}}{{\sim}q.}$$

As a counterexample let

                              p: Toronto is in Alaska,

and q: Toronto is in Canada.

Then $p \lor q$ is true and ${\sim}p$ is true; but ${\sim}q$ is false, for Toronto is in Canada. This shows that the conclusion is not a logical consequence of the premises.   ∎

Example 7.

        Two sides of the given triangle are equal. If the given triangle has two equal sides then it is isosceles. If the given triangle is isosceles, the angles opposite the equal sides are equal.

        The given triangle has two equal angles.

Let p: The given triangle has two equal sides,

              q: The given triangle is isosceles,

and r: The angles opposite the equal sides are equal.

The inference pattern is

$$\frac{\begin{array}{c} p \\ p \to q \\ q \to r \end{array}}{r.}$$

Argument.

(1)	$p \to q$	P	
(2)	$p \to r$	P	
(3)	$p \to r$	(1), (2), and T4	
(4)	p	P	
(5)	r	(3), (4), and T3	∎

This example illustrates a type of valid inference frequently used in mathematics without any mention of its logical structure. It is customary for the mathematician to assume that his arguments are logical. His task is to give reasons why the statements (which are the premises of the logical structure) are true in the framework of the mathematical system (geometry, here) which he is using.

Each of the examples which we have considered has had a single tf-statement as its conclusion. Let us consider the strategy needed to establish a conclusion which is a conditional. If we denote the conditional by $w \to s$, then the inference pattern can be represented by

$$(\text{conjunction of premises}) \to (w \to s).$$

If we let t represent the conjunction of the premises the inference pattern is

$$t \to (w \to s).$$

This is equivalent to $(t \wedge w) \to s$, by Tautology T14. Therefore, the conclusion $w \to s$ can be established by showing that s is a logical consequence of the given premises and w.

Rule III.   Rule for Conditional Conclusion

To show that given premises imply a conditional conclusion, show that the given premises and the antecedent of the conditional imply the consequent of the conditional.

Example 8.

$$(s \vee t) \to w$$
$$\frac{\sim s \to \sim w}{t \to s.}$$

Argument.

(1)	$\sim s \to \sim w$	P
(2)	$w \to s$	(1), T6
(3)	$(s \lor t) \to w$	P
(4)	$(s \lor t) \to s$	(2), (3), and T4
(5)	Assume t	Antecedent of the conditional conclusion
(6)	$s \lor t$	(5), T21
(7)	s	(4), (6), and T3
(8)	$t \to s$	(5), (7) Rule for conditional conclusion ∎

The following specific instance of the inference pattern in Example 8 shows how the statements accepted as true affect the conclusion.

If you are interested in frontier history or you are just traveling leisurely through the west, you will leave the main thoroughfares. If you are not interested in frontier history you will not leave the main thoroughfares.

If you are traveling leisurely then you are interested in frontier history.

Indirect Argument

Indirect arguments are based upon the fact that a conclusion must be true or false. If it can be shown that the negation of a conclusion leads to the negation of one of the premises, or the negation of some other statement which is accepted as true, then the conclusion cannot be false. If it cannot be false, then it must be true. The negation of a premise or some other statement known to be true presents the impossible situation of $p \land \sim p$ which is referred to as a contradiction. Indirect arguments are a powerful tool in mathematics. The need for negating conclusions for this type of argument explains the emphasis which is placed upon correct negation in this book.

The following examples show how indirect arguments can be used to obtain certain tautologies from other tautologies. It is assumed that the tautologies and theorems used have already been established by proof-tables. Care should be taken not to produce circular arguments by using the tautology that we are trying to establish as a reason in the argument.

Example 9.

$$p \to q$$
$$\overline{\sim q \to \sim p.}$$

Argument.

(1)	Assume $\sim(\sim q \to \sim p)$	Indirect argument.
(2)	$\sim q \wedge p$	(1), T19
(3)	$\sim q$	(2), T10,
(4)	p	(2), T10,
(5)	$p \to q$	P
(6)	q	(4), (5), T3
(7)	$q \wedge \sim q$	(3), (6), A contradiction.
(8)	Therefore $\sim q \to \sim p$	(1), (7), T5 ∎

Example 10.

$$r \vee \sim s$$
$$s$$
$$\overline{r.}$$

Argument.	(1)	Assume $\sim r$	Indirect argument
	(2)	$r \vee \sim s$	P
	(3)	$\sim r \to \sim s$	(2) and Theorem 4
	(4)	$\sim s$	(1), (3), and T3
	(5)	s	P
	(6)	$\sim s \wedge s$	(4), (5), Contradiction
	(7)	Therefore r	(1), (6), T5 ∎

Contrapositive Argument

By the Law of Contraposition $(p \to q) \leftrightarrow (\sim q \to \sim p)$. When it is expedient we can show that $\sim q \to \sim p$ is true instead of showing that $p \to q$ is true.

Example 11.

$$(w \wedge r) \to s$$
$$\overline{w \to (r \to s)}$$

According to this inference pattern we need to show that $[(w \wedge r) \to s] \to [w \to (r \to s)]$. Let us instead establish the contrapositive statement $\sim[w \to (r \to s)] \to \sim[(w \wedge r) \to s]$.

Argument.

(1)	$\sim[w \rightarrow (r \rightarrow s)]$	Contrapositive argument
(2)	$w \wedge \sim(r \rightarrow s)$	(1), T19
(3)	$w \wedge r \wedge \sim s$	(2), T19
(4)	$\sim[(w \wedge r) \rightarrow s]$	(3), T19

The contrapositive proof corresponds to one of the rules for establishing an implication; namely, show that whenever the consequent is false then the antecedent must be false.

Necessary and Sufficient Conditions

The words "necessary" and "sufficient" are frequently used in mathematical statements. We shall explain them in terms of an everyday example. A normal elephant has four legs; therefore we often say that if the elephant is normal he necessarily has four legs. Since this is a conditional statement we can represent it as

$$(\text{normal elephant}) \rightarrow (\text{four legs}).$$

This concept can also be expressed by saying that having four legs is a necessary condition for an animal to be a normal elephant.

We now ask whether four legs is sufficient to make a normal animal an elephant. Since there are many animals which have four legs but are not elephants the requirement of four legs is not sufficient to make the animal an elephant. There must be other requirements, such as a trunk and large floppy ears, which would rule out the other four legged animals.

This example can be viewed from the opposite direction. It was viewed with emphasis on producing a *normal elephant*. Now let us consider it with a view toward producing *four legs*.

Is being an elephant a necessary condition for a normal animal having four legs. That is, if a normal animal has four legs is it necessarily an elephant? Obviously not. Is being an elephant sufficient to cause a normal animal to have four legs. Obviously yes.

From this discussion we see that $p \rightarrow q$ can be read

"q is a necessary condition for p"

and also as

"p is a sufficient condition for q".

Some examples may make these concepts clearer. These examples can readily be introduced in outline form, followed by the usual statement.

Example **12.**   (Isosceles triangle) $\leftrightarrow$ (two equal angles)

A necessary and sufficient condition that a triangle be isosceles is that it have two equal angles.

(Also: A necessary and sufficient condition that a triangle have two equal angles is that it be isosceles.)

Example **13.**   (Congruent triangles) $\rightarrow$ (mutually equiangular)

A necessary condition that two triangles be congruent is that they be mutually equiangular.

A sufficient condition that two triangles be mutually equiangular is that they be congruent.

Example **14.**   (Divisible by 6) $\leftrightarrow$ (divisible by 2 and 3)

A necessary and sufficient condition that a whole number be exactly divisible by 6 is that it be exactly divisible by both 2 and 3.

Example **15.**   (Greater than 7) $\rightarrow$ (greater than 3)

A necessary condition that a number be greater than 7 is that it be greater than 3.

A sufficient condition that a number be greater than 3 is that it be greater than 7.

The words "if and only if" are often used in mathematics to express necessary and sufficient conditions. Examples 12 and 14 are rephrased using this terminology.

A triangle is isosceles if and only if it has two equal angles.

A whole number is exactly divisible by 6 if and only if it is exactly divisible by both 2 and 3.

Concluding Remark. The portion of logic which we have considered thus far is often referred to as the *sentential calculus* (or the propositional calculus). It should be observed that the actual content of the statements (or propositions) was not stressed. Instead the fact that each statement had a truth-value was used to form truth-tables for *arbitrary* statements combined by connectives or modified by negation. Proceeding in this manner, we obtained laws of logic which are independent of the content of the statements and their truth-value.

EXERCISES

1. Determine whether each of the following inference patterns is valid or invalid. If the inference pattern is invalid, indicate a combination of truth-values which will produce a counterexample. If the inference pattern is valid, produce some evidence which will confirm its validity.

(a) $r \to s$
$\sim s$
$\overline{\quad\quad}$
$\sim r.$

(b) $r \to s$
$p \to q$
$r \lor p$
$\overline{\quad\quad}$
$s \lor q.$

(c) $r \to s$
$\sim r$
$\overline{\quad\quad}$
$\sim s.$

(d) $p \land q$
$\overline{\quad\quad}$
$p.$

(e) $\sim q$
$\overline{\quad\quad}$
$\sim(p \land q).$

(f) $p \to (r \to s)$
$\sim r \to \sim p$
p
$\overline{\quad\quad}$
$s.$

(g) $(p \land q) \to \sim t$
$w \lor r$
$w \to p$
$r \to q$
$\overline{\quad\quad\quad}$
$(w \lor r) \to \sim t.$

(h) $\sim t \to \sim r$
$\sim s$
$t \to w$
$r \lor s$
$\overline{\quad\quad}$
$w.$

(i) $\sim r \to (s \to \sim t)$
$\sim r \lor w$
$\sim p \to s$
$\sim w$
$\overline{\quad\quad}$
$t \to p.$

(j) $\sim(q \lor r) \to \sim q$
$s \to \sim r$
$q \to \sim p$
$\overline{\quad\quad\quad}$
$p \to \sim s.$

(k) $p \to q$
$q \to r$
$r \to s$
$\overline{\quad\quad}$
$s.$

(l) If today is Thursday, then yesterday was Wednesday.
Yesterday was Wednesday.
$\overline{\qquad\qquad\qquad\qquad\qquad\qquad\qquad}$
Today is Thursday.

(m) If the parakeet likes celery, then Jim will buy celery.
The parakeet likes celery.
$\overline{\qquad\qquad\qquad\qquad\qquad\qquad\qquad}$

(n) If the innkeeper explained, there is no reason for argument.
The innkeeper explained.
$\overline{\qquad\qquad\qquad\qquad\qquad\qquad\qquad}$
There is no reason for argument.

(o) If Los Angeles is not in California, then golf balls are not sold in Chicago. Golf balls are sold in Chicago.

Los Angeles is in California.

(p) If the cup is gold, then it is lighter than water. If the cup is lighter than water, then Janie can carry it.

If the cup is gold, then Janie can carry it.

(q) If wishes are horses, beggars can ride. Beggars can ride.

Wishes are horses.

(r) If the week has seven days, then fish have wings. If there aren't fifty-two weeks in a year then fish do not have wings.

If the week has seven days, then there are fifty-two weeks in the year.

(s) If wages are raised, buying increases. If there is a depression wages cannot be raised.

If there is a depression, buying cannot increase.

(t) The given triangles are similar. If the given triangles are mutually equiangular then they are similar.

The triangles are mutually equiangular.

(u) If the wire at the tip of the kite caught the electricity in the clouds then it would pass through the thoroughly wet twine and then through the poor conductor made of dry silk ribbon. If electricity passed first through the wet twine and then through the dry silk ribbon Franklin would be protected from the shock.

Franklin would not be protected from the shock if the wire at the tip of the kite did not catch the electricity from the clouds.

(v) If the package is not properly addressed or is too large, then it will not be accepted by the Post Office. This package is not too large. If Thomas addressed this package, then it is properly addressed.

If Thomas addressed this package, then it will be accepted by the Post Office.

(w) If Marge or Frank needs a vacation, then Kate deserves an assistant.

If Frank needs a vacation, then Kate deserves an assistant.

2. Show that the following inference is valid

$$[p \wedge (p \to q) \wedge (q \to r) \wedge (r \to s) \wedge (s \to t) \wedge (t \to u)] \to u,$$

    (a) by using only the Law of Detachment.

    (b) by using the Law of Syllogism except for the last step.

3. For each of the following pairs of elements state all necessary and sufficient relationships that exist between the two elements of the pair. (Freedom of expression is allowed.)

    (a) A biped; a normal duck.

    (b) Equilateral triangle; equiangular triangle.

    (c) Equilateral triangle; isosceles triangle.

    (d) A right angle; a right triangle.

    (e) A parallelogram; a square.

    (f) A living person; air to breathe.

    (g) Less than 5; less than -2.

    (h) Even number; of the form $2n$, where n is a whole number.

    (i) Integer; rational number.

    (j) Worth a dime; worth ten cents.

4. Use an indirect argument to verify the following valid inferences.

    (a) $q \to t$ (b) $\sim p \to (q \to \sim w)$

        $s \to r$ $\sim s \to q$

        $\dfrac{q \vee s}{t \vee r.}$ $\sim t$

                               $\dfrac{\sim p \vee t}{w \to s.}$

5. Use a contrapositive argument to verify the following valid inference.

$$\frac{w \to (r \to s)}{(w \wedge r) \to s\,.}$$

The Restricted
Predicate Calculus

We now turn our attention to that part of logic which deals with the *content* of statements.

12. OPEN STATEMENTS

Throughout mathematics there are many statements which contain symbols or words as place holders for mathematical objects. Similar statements occur also in everyday speech. Many of these statements become tf-statements when the symbols, or certain words, are replaced by specific objects from a designated set.

The statements

(1) The rational number x is greater than 50,
(2) He is a Nobel Prize winner,
(3) $z + y = 6$, where z and y are integers,
(4) By the campfires v listened to w, a fur trader, tell of the wonderful country across the mountains and down the Ohio, not knowing that one day w would show him the way to Kentucky,

are not tf-statements because they have no truth values.

Replacing x in statement (1) by the number 7 produces a false statement, and replacing it by 121.7 produces a true statement.*

The pronoun in (2) must be replaced by a specific name before the statement is declared true or false.

For $z = 8$, $y = -2$, statement (3) is true. Also when $z = y = 3$ it is true. If $z = 11$ and $y = -1$, it is false.

If the letter v is replaced by "Daniel Boone" and each occurrence of the letter w is replaced by "John Findley" the statement resulting from (4) is true.

Statements of this type will be called *open statements*. It should be observed that for a specific replacement all occurrences of a symbol should be replaced by the *same* object. For example, if "John Findley" is substituted for one occurrence of w in statement (4), then it must be substituted for both occurrences. The symbol w cannot represent two different objects in the same statement.

Definition. *An **open statement** is a declarative sentence which*

(i) *contains one or more symbols,*

(ii) *is not a tf-statement, but*

(iii) *produces a tf-statement when each of its symbols is replaced by a specific object from a designated set.*

In this definition a pronoun is equivalent to a symbol such as x.

For statements (2) and (4) no sets were designated since the nature of the objects involved is indicated by the statements themselves. They obviously refer to human beings, living or dead. By naming a specific set of human beings we could restrict the symbols in either statement to a smaller set.

The set of objects which the symbols in an open statement can represent is the *universe*, or the *universe of discourse*, of the open sentence. In some cases the universe will be literally everything; though it frequently will be smaller. In order to insure the validity of certain statements we shall require it to be nonempty; that is, it must contain at least one object.†

---

* The decimal 121.7 is a rational number since it can be written as 1217/10, which is the quotient of two integers.

† In many cases it is convenient to allow an empty universe. See Exner and Rosskopf, *Logic in Elementary Mathematics* (New York, McGraw-Hill, 1959), p. 75.

Open statements will be indicated by capital letters, followed by the symbols involved. This will distinguish them from tf-statements which are represented by small letters. Statement (1) can be represented by Px; statement (3) by Qzy; and statement (4) by Rvw. If statement (2) is replaced by

y is a Nobel Prize winner

then it can be represented by Sy. Thus,

Px: The rational number x is greater than 50.

Sy: y is a Nobel Prize winner.

Qzy: $z + y = 6$, where z and y are integers.

Replacements are indicated by substituting an object from the designated set for each variable.* Thus,

$P7$: The rational number 7 is greater than 50.

Pa: The rational number a is greater than 50.

Py: The rational number y is greater than 50.

$Q\,3{,}2$: $3 + 2 = 6$.

S George Washington: George Washington is a
            Nobel Prize winner.

If we let w represent George Washington this last replacement can be more simply represented. Thus,

Sw: George Washington is a Nobel Prize winner.

Open statements can be combined with other open statements and also with tf-statements to form new open statements.

If r: 12 is divisible by 3,   then

$r \wedge Px$: 12 is divisible by 3, and the rational number x is
            greater than 50, and

$Px \wedge Qzy$: The rational number x is greater than 50, and $z + y = 6$.

Similarly,

$(Px \wedge Qzy) \rightarrow r$: If the rational number x is greater than 50
            and $z + y = 6$, then 12 is divisible by 3,

is always true because of the true consequent.

---

* In sections where the tautologies are being referred to as T1, T2, T3, etc., we shall not use Tx to represent an open sentence. This will avoid the confusion that might be caused by interpreting T5 as the replacement of x by 5 in the open sentence Tx. Thus the letter T will be reserved for references to the tautologies.

It should be observed that if the universe of

$$Dx\colon 12/x \text{ is an integer,}$$

is restricted to the numbers $\{2, 3, 4, 5\}$, and if the universe of

$$Hx\colon x \text{ is a negative number,}$$

is restricted to the rational numbers from -1 to 2, inclusive, then there is only one number, namely 2, which lies in both universes. Thus such statements as $Dx \wedge Hx$, $Dx \vee Hx$, $\sim Dx \rightarrow \sim Hx$ could be restricted to the universe containing only the number 2. It is also possible to consider a larger universe for one of these composite statements, such as the rational numbers between -1 and 2, except for $x = 0$, along with the numbers 3, 4, and 5; since all of these are objects for which each of the statements Dx and Hx is true or false. (Observe that the number 0 was not included in the universe because $12/0$ is meaningless.) The universe might be further enlarged to contain all objects for which the composite statement under consideration is either true or false.

If, for some reason, we need to consider the statement Dx for a specific x and at the same time consider Hx for a different x, it is often convenient to introduce another symbol and write $Dx \wedge Hy$ rather than $Dx \wedge Hx$, because in the statement

$$Dx \wedge Hx\colon 12/x \text{ is an integer and } x \text{ is a negative number,}$$

x must be replaced in both occurrences by the same number, while

$$Dx \wedge Hy\colon 12/x \text{ is an integer and } y \text{ is a negative number,}$$

allows x to be replaced by one number and y by a different number.

13. QUANTIFIERS

Certain statements involve words that indicate quantity such as "all", "some", "none", or "one". They answer the question "How many?" Since such words indicate quantity they are called *quantifiers*. Consider the following examples:

(1) All birds are small.
(2) Some men are tall.

(3) No balloon is perfectly round.

(4) There is an individual who cannot do the work.

An analysis of mathematical sentences involving quantifiers indicates that the two main quantifiers are "all" and "some", where "some" is interpreted to mean "at least one".

Example (1) uses *"all"*; example (2) can be restated as "There is *at least one* tall man"; example (3) means that *all* balloons fail to be perfectly round; and (4) indicates that *at least one* individual cannot do the work.

The quantifier "all" is the *universal quantifier*. We shall denote it by the symbol ∀ x, which is an inverted A followed by an x. It represents each of the following phrases, since they all have essentially the same meaning.

For all x,	All things x are such that,
For every x,	Everything x is such that,
For each x,	Each thing x is such that.

The quantifier "some" is the *existential quantifier*. We shall denote it by the symbol ∃ x, which is a reversed E followed by an x. It represents each of the following phrases, since they have essentially the same meaning.

"For some x",
"Some x is such that",
"There exists an x such that",
"There is an x such that",
"There is at least one x such that".

14. STATEMENTS INVOLVING ONE QUANTIFIER

We now write the following statements in symbolic form,

(1) Something is green.

(2) Everything is green.

(3) Nothing is green.

(4) Something is not green.

Statement (1) can be rephrased as "There is an x such that x is green," where x belongs to the set of all objects which can be classified as "green" or "not green".
If Gx: x is green, then this statement can be written symbolically as $\exists x \, [Gx]$.

Statement (2) rephrased is "For all x, x is green," and it can be written symbolically as $\forall x \, [Gx]$.

Statement (3) means "For all x, x is not green," and symbolically written is $\forall x \, [\sim Gx]$.

Statement (4) means "There is an x such that x is not green," and it can be denoted by $\exists x \, [\sim Gx]$.

In summary,

$$\exists x \, [Gx]: \text{Something is green,}$$
$$\forall x \, [Gx]: \text{Everything is green,}$$
$$\forall x \, [\sim Gx]: \text{Nothing is green,}$$
$$\exists x \, [\sim Gx]: \text{Something is not green.}$$

We observe that even though

$$Gx: x \text{ is green,}$$

is an open statement, and therefore not a tf-statement, the statements obtained from it by prefixing quantifiers; namely

$$\exists x \, [Gx] \quad \text{which means "Something is green",}$$

and

$$\forall x \, [Gx] \quad \text{which means "Everything is green",}$$

are tf-statements. Therefore, we see that an open statement containing only one symbol can be made into a tf-statement by prefixing the existential quantifier, or the universal quantifier. Such a statement is called a *closed statement* since its only symbol is *covered by a quantifier*.

We now have two ways of obtaining a tf-statement from an open statement; namely,

(1) by replacing the symbol by an object which it represents, or
(2) by prefixing either the existential quantifier, or the universal quantifier.

Definition. *The specific object which replaces a symbol in an open or closed statement is a* **replacement;** *and the statement obtained by replacing* *the symbols by specific objects is a* **replacement instance** *of the open or closed statement.*

For example,

John Smith is a fireman,

is a *replacement instance* of

x is a fireman,

obtained by replacing x by the *replacement* John Smith.

The fact that the truth of a quantified statement depends upon the universe of discourse will be shown in terms of a specific open statement involving one symbol.

Example.   Let Qy: y is less than 5.

For each universe given below we shall write four true statements using the quantifiers ∀ y and ∃ y.

(a) $\{-1, 0, 2, .75, -10\}$
(b) $\{3, -2, 7, 8.2\}$
(c) $\{6, 15, 32\}$

With universe (a) we can produce the statements

-1 is less than 5,	.75 is less than 5,
0 is less than 5,	-10 is less than 5.
2 is less than 5,	

All of these statements are true. Therefore, we state that ∀ y $[Qy]$ is a true statement in this universe. There does not exist a number in the universe which is not less than 5. We therefore state that ∃ y $[\sim Qy]$ is false. The negation of this false statement is $\sim$∃ y $[\sim Qy]$. This is a true statement. We observe that ∀ y $[Qy]$ and $\sim$∃ y $[\sim Qy]$ make the same assertion. The first says that for every number in the universe the statement is true (that is, *all true*), and the second says there is no number in the universe for which the statement is false (that is, *none false*). Are there other quantifying statements that can be made? We can ask whether there is a number for which the statement is true. Obviously, there is, since the statement is true for all numbers in the universe. We therefore declare that ∃ y $[Qy]$ is a true statement. Is there another statement which makes the same true assertion? Saying that the statement is true for one number also says that it is not false for all numbers. That is, it is false that each number in the universe produces a false statement. Therefore $\forall y \ [\sim Qy]$ is false, and its negation $\sim\forall y \ [\sim Qy]$ must be true. We observe that $\exists y \ [Qy]$ makes the same assertion as $\sim\forall y \ [\sim Qy]$; the first means *"one true"* and the second means *"not all false"*.

We have thus produced four true quantified statements using Qy and the first universe (a). They are $\forall y \ [Qy]$, $\sim\exists y \ [\sim Qy]$, $\exists y \ [Qy]$, and $\sim\forall y \ [\sim Qy]$; and these are read, respectively,

> For all y, Qy,
> There does not exist a y such that $\sim Qy$,
> There exists a y such that Qy,
> It is not true that for all y, $\sim Qy$.

In all cases "y" means "y in the universe (a)". In terms of the specific statement and the specific universe (a) these could be read:

> Every number in universe (a) is less than 5,
> There is no number in universe (a) which is not less than 5,
> There is a number in universe (a) which is less than 5,
> It is false that all numbers in universe (a) are not less than 5.

Let us now consider the statements obtained from Qy, *using universe* (b). We observe that "3 is less than 5" but "7 is not less than 5". Therefore there is a number in the universe for which Qy is true and one for which it is false. We, therefore, obtain two true statements $\exists y \ [Qy]$ and $\exists y \ [\sim Qy]$. What does $\exists y \ [\sim Qy]$ mean? It means that the statement is not true for all numbers in the universe. Therefore $\sim\forall y \ [Qy]$ is a true statement. What does $\exists y \ [Qy]$ mean? It means that not all of the numbers produce false statements. Therefore, $\sim\forall y \ [\sim Qy]$ is a true statement. The four true quantified statements are $\exists y \ [\sim Qy]$, $\sim \forall y \ [Qy]$, $\exists y \ [Qy]$, and $\sim\forall y \ [\sim Qy]$.

Finally, we consider *universe* (c). Observe that $\exists y \ [\sim Qy]$ and $\sim\exists y \ [Qy]$. Therefore, $\sim\forall y \ [Qy]$ and $\forall y \ [\sim Qy]$. The four true statements are $\exists y \ [\sim Qy]$, $\sim\forall y \ [Qy]$, $\sim \exists y \ [Qy]$, $\forall y \ [\sim Qy]$.

From this example we learn that the truth of a quantified statement such as $\forall y \ [Qy]$ depends upon the universe. This statement was true only in universe (a). Similarly, $\forall y \ [\sim Qy]$ was true only in universe (c).

This example also seems to indicate that certain concepts involving quantifiers can be stated in two ways. We cannot draw conclusions on the basis of one specific example. Therefore, let us consider an arbitrary open sentence Px. If every statement obtained from Px by replacing x by a specific object from the universe is true, does it follow that there are no false statements? Obviously, yes, since no statement can be both true and false. Furthermore, if there are no false statements, then all statements are true, for each statement must be either true or false. Therefore, "all true" means the same as "none false". A similar consideration would lead us to the conclusion that "all false" means the same as "none true". What does "not all false" mean? It means that for at least one a in the universe the statement Pa is true. Conversely, if one statement Pa is true, does it follow that not all statements are false? Obviously, yes. A similar discussion can be given for "at least one false" and "not all true".

We conclude that:

"all true" means the same as "none false",
"all false" means the same as "none true",
"not all true" means the same as "at least one false",
and   "not all false" means the same as "at least one true".

Therefore, the following quantified statements are equivalences.*

$$\forall\, x\,[Px] \leftrightarrow \sim\!\exists\, x\,[\sim\!Px],$$
$$\forall\, x\,[\sim\!Px] \leftrightarrow \sim\!\exists\, x\,[Px],$$
$$\sim\!\forall\, x\,[Px] \leftrightarrow \quad\exists\, x\,[\sim\!Px],$$
$$\sim\!\forall\, x\,[\sim\!Px] \leftrightarrow \quad\exists\, x\,[Px].$$

The last two statements can be obtained from the first two by negating both sides of each equivalence.

The equivalences also provide information about the negation of this type of quantified statement. In the first statement we have $\forall\, x\,[Px]$. Its negation $\sim\!\forall\, x\,[Px]$ occurs in the third statement and is equivalent to $\exists\, x\,[\sim\!Px]$. Thus the negation of "all true" is "at least one false". Further observation shows that the negations come in pairs: the statements "all true" and "at least one false" are negations

---

* We showed that whenever "all true" is true then "none false" is true, and whenever "none false" is true then "all true" is true; therefore, "all true" and "none false" are equivalent statements. (See "Implication and Equivalence".) The other equivalences were established in the same manner.

of each other; and the statements "all false" and "at least one true" are negations of each other.

Statement	Negation
$\forall x \, [Px]$	$\exists x \, [\sim Px]$
$\exists x \, [\sim Px]$	$\forall x \, [Px]$
$\forall x \, [\sim Px]$	$\exists x \, [Px]$
$\exists x \, [Px]$	$\forall x \, [\sim Px]$

We see that the negation of a statement involving the universal quantifier is a statement involving the existential quantifier, and conversely the negation of a statement involving an existential quantifier is a statement involving a universal quantifier. We also observe that if a statement contains Px its negation contains $\sim Px$; if it contains $\sim Px$, its negation contains Px.

This suggests that in order to negate a quantified statement involving one quantifier we should change the quantifier from universal to existential, or from existential to universal, and negate the statement which it quantifies. We shall consider this as a possible rule and investigate it further.

Let us now consider the following statements which are slightly more involved than the four statements which we have just discussed.

(5) All men are giants.
(6) No men are giants.
(7) Some men are giants.
(8) Some men are not giants.

If the universe for the statement "All men are giants" consists only of men then this statement is merely $\forall x \, [Gx]$, where

$$Gx\colon x \text{ is a giant,}$$

and this statement is essentially of the same type as "Everything is green". However, if the universe consists of objects some of which are not men, a further refinement is necessary. Let

$$Mx\colon x \text{ is a man,} \qquad \text{and} \qquad Gx\colon x \text{ is a giant.}$$

Then "All men are giants" is of the form $\forall x \, [Px]$, where Px represents some combination of Mx and Gx. Should Px be replaced by $Mx \wedge Gx$, $Mx \vee Gx$, $Mx \rightarrow Gx$, or $Mx \leftrightarrow Gx$?

To determine which sentential connective should be used assume that b is an object in the universe. "All men are giants" makes no statement about objects in the universe which are not men. If the object is a man, then he is, or is not, a giant. If there is one man who is not a giant, then the given statement is false, otherwise it is true. Thus the given statement can be false only when there is an object b in the universe such that Mb is true and Gb is false. This shows that a rephrasing of statement (5) is

For all x, if x is a man, then x is a giant,

and it can be written as

$$\forall x \, [Mx \rightarrow Gx].$$

The reader should convince himself that $Mx \wedge Gx$ would not be a correct rephrasing, for $Mb \wedge Gb$ would be false when Mb is false; that is, for objects that are not men. Similarly $Mx \vee Gx$ is not correct, for $Mb \vee Gb$ would be false when b is neither a man nor a giant.

Statement (6) means "For all x, if x is a man, then x is not a giant," and it can be written as

$$\forall x \, [Mx \rightarrow \sim Gx].$$

The statement, "Some men are giants" means that something is both a man and a giant. Thus statement (7) means "There is an x, such that x is a man and x is a giant," and it can be written as

$$\exists x \, [Mx \wedge Gx].$$

Statement (8) means "There is an x, such that x is a man and x is not a giant," and can be written as

$$\exists x \, [Mx \wedge \sim Gx].$$

In summary,

$\forall x \, [Mx \rightarrow Gx]$: All men are giants,
$\forall x \, [Mx \rightarrow \sim Gx]$: No men are giants,
$\exists x \, [Mx \wedge Gx]$: Some men are giants,
$\exists x \, [Mx \wedge \sim Gx]$: Some men are not giants.

Caution should be exercised in rephrasing statements (7) and (8). One might be inclined to restate (7) as "There is an x such that if x is a man, then x is a giant", which would have the symbolic representation $\exists\, x\, [Mx \to Gx]$. Since, by Theorem 4, $(Mb \to Gb) \leftrightarrow (\sim Mb \lor Gb)$, for every b in the universe, this can be written as $\exists\, x\, [\sim Mx \lor Gx]$. This says "Something is not a man or it is a giant". Therefore, this would be true of all universes which contain one object which is not a man. This in no way forces something to be both a man and a giant.

Another way of looking at statement (7) is to consider it as the negation of (6). To deny that "No men are giants" is to say that "Some men are giants". The symbolic form of (6) is $\forall\, x\, [Px]$, where Px is $Mx \to \sim Gx$. Its negation is $\exists\, x\, [\sim Px]$, which is $\exists\, x\, [\sim(\sim Mx \lor \sim Gx)]$. Since, by T18, $\sim(\sim Mb \lor \sim Gb) \leftrightarrow (Mb \land Gb)$, for every b in the universe, this statement can be written as $\exists\, x\, [Mx \land Gx]$, which is the symbolic form first obtained.

We observe that statements (6) and (7) are negations of each other; and statements (5) and (8) are negations of each other.

The discussions in this section show that there are four main types of statements involving a single quantifier; namely, $\forall\, x\, [Px]$, $\exists\, x\, [Px]$, $\forall\, x\, [\sim Px]$, and $\exists\, x\, [\sim Px]$, where Px may be a simple open statement or a more complicated one, such as,

Px: x is green,
Px: If x is a man, then x is a giant,

or

Px: x is wise, x is strong, and x will succeed if x controls x.

(The last open statement corresponds to the statement "He is wise and strong and will succeed if he controls himself.")

The following chart shows when each main type of quantified statement is true and when it is false. First read the heading for a column, then the entry in which you are interested. For example, if we seek information about $\forall\, x\, [\sim Px]$ we observe that this is the third entry in the first column. The third entry in each of the other two columns gives information about this third quantified statement. For each column we read the heading followed by the third entry to obtain,

"*The statement* $\forall\, x\, [\sim Px]$ *is true* if for all c, Pc is false; it *is false* if for at least one c, Pc is true."

Let c represent an object in the universe of the quantified statement.

The statement	is true	is false
∀ x $[Px]$	if for all c, Pc is true	if for at least one c, Pc is false
∃ x $[Px]$	if for at least one c, Pc is true	if for all c, Pc is false
∀ x $[{\sim}Px]$	if for all c, Pc is false	if for at least one c, Pc is true
∃ x $[{\sim}Px]$	if for at least one c, Pc is false	if for all c, Pc is true

From this chart we can readily see that the condition under which ∀ x $[Px]$ is true is the condition under which ∃ x $[{\sim}Px]$ is false. It is "for all c, Pc is true". Also, the condition under which ∀ x $[Px]$ is false is the condition under which ∃ x $[{\sim}Px]$ is true. It is "for at least one c, Pc is false". This agrees with our previous observation that ∀ x $[Px]$ and ∃ x $[{\sim}Px]$ are negations of each other. Similarly, the chart shows that ∀ x $[{\sim}Px]$ and ∃ x $[Px]$ are negations of each other.

We now accept the rule which we suggested earlier in this section for the negation of this type of statement.

Rule for Negating a Statement Covered by one Quantifier

To negate a statement covered by one quantifier change the quantifier from universal to existential, or from existential to universal, and negate the statement which it quantifies.

Examples of Statement Analysis

A few examples of statement analysis will provide further instruction in changing statements to the symbolic form. We shall also classify each statement as open or closed. A sentence is closed only if each of its symbols is covered by a quantifier. If there is one symbol which is not covered by a quantifier, then the statement is open.

Example 1. $x + 7$ *is greater than* $x + 3$ *only if* 7 *is greater than* 3.

This is an open statement since the symbol x is not covered by a quantifier. Let

q: 7 is greater than 3,   and Px: $x + 7$ is greater than $x + 3$.

Since the conditional $p \to q$ can be read "p only if q" as well as "if p then q", the statement is of the form

$(x + 7$ is greater than $x + 3) \to (7$ is greater than $3)$,

which can be written as $Px \to q$.

Example 2. $x + 7$ *is greater than* $x + 3$, *if* 7 *is greater than* 3.
Using the same notation as in Example 1, we can symbolize this statement as $q \to Px$. This is also an open statement.

Example 3. If the preceding example is interpreted to mean "For all x, $x + 7$ is greater than $x + 3$, if 7 is greater than 3," then it could be written as $q \to \forall x [Px]$. or as $\forall x [q \to Px]$. This is a closed statement.

Example 4. *Some people who trust others are rewarded.*
In the universe of people this can be rephrased as follows, "For some x, x trusts others and x is rewarded," and this can be written symbolically as $\exists x [Tx \land Rx]$, where

Tx: x trust others   and Rx: x is rewarded.

If a larger universe is used, let Px: x is a person, then the symbolic form is $\exists x [Px \land Tx \land Rx]$. Both statements are closed.

Example 5. *If a hurricane comes, all of the property will be destroyed.*
This closed statement can be rephrased as follows, "If a hurricane comes, then for all x, if x is property, then x will be destroyed." Let

h: a hurricane comes, Px: x is property,   and Dx: x will be destroyed, then we obtain $h \to \forall x [Px \to Dx]$.

Example 6. *If everything is beautiful, then something is beautiful.*
We rephrase this closed statement as follows, "If for each x, x is beautiful, then for some x, x is beautiful," and symbolize it as $\forall x [Bx] \to \exists x [Bx]$, where Bx: x is beautiful.

Example 7. *Jane must do her work on time or someone will be late for the meeting.*
This is a disjunction, "(Jane must do her work on time) $\lor$ (someone will be late for the meeting)". The second part of the statement involves a quantifier; therefore, it can be written as

(Jane must do her work on time) $\lor$ $\exists x [x$ will be late for the meeting].

This is of the form $t \vee \exists x [Lx]$, where

> t: Jane must do her work on time,

and Lx: x will be late for the meeting.

This is a closed statement.

This sentence also can be written as a conditional since it means the same as

> "If Jane does not do her work on time
> then someone will be late for the meeting,"

which can be symbolized as $\sim d \rightarrow \exists x [Lx]$, where

> d: Jane does her work on time.

Observe also that the same meaning is conveyed by the statement

> "Unless Jane does her work on time
> someone will be late for the meeting."

Thus the connective "unless" frequently has the meaning "if $\cdots$ not, then", which is a combination of "not" and "if $\cdots$ then".

Example 8.   *Janet loses everything.*

A restatement is "For all x, Janet loses x." It has the symbolic representation $\forall x [Jx]$, where Jx: Janet loses x. This is a closed statement.

Example 9.   *If anyone is good then John is good.*

> (Anyone is good) $\rightarrow$ (John is good).

This means

> (There is an x, such that x is good) $\rightarrow$ (John is good).

Let Gx: x is good; then the statement is of the form

$$\exists x [Gx] \rightarrow G \text{ John.}$$

This is a closed statement.

Example 10.   *He is ambitious or no one is ambitious.*

Let us use all people as the universe. The statement form is

> (He is ambitious) $\vee$ (no one is ambitious)

which can be refined to

> (y is ambitious) $\vee$ (for all x, x is not ambitious).

Let Ay: y is ambitious; then the statement can be represented by

$$Ay \ \vee \ \forall x \ [\sim\!Ax].$$

This is an open statement because y is not covered by a quantifier.

Example 11. *If every member of the Plan Committee is a Democrat or an independent voter, and if there is no Republican member of the Building Committee, then the Republicans may not have adequate representation.*

We first indicate the dominant structure of the statement

$$\left[\begin{pmatrix} \text{Every member of} \\ \text{the Plan Commit-} \\ \text{tee is a Democrat} \\ \text{or an independent} \\ \text{voter} \end{pmatrix} \wedge \begin{pmatrix} \text{there is no Re-} \\ \text{publican mem-} \\ \text{ber of the} \\ \text{Building Com-} \\ \text{mittee} \end{pmatrix} \right] \rightarrow \begin{pmatrix} \text{the Republicans} \\ \text{may not have ade-} \\ \text{quate representa-} \\ \text{tion} \end{pmatrix}.$$

This is of the form $p \wedge q \rightarrow r$. However, the analysis of the antecedent can be refined.

$$\begin{pmatrix} \text{For every } x, \text{ if } x \text{ is a member} \\ \text{of the Plan Committee, then} \\ x \text{ is a Democrat or an inde-} \\ \text{pendent voter} \end{pmatrix} \wedge \sim \begin{pmatrix} \text{there is a } y, \text{ such that } y \text{ is a} \\ \text{member of the Building Com-} \\ \text{mittee and } y \text{ is a Republican} \end{pmatrix}.$$

Let Mx: x is a member of the Plan Committee,

  Dx: x is a Democrat,

  Ix: x is an independent voter,

  By: y is a member of the Building Committee

  Ry: y is a Republican

and r: the Republicans may not have adequate representation.

Then the symbolic form of this closed statement is

$$\{\forall x \ [Mx \rightarrow (Dx \vee Ix)] \wedge \sim\!\exists y \ [By \wedge Ry]\} \rightarrow r.$$

EXERCISES

1. Let Px: x is an even integer; where x is one of the integers 1, 2, 3, 4, 5, 6, or 7.

(a) For which of the numbers is Px true?

(b) For which of the numbers is Px false?

(c) What is the truth-value of each of the following?

$$(P6 \vee P7) \wedge P3; \quad P3 \rightarrow P7; \quad P1 \rightarrow (P2 \vee P5).$$

2. Let the universe consist of all integers, and let
Px: x is a prime, $\qquad Rx$: x is divisible by 7,
Qx: x is positive, $\qquad Sx$: x is a perfect square,
Ex: x is even, $\qquad Tx$: x is greater than 2,
and $\quad h$: 12 is less than 5.

Express each of the following statements in symbolic form:

(a) x is even or x is a perfect square.

(b) x is a prime and x is greater than 2.

(c) If x is a perfect square then x is even and x is greater than 2.

(d) x is a prime if and only if it is not a perfect square.

(e) If x is not positive, then x is not a perfect square.

(f) If x is even and x is divisible by 7, then x is not a prime.

(g) x is a prime only if x is positive.

Express the following as sentences.

(h) $(Px \wedge Tx) \rightarrow \sim Ex$ $\qquad$ (i) $(Qx \rightarrow Sx) \rightarrow \sim Tx$

(j) $\sim Px \wedge \sim Tx \wedge \sim Sx$ $\qquad$ (k) $(\sim Sx \vee \sim Qx) \wedge h$

3. Write each of the following in symbolic form. Assume that the universe consists of literally everything.

(a) All cats have tails. $\qquad$ (b) Not everything is mine.

(c) Someone is teasing. $\qquad$ (d) In the stone age of science

(e) It is not true that all roads $\qquad$ fiction, back in the twen-
lead to Rome. $\qquad$ ties, nobody thought much
about cooking in space.

4. Let the universe consist of cities in Scotland, and let Px: x is a good starting point for a journey through Scotland's past.

(a) Translate $\exists x\,[Px]$ into a sentence which does not involve x.

(b) Give a second sentence which is equivalent to the answer for part (a).

5. For each of the given universes, write symbolic statements which represent the sentences:

Each male Indian wears a headdress.

There is a male Indian who wears a headdress.

No male Indian wears a headdress.

There is a male Indian who does not wear a headdress.

Universes:

(a) All male Indians; $\qquad$ (c) All men;

(b) All Indians; $\qquad$ (d) Everything.

6.   (i)   Write each of the following statements in symbolic form.
     (ii)   Write its negation in symbolic form.
    (iii)   Write its negation as a sentence containing no symbols.
          (*a*) Nothing is correct.
          (*b*) Everything is bright.
          (*c*) Something is missing.
          (*d*) Something is not white.

7. For the following sentences, use a universe consisting of everything, and follow the instructions in the preceding exercise.
          (*a*) Some men are misers.
          (*b*) No dogs are intelligent.
          (*c*) Some birds cannot fly.
          (*d*) All babies are illogical.
          (*e*) All of the guests have arrived.

8. For each open statement and its associated universe give four true symbolic statements involving quantifiers.

Statement	Universe
(*a*) Ax: x is even.	$\{-1, 0, 1, 2\}$.
(*b*) Bx: $x + 5 = 7$.	$\{5, 6, 7, 8, 9\}$.
(*c*) Cx: x is a prime integer.	$\{5, 7\}$.
(*d*) Dx: $x^2 - 5x + 6 = 0$	$\{-3, 3, 2\}$.

9. For the statement, Px: x is a state belonging to the United States; give four true quantified statements associated with each of the following universes.
          (*a*) {New Mexico, Alaska, Chicago, California}
          (*b*) {Kentucky, Oklahoma}
          (*c*) {Mexico, New York City}

10. Classify each of these statements as open or closed and write each in symbolic form. If a restricted universe is used indicate this universe.
  (*a*) Some snakes are poisonous, and all snakes are ugly.
  (*b*) If all that glitters is gold, then the sun is gold.
  (*c*) x is bright or John is wrong.
  (*d*) All people grow old too soon and become smart too late.
  (*e*) Tom gave something to Mary and Mary gave it to Victor.
  (*f*) Whether it rains or the sun shines, someone is not satisfied.

(g)   If he is president, then someone will be president.

(h) x is an odd number and x is a prime.

(i)   There exists an x such that x is odd and x is a prime.

(j)   For all x, x is odd or x is a prime.

(k)   Nothing is both right and wrong.

(l)   If Franklin does learn something he will not remember it.

(m) If all seniors take sophomores to the prom then all juniors will object.

(n)   There is a student who likes mathematics but not history.

(o)   If someone will go, but not all will go, then enough people will be left to do everything.

(p)   He must be true to himself.

(q)   Each person must be true to himself.

(r)   The investigator has the facts or someone is hiding information.

15. LOGICALLY VALID STATEMENT PATTERNS

In the statement calculus we discussed some composite tf-statement patterns that are always true even though the elementary components are replaced by other tf-statements. These statement patterns were called tautologies or logically valid sentential statement patterns in order to emphasize the fact that the form of each composite statement is of prime importance.

The restricted predicate calculus, which we are now studying, is that part of logic which emphasizes the content of the statements. Are there, in the restricted predicate calculus, statements involving open statements or quantifiers which play a role similar to the logically valid sentential statement patterns? Before answering this question we observe that either an open statement or a statement closed by quantifiers has more than elementary components. It has also an associated universe. Therefore, changes in elementary components can involve changes in the associated universes.

The Law of the Excluded Middle, denoted by T1, is $p \lor \sim p$. Let us consider some statements which have the same form. First, can we draw any conclusions about $Gx \lor \sim Gx$, where Gx represents an open statement containing only one symbol x, and no restrictions are placed on the associated universe, except that it be nonempty? We can understand more fully the meaning of $Gx \lor \sim Gx$ by taking a specific example and then later considering what happens when the statement and the associated universe are changed.

Let Gx: x is an integer, with the associated universe of all rational numbers. Then $Gx \lor \sim Gx$ means x is an integer, or x is not an integer, and specific replacements for x produce

> 5/7 is an integer, or 5/7 is not an integer,
>
> -3 is an integer, or -3 is not an integer,
>
> 5.26 is an integer, or 5.26 is not an integer.

Since each replacement is of the form $p \lor \sim p$, which is a logically valid statement pattern we conclude that only true statements can be obtained from $Gx \lor \sim Gx$ for this specific Gx and its associated universe. What of other open statements and their universes?

We can discuss the problem in general by considering a general open statement Px and its associated universe. If b is an object in the universe then when b replaces x in the statement $Px \lor \sim Px$ the statement $Pb \lor \sim Pb$ is obtained. Since Pb is a tf-statement, this is a statement of the form $q \lor \sim q$ and is therefore true. This general argument shows that $Px \lor \sim Px$ is always a true statement regardless of what open statement Px represents and regardless of what universe is involved. To emphasize this fact we can say that there is no open statement Px, regardless of its associated universe, such that replacements from the universe will produce a false instance of the statement $Px \lor \sim Px$. We therefore conclude that $Px \lor \sim Px$ is a logically valid statement.

The statements $\forall x \, [Px] \lor \sim \forall x \, [Px]$ and $\exists x \, [Px] \lor \sim \exists x \, [Px]$ also have the form of $p \lor \sim p$, the Law of the Excluded Middle. The statement $\forall x \, [Px]$ is true if every replacement instance obtained by replacing x by an object of the universe is true. Otherwise it is false, and $\forall x \, [Px]$ and $\sim \forall x \, [Px]$ always have opposite truth-values. Therefore $\forall x \, [Px] \lor \sim \forall x \, [Px]$ is always true regardless of what statement $\forall x \, [Px]$ represents and regardless of its associated universe. A similar conclusion follows for $\exists x \, [Px] \lor \sim \exists x \, [Px]$.

What can be said of the statement $(Qx \to Rx) \lor \sim (Qx \to Rx)$? The conditional $Qx \to Rx$ is an open statement which can be represented by Px. This statement is therefore of the form $Px \lor \sim Px$ and is therefore always true. Similarly $(\forall x [Qx \rightarrow Rx] \rightarrow w) \lor$ $\sim(\forall x [Qx \rightarrow Rx] \rightarrow w)$ is always true. In fact, it soon becomes apparent that every statement having the form $p \lor \sim p$ is always true.

This immediately raises the question as to whether every statement having the form of a logically valid statement pattern is always true. In order to investigate this question let us consider what happens when the elementary statements p and q of a logically valid statement, such as $[(p \rightarrow q) \land \sim q] \rightarrow \sim p$, are replaced by open statements. Regardless of whether we substitute Px, $Px \rightarrow Rx$, or even a more complicated statement for p, when an object c in the universe of the statement replaces x, the resulting statements, such as Pc and $Pc \rightarrow Rc$, have truth-values; and each of the statements $\sim Pc$ and $\sim(Pc \rightarrow Rc)$, has a truth-value opposite to the statement it negates. Similarly, if Qx, or $Qx \lor Tx$, or a more complicated open statement is substituted for q, then its negation must replace $\sim q$. For a specific c of the universe, Qc, or $Qc \lor Tc$, has a truth-value and its negation has the opposite truth-value. Thus, replacing p and q by open statements merely changes the *method* of producing the combinations of truth-values which result from the tf-statements. Instead of having a tf-statement such as p in the given statement we have an open statement Px which is not a tf-statement, but produces tf-statements such as Pa, Pb, Pc, and Pd, when x is replaced by the objects a, b, c, and d of the universe. But the statement $[(p \rightarrow q) \land \sim q] \rightarrow \sim p$ is true regardless of what tf-statement replaces p or q, and is therefore true regardless of the resulting combination of truth-values. It is true for *all* possible combinations. Since Px, if it replaces p, can only produce a set of tf-statements which one by one replace p, then replacing p by Px must produce a new statement which is also always true. Similarly replacing q by Qx produces a new statement which is always true. We conclude that this logically valid statement pattern will produce a statement which is always true when p and q are replaced by open statements. Actually our argument was general enough for us to conclude that if elementary statements such as p, q, and r of a tautology are replaced by open statements then the resulting statement will always be true.

Is the result essentially different when p and q are replaced by closed statements or by a mixture of open and closed statements?

Let us consider $[(Px \rightarrow \forall x [Qx]) \wedge \sim\forall x [Qx]] \rightarrow \sim Px$, which we obtain from $[(p \rightarrow q) \wedge \sim q] \rightarrow \sim p$ by replacing p by Px and q by $\forall x [Qx]$. This statement has a universe of discourse. With respect to this universe $\forall x [Qx]$ has a fixed truth-value and $\sim\forall x [Qx]$ has the opposite truth-value. For each c of the universe Px and $\sim Px$ have opposite truth-values; therefore for this specific universe and a specified c of the universe Px and $\forall x [Qx]$ produce a combination of truth-values. The result produced in the given statement by this combination of truth-values is exactly the same as the result produced in the logically valid statement pattern $[(p \rightarrow q) \wedge \sim q] \rightarrow \sim p$ by the truth-value combination, where p has the same truth-value as Pc, and q has the same truth-value as $\forall x [Qx]$. However, this logically valid statement pattern is true for *all* combinations of truth-values of the component parts. Therefore it is true for this particular combination. A different choice for c may produce a different truth-value for Pc, but the truth-value of $\forall x [Qx]$ remains the same for this specific universe. Thus a change in the truth-value of Pc merely causes Pc and $\forall x [Qx]$ to produce a different combination of truth-values. Furthermore, changing the universe of the statements substituted for p and q, or making different replacements for p and q merely produces a different combination of truth-values.

By this same type of analysis we can see that any statement involving open or closed statements is always true if it has the form of a logically valid sentential statement pattern. Thus each of the tautologies gives rise to many logically valid statement patterns. Our definition of a logically valid statement pattern can now be modified to include a larger set of elementary statements.

Definition. *A statement pattern involving some combination of tf-statements, open statements, and closed statements is a logically valid statement pattern if leaving the sentential connectives and quantifiers unchanged in its symbolic form but replacing its elementary tf-statements by other tf-statements and replacing its statements involving symbols by other statements involving the same number of symbols, produces a true statement for each replacement instance.*

This definition states in a positive way that there are no false examples of the statement pattern.

Our previous discussion supports the following conclusion.

A statement pattern having the form of a logically valid statement pattern is also a logically valid statement pattern.

Remark. In what follows we shall often shorten "statement pattern" to "statement" or "pattern" when the meaning is clear.

There are logically valid statement patterns other than those obtained from tautologies. For example, the equivalences listed on page 296, such as,

$$\forall x \, [Px] \leftrightarrow \sim\exists x \, [\sim Px]$$

are true because of the meaning of the quantifiers. We shall now introduce some other biconditionals and also some conditionals. The reader should thoroughly understand the section on implication and equivalence. In particular, he must understand the short cuts explained there for showing that a conditional or a biconditional is *always* true.

Even though we are able to show that sentential statements are tautologies by means of proof tables there is no *simple* mechanical device which will establish the validity of statements involving quantifiers. There is a complicated systematic process for statements whose elementary parts contain at most one symbol, but no such process exists for statements whose elementary parts contain two or more symbols.* We shall now establish some statements by considering the meaning of the quantifiers and the sentential connectives.

Let us consider the statement

If everything is green, then something is green.

This statement is of the form $\forall x \, [Gx] \rightarrow \exists x \, [Gx]$, where $Gx: x$ is green. If everything is green in some particular universe, and every universe must be nonempty, then there is a c such that c is green. Therefore, this conditional is always true in this particular universe and is an implication in this universe. The general case corresponding to this statement is $\forall x \, [Px] \rightarrow \exists x \, [Px]$. If $\forall x \, [Px]$ is true, then Pb is a true statement for every b in the universe. Since the universe has at least one object c in it, and for all objects in the universe the statement is true, then Pc must be true. Thus, $\exists x \, [Px]$ is true. This shows that

---

* In 1936, Alonzo Church proved that no decision procedure exists for statements involving two or more symbols.

whenever the antecedent is true then the consequent is true, and
therefore

$$\forall\, x\, [Px] \rightarrow \exists\, x\, [Px]$$

is a logically valid statement.

Is the statement

If all men are giants, then some men are giants,

of the form $\forall\, x\, [Px] \rightarrow \exists\, x\, [Px]$? If the universe is restricted to men and
$Px\!:\! x$ is a giant, then this statement is of the required form. Observe,
however, that in a universe containing some objects other than men,
we have

(all men are giants) $\rightarrow$ (some men are giants)

$$\forall\, x\, [Mx \rightarrow Gx] \rightarrow \exists\, x\, [Mx \wedge Gx],$$

which is not of this form. In a universe which contains no men, the
antecedent could be true when the consequent is false. This, of course,
has nothing to do with the validity of $\forall\, x\, [Px] \rightarrow \exists\, x\, [Px]$.

Let us consider the statements:

If all types of fish eat worms, then the catfish eats worms.
If all kinds of dogs bark, then the collie barks.
If all square integers are nonnegative, then 4 is nonnegative.

In the universe of types of fish, let $Ex\!:\! x$ eats worms. Then the first
statement is of the form $\forall\, x\, [Ex] \rightarrow E$ catfish.

In the universe of kinds of dogs, let $Bx\!:\! x$ barks. Then the second
statement has the form $\forall\, x\, [Bx] \rightarrow B$ collie.

In the universe of square integers, let $Nx\!:\! x$ is nonnegative. Then
the third statement is of the form $\forall\, x\, [Nx] \rightarrow N4$.

Statements of this type have the general form

$$\forall\, x\, [Px] \rightarrow Py,$$

where y represents any one of the objects in the universe. The logical
validity of this statement follows immediately from the fact that if Pc
is true for all elements c of a universe then it is true for a specific
object in the universe. Therefore, whenever $\forall\, x\, [Px]$ is true, then Py is
true and this is a logically valid statement.

The next statement that we shall consider is

$$Py \rightarrow \exists\, x\, [Px],$$

which says that if a statement is true of y then there is something for which the statement is true. The truth of this statement is a consequence of the meaning of the existential quantifier. The statement ∃ x [Px] is true if and only if there exists at least one object in the universe for which Px is true. Therefore, if Py is true then ∃ x [Px] is true and the statement is logically valid.

Consider the statement

Everything is large and green.

Does this statement mean the same as

Everything is large and everything is green?

Let Lx: x is large,   and Gx: x is green.

The first statement is of the form ∀ x [Lx ∧ Gx] and the second one is of the form ∀ x [Lx] ∧ ∀ x [Gx]. If these two statements are equivalent then we should be able to show that a statement of the form

$$∀ x [Lx ∧ Gx] ↔ (∀ x [Lx] ∧ ∀ x [Gx])$$

is a logically valid statement. For this specific example this equivalence represents the statement "Everything is large and green if and only if everything is large and everything is green."

In order to present a general argument we ask whether the statement

$$∀ x [Px ∧ Qx] ↔ (∀ x [Px] ∧ ∀ x [Qx])$$

is a logically valid statement pattern. If ∀ x [Px ∧ Qx] is true, then for each c in the universe Pc ∧ Qc is true. Therefore, for each c, Pc is true; and for each c, Qc is true. Thus ∀ x [Px] ∧ ∀ x [Qx] is true. This shows that

$$∀ x [Px ∧ Qx] → (∀ x [Px] ∧ ∀ x [Qx]).$$

If ∀ x [Px] ∧ ∀ x [Qx] is true, then for each c in the universe Pc is true; and for each c, Qc is true. Therefore Pc ∧ Qc is true for each c, and ∀ x [Px ∧ Qx] is true. This shows that

$$(∀ x [Px] ∧ ∀ x [Qx]) → ∀ x [Px ∧ Qx],$$

and

$$∀ x [Px ∧ Qx] ↔ (∀ x [Px] ∧ ∀ x [Qx])$$

is a logically valid statement.

This statement is a type of distributive law. It shows that the universal quantifier "distributes through a conjunction" and also that the universal quantifier can be "factored out of a conjunction". Are there other distributive laws? There should be at least one more, for if two statements always have the same truth-value then their negations always have the same truth-value.

Let us consider the negations of the two statements involved in the equivalence which we have just established.

$$\sim\!\forall\, x\, [Px \land Qx] \leftrightarrow \sim\!(\forall\, x\, [Px] \land \forall\, x\, [Qx]),$$
$$\exists\, x\, [\sim\!(Px \land Qx)] \leftrightarrow \sim\!\forall\, x\, [Px] \lor \sim\!\forall\, x\, [Qx],$$
$$\exists\, x\, [\sim\!Px \lor \sim\!Qx] \leftrightarrow \exists\, x\, [\sim\!Px] \lor \exists\, x\, [\sim\!Qx].$$

In order to obtain symbols with no negation signs attached, let us replace $\sim\!Px$ by Rx and $\sim\!Qx$ by Sx in the last equivalence. We then have

$$\exists\, x\, [Rx \lor Sx] \leftrightarrow \exists\, x\, [Rx] \lor \exists\, x\, [Sx].$$

This is a logically valid statement.

The reader might observe that the statement

(1) $\forall\, x\, [Px \land Qx] \leftrightarrow (\forall\, x\, [Px] \land \forall\, x\, [Qx])$

is not essentially different from

(2) $\forall\, x\, [\sim\!Px \land \sim\!Qx] \leftrightarrow (\forall\, x\, [\sim\!Px] \land \forall\, x\, [\sim\!Qx])$

or from

(3) $\forall\, x\, [Rx \land Sx] \leftrightarrow (\forall\, x\, [Rx] \land \forall\, x\, [Sx]).$

In (1), the basic statements involved are represented by Px and Qx, but the statement remains true regardless of what open statements replace Px and Qx. Statement (2) can be obtained from statement (1) by replacing Px and Qx by $\sim\!Px$ and $\sim\!Qx$, respectively; and (3) can be obtained from (1) by replacing Px and Qx by Rx and Sx, respectively. Each of these represents the same logically valid statement pattern.

The statement just obtained by negating each part of the equivalence

$$\forall\, x\, [Px \land Qx] \leftrightarrow (\forall\, x\, [Px] \land \forall\, x\, [Qx])$$

was

(4) $\exists\, x\, [\sim\!Px \lor \sim\!Qx] \leftrightarrow \exists\, x\, [\sim\!Px] \lor \exists\, x\, [\sim\!Qx].$

This represents the same statement pattern as

(5) $\exists x \, [Px \lor Qx] \leftrightarrow \exists x \, [Px] \lor \exists x \, [Qx].$

If we had started with (2), which is another form of (1), the result of carrying through the steps of the negations would have been (5). A specific example of this logically valid pattern is the statement

Something is large or green if and only if something is large or something is green.

This statement pattern is also a distributive pattern. It shows that the existential quantifier "distributes through disjunction" and can be "factored out of disjunction".

It is only natural to ask if there are other distributive laws. Does the universal quantifier distribute through disjunction? Does the existential quantifier distribute through conjunction?

Let us consider the statement forms $\forall x \, [Px \lor Qx]$ and $\forall x \, [Px] \lor \forall x \, [Qx]$. A specific example of the first is

For all x, x is large or x is green.

This can be rephrased as

Everything is large or green.

An example of the second statement form is

For all x, x is large; or for all x, x is green,

and this can be rephrased as,

Everything is large, or everything is green.

We can readily see that the first of these statements can be true without the second one being true. For example, for a universe consisting of three large marbles and two green marbles the statement "Everything is large or green," is true. However, the statement "Everything is large, or everything is green," is false. Therefore, the first statement does not imply the second statement. Does the second imply the first? According to our specific example it seems to, for if all of the marbles are large, or if all of them are green then each of the marbles would certainly possess one of the two properties of being large or being green. Let us return to the general statement forms and

consider the case where ∀ x [Px] ∨ ∀ x [Qx] is true. Since this is a
disjunction, one of the statements ∀ x [Px] and ∀ x [Qx] must be true.
When Pb is true for all b, then Pb ∨ Qb is true for all b. Similarly when
Qb is true for all b, then Pb ∨ Qb is true for all b. In both cases
∀ x [Px ∨ Qx] is true. Therefore,

$$(∀ \; x \; [Px] ∨ ∀ \; x \; [Qx]) → ∀ \; x \; [Px ∨ Qx]$$

is a logically valid statement.

We now present a *second method* for verifying the preceding statement. We shall verify it by showing that if the consequent is false
then the antecedent is false. If ∀ x [Px ∨ Qx] is false there must be
some c in the universe for which Pc ∨ Qc is false. But this disjunction
is false only when both Pc and Qc are false. Therefore there is an
object c in the universe for which neither Pc nor Qc is true. Therefore,
Px and Qx have false instances and the statement ∀ x [Px] ∨ ∀ x [Qx]
is false. Since a false consequent forces a false antecedent, the statement is always true and is therefore logically valid. This method frequently provides a short proof.

The statement ∃ x [Px ∧ Qx] → (∃ x [Px] ∧ ∃ x [Qx]) is also a
logically valid statement pattern. We shall leave its verification as
an exercise.

As our final investigation let us consider the statement

> *If all men are giants then everything is a man only if
> everything is a giant.*

This statement pattern is ∀ x [Mx → Gx] → (∀ x [Mx] → ∀ x [Gx]).
Let us show that a false consequent insures a false antecedent. If
∀ x [Mx] → ∀ x [Gx] is false then ∀ x [Mx] is true and ∀ x [Gx] is
false. Therefore, there is an object c in the universe for which Gc is
false. Since ∀ x [Mx] is true, then for all x, Mx is true. In particular,
Mc is true. Therefore, c is an object in the universe for which Mc is
true and Gc is false. Therefore, Mc → Gc is false. Therefore,
∀ x [Mx → Gx] is false. Since a false consequent forces a false antecedent the statement can never be false. It is therefore logically valid.

We shall leave the verification of ∀ x [Px → p] → (∃ x [Px] → p)
as an exercise.

Each of the logically valid statements just verified gives rise to
many other logically valid statements, since every statement having

the form of a logically valid statement pattern is a logically valid statement. If we were asked to show that the following statement is logically valid we should try to show that it has the form of a logically valid statement pattern:

$$\forall \, x \, [(Mx \rightarrow Gx) \wedge \sim(Rx \vee Sx)] \leftrightarrow$$
$$(\forall \, x \, [\sim Mx \vee Gx] \wedge \forall \, x \, [\sim Rx \wedge \sim Sx])$$

If we replace $Mx \rightarrow Gx$ by Px we can also replace $\sim Mx \vee Gx$ by Px, for $Mc \rightarrow Gc \leftrightarrow \sim Mc \vee Gc$, for each c of the universe. Similarly, if we replace $\sim(Rx \vee Sx)$ by Qx, we can also replace $\sim Rx \wedge \sim Sx$ by Qx. Then the statement becomes

$$\forall \, x \, [Px \wedge Qx] \leftrightarrow (\forall \, x \, [Px] \wedge \forall \, x \, [Qx])$$

a logically valid statement pattern. Therefore, the given statement is logically valid.

For convenient reference we list here some logically valid statements which do not have the form of previously listed tautologies. We have established the validity of most of these by arguments which depend upon the meaning of the quantifiers and the sentential connectives.

Logically Valid Statements

LV1. $\forall \, x \, [Px] \leftrightarrow \sim \exists \, x \, [\sim Px]$.
LV2. $\forall \, x \, [\sim Px] \leftrightarrow \sim \exists \, x \, [Px]$.
LV3. $\forall \, x \, [Px] \rightarrow \exists \, x \, [Px]$.
LV4. $\forall \, x \, [Px] \rightarrow Py$.
LV5. $Py \rightarrow \exists \, x \, [Px]$.
LV6. $\forall \, x \, [Px \wedge Qx] \leftrightarrow (\forall \, x \, [Px] \wedge \forall \, x \, [Qx])$.
LV7. $\exists \, x \, [Px \vee Qx] \leftrightarrow (\exists \, x \, [Px] \vee \exists \, x \, [Qx])$.
LV8. $(\forall \, x \, [Px] \vee \forall \, x \, [Qx]) \rightarrow \forall \, x \, [Px \vee Qx]$.
LV9. $\exists \, x \, [Px \wedge Qx] \rightarrow (\exists \, x \, [Px] \wedge \exists \, x \, [Qx])$.
LV10. $\forall \, x \, [Px \rightarrow Qx] \rightarrow (\forall \, x \, [Px] \rightarrow \forall \, x \, [Qx])$.
LV11. $\forall \, x \, [Px \rightarrow p] \rightarrow (\exists \, x \, [Px] \rightarrow p)$.

EXERCISES

1. Show that each of the following is a logically valid statement.
(a) $\sim(Px \vee Qx) \leftrightarrow (\sim Px \wedge \sim Qx)$.

(b) $(\sim Px \vee \sim Qx) \leftrightarrow \sim(Px \wedge Qx)$.

(c) $(Px \rightarrow Qx) \leftrightarrow (\sim Px \vee Qx)$.

(d) $(Px \rightarrow Qy) \leftrightarrow (\sim Px \vee Qy)$.

(e) $[(Px \rightarrow Qx) \wedge (Qx \rightarrow Rx)] \rightarrow (Px \rightarrow Rx)$.

(f) $(Px \wedge Qy) \rightarrow (Px \rightarrow Qy)$.

(g) $(Pa \wedge Qy) \rightarrow Pa$.

(h) $\exists x [Px \wedge Qx] \rightarrow (\exists x [Px] \wedge \exists x [Qx])$.

(i) $\forall x [Px \rightarrow p] \rightarrow (\exists x [Px] \rightarrow p)$.

2. Using Px: x is a car, $\quad$ p: Tom is happy,

$\qquad$ Qx: x is small, $\quad$ Rx: John does not like x,

$\qquad$ Sx: x is good,

express each of the following statements in symbolic form.

(a) If b is a car and y is small, then b is a car.

(b) It is not true that x is small or x is a car if and only if x is not small and x is not a car.

(c) If whenever x is a car, then x is small; and whenever x is small John does not like x, then whenever x is a car John does not like x.

(d) If Tom is happy when each person is good, then Tom is happy if someone is good.

(e) If there is a small car, then something is small and something is a car.

(f) x is good whenever x is small if and only if x is not small or x is good.

(g) Everyone is small and everyone is good if and only if everyone is small and good.

(h) Everything is small if and only if there isn't anything which isn't small.

3. Using Px: x is bad, $\quad$ Rx: x is cheap,

$\qquad$ Qx: x is green, $\quad$ p: Tom is sad,

write a sentence which corresponds to each part of Exercise 1.

4. Show that each of the following statements is logically valid.

(a) $(Rx \wedge Sx) \rightarrow Rx$.

(b) $Sx \wedge (Qx \vee Hx) \leftrightarrow (Sx \wedge Qx) \vee (Sx \wedge Hx)$.

(c) $\forall x [(Px \rightarrow Qx) \leftrightarrow (\sim Px \vee Qx)]$.

(d) $[(Wx \rightarrow Hx) \wedge (Rx \rightarrow Qx) \wedge (Wx \vee Rx)] \rightarrow (Hx \vee Qx)$.

(e) $\exists x [\sim Px \vee \sim Qx] \leftrightarrow \exists x [\sim(Px \wedge Wx)]$.

(f) $(\forall x [Rx] \rightarrow \exists x [Qx]) \land (\exists x [Qx] \rightarrow Px) \rightarrow (\forall x [Rx] \rightarrow Px)$.
(g) $[\{(Rx \rightarrow \forall x [Qx]) \rightarrow \exists x [Hx]\} \land \forall x [\sim Hx]] \rightarrow$
     $\{Rx \land \exists x [\sim Qx]\}$.
(h) $\{(Rx \land \exists x [Px]) \rightarrow \forall x [Qx]\} \leftrightarrow$
     $\{Rx \rightarrow (\exists x [Px] \rightarrow \forall x [Qx])\}$.

16. STATEMENTS INVOLVING TWO QUANTIFIERS

If an open statement involves two different symbols such as x and y, more than one quantifier is needed to produce a closed sentence. For example, the open statement

$$Pxy: x \text{ influences } y$$

is not closed if it is preceded by $\exists x$ or $\forall x$; for $\exists x [Pxy]$ represents the statement

There is an x, such that x influences y.

This can be rephrased as

There is someone who influences y,

or merely

Someone influences y.

Also $\forall x [Pxy]$ represents the statement

For each x, x influences y.

This can be rephrased as

Everyone influences y.

The two resulting statements "Someone influences y" and "Everyone influences y" are open statements. They will produce tf-statements if y is replaced by the name of a specific person, such as, John Smith. They will also produce tf-statements if each statement is preceded by $\exists y$ or $\forall y$.

Thus,

$$\exists\, y \text{ [Someone influences } y],$$
$$\exists\, y \text{ [Everyone influences } y],$$
$$\forall\, y \text{ [Someone influences } y],$$
$$\forall\, y \text{ [Everyone influences } y],$$

are closed statements.

The *first* of these four statements can be stated as

There is a y, such that someone influences y,

or as

There is somebody whom someone influences.

Since Pxy: x influences y, and $\exists\, x\, [Pxy]$: Someone influences y, this statement which we have written as $\exists\, y$ [Someone influences y] can be written as $\exists\, y\, [\exists\, x\, [Pxy]]$, or more simply as $\exists\, y\, \exists\, x\, [Pxy]$.

The *second* statement can be stated as

There is a y such that everyone influences y,

or as

There is somebody whom everyone influences.

It can be written symbolically as $\exists\, y\, \forall\, x\, [Pxy]$.

The *third* statement can be stated as

For each y, someone influences y,

or as

Everybody is influenced by someone.

Its symbolic form is $\forall\, y\, \exists\, x\, [Pxy]$.

The *fourth* statement can be stated as

For each y, everyone influences y

or as

Everybody is influenced by everyone.

Its symbolic form is $\forall\, y\, \forall\, x\, [Pxy]$.

Let us return to Pxy: x influences y, and consider what happens when this statement is preceded by $\exists\, y$ or $\forall\, y$. We obtain $\exists\, y$ [x influences y] which means

There exists y, such that x influences y.

This can be rephrased as

> x influences somebody.

Similarly $\forall\, x\, [Pxy]$ means

> For each y, x influences y,

or

> x influences everybody.

If we precede these statements by $\exists\, x$ and $\forall\, x$ we obtain the statements

> $\exists\, x\, [x$ influences somebody$]$, or $\exists\, x\, \exists\, y\, [Pxy]$,
> $\forall\, x\, [x$ influences somebody$]$, or $\forall\, x\, \exists\, y\, [Pxy]$,
> $\exists\, x\, [x$ influences everybody$]$, or $\exists\, x\, \forall\, y\, [Pxy]$,
> $\forall\, x\, [x$ influences everybody$]$, or $\forall\, x\, \forall\, y\, [Pxy]$.

The *first* of these four statements means

> There is an x such that x influences somebody,

or

> Someone influences somebody.

The *second* statement means

> For every x, x influences somebody,

or

> Everyone influences somebody.

The *third* statement means

> There is an x, such that x influences everybody,

or

> Someone influences everybody.

The *fourth* statement means

> For every x, x influences everybody,

or

> Everyone influences everybody.

In summary, we have, for Pxy: x influences y,

∃ y ∃ x $[Pxy]$: There is somebody whom someone influences.
∃ y ∀ x $[Pxy]$: There is somebody whom everyone influences.
∀ y ∃ x $[Pxy]$: Everybody is influenced by someone.
∀ y ∀ x $[Pxy]$: Everybody is influenced by everyone.
∃ x ∃ y $[Pxy]$: Someone influences somebody.
∀ x ∃ y $[Pxy]$: Everyone influences somebody.
∃ x ∀ y $[Pxy]$: Someone influences everybody.
∀ x ∀ y $[Pxy]$: Everyone influences everybody.

Let us examine these statements. Which ones have the same meaning? Do ∃ y ∃ x $[Pxy]$ and ∃ x ∃ y $[Pxy]$ have the same meaning? Does the statement "There is somebody whom someone influences," mean the same as "Someone influences somebody?" Each of these symbolic statements means "There exists x, and there exists y such that x influences y." If Frank Crank influences Jim Slim then Frank Crank and Jim Slim are replacements for x and y, respectively, which makes each of the statements true. If there is no pair which makes the statements true, then each is false. We conclude that these statements are equivalent. Therefore,

$$∃ x ∃ y [Pxy] ↔ ∃ y ∃ x [Pxy].$$

Consider next ∀ y ∀ x $[Pxy]$ and ∀ x ∀ y $[Pxy]$. Since "Everybody is influenced by everyone," and "Everyone influences everybody," have the same meaning, we conclude that these statements are equivalent. Therefore,

$$∀ x ∀ y [Pxy] ↔ ∀ y ∀ x [Pxy].$$

Let us now consider ∃ y ∀ x $[Pxy]$ and ∀ x ∃ y $[Pxy]$. The first of these two statements means "There is someone whom everyone influences," and the second means "Everyone influences somebody." These two statements are not the same, for the first states that there is a y, which we shall call Daniel Small, such that everyone influences him. Thus,

Joe Doe influences Daniel Small.
Tim Kent influences Daniel Small.
Frank Crank influences Daniel Small.
Jim Slim influences Daniel Small.

The second states that for each x, such as Jane Trent, there is some-one whom x influences. Thus the second produces pairs such as

> Jane Trent influences Ken Wright.
> Frank Crank influences Daniel Small.
> Harold Smith influences Tom Olds.

It is evident that the first one pairs everyone with Daniel Small, so that it also produces pairs. The second one does not, however, pair everyone with a single individual; therefore, it can be true without making the first statement true. This shows that when the statement "There is someone whom everyone influences," is true then the state-ment "Everyone influences someone," is true. Therefore

$$\exists\, y\, \forall\, x\, [Pxy] \rightarrow \forall\, x\, \exists\, y\, [Pxy],$$

is a logically valid statement. The converse of this statement is not logically valid.

Finally, we consider

$$\forall\, y\, \exists\, x\, [Pxy] \qquad \text{and} \qquad \exists\, x\, \forall\, y\, [Pxy].$$

The first of these two statements is "Everybody is influenced by someone," and the second is "Someone influences everybody." The first says that for each y, there is an x such that x influences y. There-fore, given Ken Wright, there is someone: namely, Jane Trent who influences him. Thus again there are pairs.

> Jane Trent influences Ken Wright.
> Frank Crank influences Daniel Small.

The second states that there is someone, say Kenneth Strong, who influences everyone. Thus,

> Kenneth Strong influences Jane Trent.
> Kenneth Strong influences Daniel Small.
> Kenneth Strong influences Harold Smith.

It is evident from this discussion that

$$\exists\, x\, \forall\, y\, [Pxy] \rightarrow \forall\, y\, \exists\, x\, [Pxy]$$

is a logically valid statement, but the converse statement is not logically valid.

After these statements are established, it is easy to see that two chains of implications exist. For simplicity, the quantified statement is omitted.

$$\forall\, x\, \forall\, y \to \exists\, y\, \forall\, x \to \forall\, x\, \exists\, y \to \exists\, x\, \exists\, y$$
$$\forall\, y\, \forall\, x \to \exists\, x\, \forall\, y \to \forall\, y\, \exists\, x \to \exists\, y\, \exists\, x$$

Some additional examples will help clarify the concepts of double quantification.

Example 1. In the universe of all integers let Qxy: $x + 2y = 5$. Then $\exists\, x\, \exists\, y\, [Qxy]$ means that there is an integer x and there is an integer y such that $x + 2y = 5$. This statement is true when x is 7 and y is -1, since $7 + 2(-1) = 5$. Therefore it is always true for this particular universe. There are other choices of x and y for which this statement is true, but the symbolic statement merely says that there is at least one choice for x and at least one choice for y which will make the statement true.

Example 2. The symbolic form $\forall\, x\, \forall\, y\, [Qxy]$ means that for each x and each y, $x + 2y = 5$. This is obviously false, for if x is 12 and y is -2, $12 + 2(-2) \neq 5$.

Example 3. On the other hand, if

$$Rxy: (x + 2y)(x - y) = x^2 + xy - 2y^2$$

then $\forall\, x\, \forall\, y\, [Rxy]$ is true, for there are no choices for x and y which fail. Thus when x is 5 and y is 3,

$$[5 + 2(3)][5 - 3] = 5^2 + 5(3) - 2(3^2),$$
$$11 \cdot 2 = 25 + 15 - 18,$$
$$22 = 22;$$

and when x is 0 and y is 1,

$$(0 + 2 \cdot 1)(0 - 1) = 0^2 + 0 \cdot 1 - 2(1^2),$$
$$2(-1) = -2,$$
$$-2 = -2,$$

and so on.

Example 4. The form $\exists\, x\, \forall\, y\, [Qxy]$ means that there is an x, such that for all y, $x + 2y = 5$. This is false since no fixed value of x will make this true for all y.

Example 5.   The form $\forall\, y\, \exists\, x\, [Qxy]$ means that for each y, there is an x such that $x + 2y = 5$. Let y be a fixed integer b, then $x = 5 - 2b$, and for each specific value of b there is a value of x which is an integer and which will make the statement true. Therefore, this statement is true.

Examples 6-7.   What can be said about $\exists\, x\, \forall\, y\, [Rxy]$ and $\forall\, y\, \exists\, x\, [Rxy]$? The first says that there exists an x, such that for all y,

$$(x + 2y)(x - y) = x^2 + xy - 2y^2.$$

This means that there is a specific value for x, such as b, for which $(b + 2y)(b - y) = b^2 + by - 2y^2$ is true of all y. This is a true statement. In fact, every fixed value of x has this property. The second form says that for each y, there is an x such that

$$(x + 2y)(x - y) = x^2 + xy - 2y^2.$$

Assume that y is c. Then this says that there is an x for which $(x + 2c)(x - c) = x^2 + cx - 2c^2$. Every value of x satisfies this, therefore it is true.

We should observe here that when $\forall\, x\, \forall\, y\, [Rxy]$ is a true statement then for *all* pairs a and b the statement Rab is true; therefore, the specific pairs indicated by $\forall\, x\, \exists\, y\, [Rxy]$, $\exists\, y\, \forall\, x\, [Rxy]$, $\forall\, y\, \exists\, x\, [Rxy]$, $\exists\, x\, \forall\, y\, [Rxy]$, and $\exists\, x\, \exists\, y\, [Rxy]$ exist, and all of these statements are also true.

Example 8.   Let us consider the form $\forall\, x\, \exists\, y\, [Qxy]$. This means for each integer x, there is an integer y such that $x + 2\,y = 5$. Let x be 2, then if $x + 2y = 5$, y must be $3/2$, which is not an integer. Therefore this statement is false.

Example 9.   Is $\exists\, y\, \forall\, x\, [Qxy]$ true? This means that there is a fixed integer y, such that for all x, $x + 2y = 5$. This is false because the value of y changes when x changes. Thus when x is 1, y must be 2. When x is 3, y must be 1. When x is -3, y must be 4, and so on. When x is an even integer, no integral value of y exists.

Example 10.   It is interesting to negate the form $\exists\, y\, \forall\, x\, [Qxy]$. Its negation can be written $\sim\!\exists\, y\, [\forall\, x\, [Qxy]]$. We now change the outside quantifier and negate the statement inside the outer set of brackets to obtain

$$\forall\, y\, [\sim\!\forall\, x\, [Qxy]].$$

Applying the rule to the inside quantifier and the statement which it quantifies we obtain

$$\forall\, y\; \exists\, x\; [\sim\!Qxy].$$

The resulting statement means that for each y, there is an x such that $x + 2y \neq 5$. This, of course, is a true statement. For example, if y is 1, then every value of x except 3 will make the statement $x + 2y \neq 5$ true. Therefore, there are many values of x for which $x + 2y \neq 5$, if y is 1. Similarly, for every other specific value of y there are values of x that satisfy the inequality.

Example **11.** In order to write the symbolic form of "Everyone respects someone and everyone needs praise," let

$$Sxy: x \text{ respects } y, \qquad \text{and} \qquad Pz: z \text{ needs praise.}$$

Then the symbolic form is $\forall\, x\; \exists\, y\; [Sxy] \wedge \forall\, z\; [Pz]$.

We should observe here that $\forall\, z\; [Pz]$ and $\forall\, x\; [Px]$ are equivalent statements. The first means "For all z, z needs praise," and the second means "For all x, x needs praise." Therefore, the given statement can be represented by

$$\forall\, x\; \exists\, y\; [Sxy] \wedge \forall\, x\; [Px]$$

which can be written

$$\forall\, x\; [\exists\, y\; [Sxy] \wedge Px].$$

Example **12.** To symbolize, "Someone influences everyone, and someone is honest," let

$$Ixy: x \text{ influences } y, \qquad \text{and} \qquad Hz: z \text{ is honest.}$$

Then the symbolic form is $\exists\, x\; \forall\, y\; [Ixy] \wedge \exists\, z\; [Hz]$. Here we cannot assume that the person who influences everyone is the same as the person who is honest; therefore, no simplification is possible.

Example **13.** The statement, "Someone influences everyone and is honest" is similar in form to Example 12; however, it has a different meaning. This sentence states that there is an honest person who influences everyone. Its symbolic form is

$$\exists\, x\; [\forall\, y\; [Ixy] \wedge Hx].$$

Example **14.** In order to symbolize the statement, "Everyone who likes fun will enjoy each of these plays," we first rephrase the statement to obtain "For all x, if x likes fun, then for each y, if y is one of these plays then x will enjoy y." Let

Lx: x likes fun,
Py: y is one of these plays,

and Exy: x will enjoy y,

then the symbolic form is

$$\forall x \left[Lx \rightarrow \forall y \left[Py \rightarrow Exy \right] \right].$$

Observe that this statement could also be rephrased to obtain "For each x, if x likes fun, and for each y, if y is one of these plays, then x enjoys y," and then it could be symbolized as

$$\forall x \forall y \left[(Lx \wedge Py) \rightarrow Exy \right].$$

These two symbolic forms are equivalent because the first one can also be written as

$$\forall x \forall y \left[Lx \rightarrow (Py \rightarrow Exy) \right],$$

and the open statements

$$Lx \rightarrow (Py \rightarrow Exy) \qquad \text{and} \qquad (Lx \wedge Py) \rightarrow Exy$$

are equivalent statements.

***Examples* 15-18.**   Let us negate statements 11 through 14. The negation of "Everyone respects someone and everyone needs praise" is

$$\sim\forall x \left[\exists y \left[Sxy \right] \wedge Px \right],$$
$$\exists x \left[\sim(\exists y \left[Sxy \right] \wedge Px) \right],$$
$$\exists x \left[\sim\exists y \left[Sxy \right] \vee \sim Px \right],$$
$$\exists x \left[\forall y \left[\sim Sxy \right] \vee \sim Px \right].$$

Thus, the negation is "There is someone who respects no one or does not need praise."

The negation of "Someone influences everyone, and someone is honest," is

$$\sim\left[\exists x \forall y \left[Ixy \right] \wedge \exists z \left[Hz \right] \right],$$
$$\sim \exists x \forall y \left[Ixy \right] \vee \sim\exists z \left[Hz \right],$$
$$\forall x \left[\sim\forall y \left[Ixy \right] \right] \vee \forall z \left[\sim Hz \right],$$
$$\forall x \exists y \left[\sim Ixy \right] \vee \forall z \left[\sim Hz \right].$$

The resulting statement is "For each x there is some y such that x does not influence y or for all z, z is not honest."

This can be rephrased as "Everyone fails to influence someone, or everyone is dishonest." Another restatement would be "No one influences everyone, or everyone is dishonest."

The negation of "Someone influences everyone and is honest," is

$$\sim\exists\, x\, [\forall\, y\, [Ixy]\, \wedge\, Hx],$$
$$\forall\, x\, [\sim(\forall\, y\, [Ixy]\, \wedge\, Hx)],$$
$$\forall\, x\, [\sim\forall\, y\, [Ixy]\, \vee\, \sim Hx],$$
$$\forall\, x\, [\exists\, y\, [\sim Ixy]\, \vee\, \sim Hx].$$

The resulting statement is, "For each x, there is a y such that x does not influence y, or x is dishonest." This can be restated as "Each person is dishonest or there is someone that he does not influence."

The negation of "Everyone who likes fun will enjoy each of these plays," is

$$\sim\forall\, x\, [Lx \rightarrow \forall\, y\, [Py \rightarrow Exy]],$$
$$\exists\, x\, [\sim(Lx \rightarrow \forall y\, [Py \rightarrow Exy])],$$
$$\exists\, x\, [Lx\, \wedge\, \sim\forall\, y\, [Py \rightarrow Exy]],$$
$$\exists\, x\, [Lx\, \wedge\, \exists\, y\, [\sim(Py \rightarrow Exy)]],$$
$$\exists\, x\, [Lx\, \wedge\, \exists\, y\, [Py\, \wedge\, \sim Exy]].$$

The resulting statement can be stated in any one of the following three ways:

> There is someone who likes fun and there is one of these plays which he does not enjoy.
> There is one of these plays which someone who likes fun does not enjoy.
> There is one of these plays which is not enjoyed by someone who likes fun.

Example **19.**   There are many statements in mathematics of the following form.*

For each u, there is a w such that if Pwx, then Qux.

The symbolic form of this statement is

$$\forall\, u\, \exists\, w\, [Pwx \rightarrow Qux],$$

---

* Such statements are found in the theory of limits. A specific example is: For each positive number ϵ there is a number δ such that when $0 < |x - 3| < \delta$, then $|x^2 - 9| < \epsilon$.

and its negation, which is important in mathematics, is

$$\sim\forall u \; \exists w \; [Pwx \rightarrow Qux],$$
$$\exists u \; [\sim\exists w \; [Pwx \rightarrow Qux]],$$
$$\exists u \; \forall w \; [\sim(Pwx \rightarrow Qux)],$$
$$\exists u \; \forall w \; [Pwx \wedge \sim Qux].$$

There is a u, such that for every w, $Pwx \wedge \sim Qux$.

17. OTHER QUANTIFIED STATEMENTS

In addition to the quantified statements that have been discussed in detail, there are a few others that should be mentioned. The following examples are slightly different from those previously discussed.

1. There are two prime integers which are integral divisors of 30.
2. There are exactly three prime integers which are integral divisors of 30.
3. There is one and only one number x such that $x + 7 = 3x$.
4. For each integer x and each integer y there is an integer z such that $x - y + 3z = 5$.
5. For all rational numbers x, y, and z: $x + (y + z) = (x + y) + z$.
6. There is an x such that for all y and z: $x + y + z = y + z$.
7. $(xy)z = x(yz)$.
8. The corresponding parts of congruent triangles are equal.
9. For each pair of points x and y there is a point z such that z is between x and y.

The fact that a certain object x in the universe of discourse has a property Px not possessed by any other object of the universe is expressed by each of the following equivalent statements.

> There is one and only one x such that Px.
> There is a unique x such that Px.
> There is exactly one x such that Px.

The statement $\exists x \; [Px]$ does not express the idea of uniqueness that is needed here, for this symbolic form means "There is at least one x such that Px." This statement is true when there are five objects x having the property Px, or even one hundred objects having this property. It merely states that there is one object x having property

Px but is noncommittal as to how many more objects in the universe have this property.

Various symbols have been introduced in mathematical literature to express the idea of an exact number of objects which possess a certain given property. We now suggest the following notation.

Let $\exists_1' x\,[Px]$: There is exactly one x such that Px,

and for each positive integer n greater than one

let $\exists_n x\,[Px]$: There are at least n objects such that Px,

and $\exists_n' x\,[Px]$: There are exactly n objects such that Px.

Thus $\exists_2 x\,[Px]$ means there are at least two objects such that Px, and $\exists_3' x\,[Px]$ means there are exactly three objects such that Px. Using this notation the reader can express the first three statements at the beginning of this section in symbolic form.

Statements 4, 5, and 6 involve three quantifiers. The principles of the preceding sections can be extended to cover them. In many statements the quantifiers are understood. This is the case in Examples 7 and 8.

The last six sentences are symbolized as follows:

4. $\forall x\,\forall y\,\exists z\,[x - y + 3z = 5]$, or $\forall x\,\forall y\,\exists z\,[Pxyz]$.
5. $\forall x\,\forall y\,\forall z\,[x + (y + z) = (x + y) + z]$, or $\forall x\,\forall y\,\forall z\,[Qxyz]$.
6. $\exists x\,\forall y\,\forall z\,[x + y + z = y + z]$, or $\exists x\,\forall y\,\forall z\,[Rxyz]$.
7. $\forall x\,\forall y\,\forall z\,[(xy)z = x(yz)]$, or $\forall x\,\forall y\,\forall z\,[Sxyz]$.
8. In the universe of triangles let Cxy: x is congruent to y, and Pxy: The corresponding parts of x and y are equal, then the symbolic form of the statement is

$$\forall x\,\forall y\,[Cxy \rightarrow Pxy].$$

9. In the universe of points let $Bxzy$: z is between x and y, then we have

$$\forall x\,\forall y\,\exists z\,[Bxzy].$$

EXERCISES

1. Write eight doubly quantified statements by quantifying the open statement "x likes y". Express each quantified statement as a sentence free of symbols.

2. For the equation $3x - 2y = 7$ write each of the following statements symbolically. Decide whether each statement is true or false. Support your decision by an example or a discussion.

(a)   There are integers which satisfy this equation.

(b)   There is an integer x which, when combined with all integers y, will satisfy this equation.

(c)   There is an integer y which, when combined with all integers x, will satisfy this equation.

(d)   For all integers x and y the equation is satisfied.

(e)   For each integer x, there is an integer y such that x and y satisfy the equation.

(f)   For each integer y, there is an integer x such that x and y satisfy the equation.

3. Let Sxy represent $(2x - 3y)^2 = 4x^2 - 12xy + 9y^2$. Determine whether each of the doubly quantified statements that can be obtained from Sxy is true or false.

4. Express each of the following quantified statements symbolically.

(a)   Everyone is indebted to someone.

(b)   Everyone knows someone whom he enjoys being with; and everyone has a type of work that he can do best.

(c)   Everyone who is healthy can do all kinds of work.

(d)   There is someone who dislikes no one.

(e)   None of Jackson's followers likes any of the independents.

(f)   If everyone teaches everyone else then everyone learns faster.

(g)   Some people are not admired by everyone.

(h)   Each of Johnson's supporters likes at least one of Harvey's supporters.

(i)   Everyone should help his neighbors, or his neighbors will not help him.

(j)   Given an integer there is always an integer larger than the given integer.

(k)   There is someone who protects every person in this organization.

(l)   Parents love their children.

(m)   There are triangles which are not similar.

5. Negate the symbolic form of each of the statements in Exercise 4 and then express the negation in everyday English free of symbols.

6. Translate each of the following quantified statements into a sentence free of symbols.

In the universe of all people,

let　　　　　　Ixy: x invites y,
　　　　　　　　Fxy: x and y are friends,
　　　　　　　　Lxy: x has y with whom he shares his leisure hours,
　　　　　　　　Axy: x agrees with y,
and　　　　　　Bxy: x and y may become friends.

(a) $\exists\, y\, \forall\, x\, [Ixy]$. 　　　　　　　(b) $\forall\, x\, [\exists\, y\, [Fxy \rightarrow Lxy]]$.
(c) $\forall\, y\, \exists\, x\, [Axy] \land \exists\, x\, \forall\, y\, [Axy]$. 　(d) $\exists\, x\, \exists\, y\, [Axy \land {\sim}Fxy]$.
(e) $\forall\, x\, \forall\, y\, [(Lxy \land Axy) \rightarrow Bxy]$.

In the universe of all points, lines, and circles,

let　Axy: x and y are distinct points,
　　$Bxyz$: y is a point between the points x and z,
　　$Mxyz$: y is the midpoint of the line segment joining x and y,
　　Cxw: x is a point on the circle w,
　　$Dxzy$: the distance between the points x and z equals the distance between the points y and z,
　　Pyz: z is a line parallel to the line y,
and　Sxy: y is a line through the point x.

(f) $\forall\, x\, \forall\, y\, [Axy \rightarrow (\exists\, z\, [Bxyz] \land \exists\, w\, [Bwxy])]$.
(g) $\forall\, x\, \forall\, y\, \exists\, z\, [Axy \rightarrow Mxzy]$.
(h) $\forall\, w\, \exists\, z\, \forall\, x\, \forall\, y\, [(Cxw \land Cyw) \rightarrow Dxzy]$.
(i) $\forall\, x\, \forall\, y\, [{\sim}Sxy \rightarrow \exists_1' z\, [Sxz \land Pyz]]$.

In the universe of integers,

let　　　　　　$Dxyz$: z is the greatest common divisor of x and y,
　　　　　　　　Uxy: $y = x + 3$,
　　　　　　　　Lxy: x is less than y,
　　　　　　　　Exy: x equals y,
　　　　　　　　Gxy: x is greater than y,
and　　　　　　$Mxyz$: z is the least common multiple of x and y.

(j) $\forall\, x\, \exists\, y\, [Uxy]$.
(k) $\forall\, x\, \forall\, y\, [{\sim}Gxy \rightarrow (Lxy \lor Exy)]$.
(l) $\exists_1'\, x\, \forall\, y\, [y + x = y] \land \exists_1'\, z\, \forall\, y\, [yz = y]$.
(m) $\forall\, x\, \forall\, y\, [\exists\, z\, [Dxyz] \land \exists\, w\, [Mxyz]]$.

18. INFERENCE AND ARGUMENT

In working with statements involving quantifiers the basic definitions of the existential and universal quantifiers should always be kept in mind.

With respect to a given discussion the objects of a given universe will be described as arbitrary, specified, or existential, according to the following definitions:

Definition. *An object is used as an **arbitrary object** in a given discussion if only those properties of the object which are possessed by every object of the universe are used in the discussion.*

In the set of even integers, x is arbitrary if we use such properties as

(a) x is exactly divisible by 2,
(b) $x + 2$ is an even integer, or
(c) the sum of x and another even integer is an even integer.

It is not arbitrary if we use such properties as

(d) x is exactly divisible by 3, or
(e) x is a power of 2,

for 10 is an even integer which is not exactly divisible by 3; neither is 10 a power of 2.

Definition. *An object is used as a **specified object** in a given discussion if it is completely identified.*

In the universe of all men, living or dead, Benjamin Franklin is a specified object. In the universe of all integers 4 is a specified object.

Definition. *An object is used as an **existential object** if the discussion shows that such an object exists in the universe but the object is not completely identified.*

The statement "There is a number larger than 7" describes an existential object. It does not specifically name a larger object. We may let $b\!\!\!/$ (read "*b* stroke") represent a number having the given property and use the statement "b is larger than 7". In this case b represents an existential object. Care must be taken not to assume more about existential objects than the premises allow.

In order to draw conclusions from quantified premises we need to know how to remove the quantifiers properly, argue with the resulting statements, and then properly prefix the correct quantifiers. A few examples will show what rules are indicated by the basic definitions of the quantifiers.

Example **1.**   Assume that in the universe of all living things the following statements are true.

Birds have wings,   and   Bald eagles are birds.

Common sense tells us that we should be able to conclude that bald eagles have wings. If we let

$$Bx: x \text{ is a bird,}$$
$$Wx: x \text{ has wings,}$$
$$Ex: x \text{ is a bald eagle,}$$

and observe that "Birds have wings" means "All birds have wings" and that "Bald eagles are birds" means "All bald eagles are birds", then we can summarize this inference as follows:

$$\begin{array}{c} \forall x \, [Bx \rightarrow Wx] \\ \underline{\forall x \, [Ex \rightarrow Bx]} \\ \forall x \, [Ex \rightarrow Wx]. \end{array}$$

In order to show that this inference is valid we must show that for each c of the universe $Ec \rightarrow Wc$. We shall give an informal discussion and then condense the argument to conform with usual procedure. Let us choose an arbitrary c from the universe, then $Ec \rightarrow Bc$ by the second premise, and $Bc \rightarrow Wc$ by the first premise; therefore, $Ec \rightarrow Wc$ by tautology T4, for each c of the universe. Therefore $\forall x \, [Ex \rightarrow Wx]$.

Unless a specified object or an existential object is named in the premises it will be convenient to use $Ex \rightarrow Bx$ or $Ey \rightarrow By$ instead of $Ec \rightarrow Bc$ in the usual formal argument. This statement involving x is obtained by dropping the universal quantifier from the second premise. This is justified by the fact that when the premise is true then $Ex \rightarrow Bx$ is true for every x in the universe. Similarly, the universal quantifier is dropped from the first premise to produce

$Bx \rightarrow Wx$. Then $[(Ex \rightarrow Bx) \wedge (Bx \rightarrow Wx)] \rightarrow (Ex \rightarrow Wx)$ since this statement has the form of a syllogism. Therefore, $Ex \rightarrow Wx$ for each x of the universe and therefore, $\forall x [Ex \rightarrow Wx]$. Here the universal quantifier has been prefixed to the statement because the statement $Ex \rightarrow Wx$ is true for an arbitrary x in the universe.

We have shown that a statement having the form of a logically valid statement pattern is also a logically valid statement. Therefore, a statement having the form of a syllogism is logically valid. Since we have reserved the word tautology for logically valid patterns involving only tf-statements, we shall not use T4 as our reason for $[(Ex \rightarrow Bx) \wedge (Bx \rightarrow Wx)] \rightarrow (Ex \rightarrow Wx)$, but shall use ST4 to mean that this statement has the form of T4. Similarly, ST1 means a statement having the form of T1, and ST8 means a statement having the form of T8.

The two rules that were used in the process of establishing the validity of this inference are now given. Informally the first says that what is true for all objects is true for each object.

Rule IV.   Universal Specification.

If a statement of the form $\forall x [Px]$ is assumed to be true (where Px may or may not contain other symbols in addition to x), then the universal quantifier may be dropped from the statement to obtain Px which is true for each object in the universe, or to obtain Pb which is true for a specific object of the universe.

Informally stated the second rule about universal quantification says that what is true of an arbitrary object is true of all objects.

Rule V.   Universal Generalization.

If a statement Gx is true of an arbitrary x of the universe (where Gx may or may not contain other symbols in addition to x) then the universal quantifier may be prefixed to obtain $\forall x [Gx]$, provided that every existential object in Gx which depends on x is covered by a quantifier.

We now present the argument for Example 1.

Statement. $\forall x [Bx \rightarrow Wx]$
$$\frac{\forall x [Ex \rightarrow Bx]}{\forall x [Ex \rightarrow Wx].}$$

Argument.

(1)	∀ x [Bx → Wx]	P
(2)	Bx → Wx	(1), Rule IV
(3)	∀ x [Ex → Bx]	P
(4)	Ex → Bx	(3), Rule IV
(5)	Ex → Wx	(2), (4), ST4
(6)	∀ x [Ex → Wx]	(5), Rule V ∎

In §11, Inference and Argument, the words "inference pattern" were used to mean the symbolic statement of the premises and conclusion of a given inference. The same terminology will be used here, even though the symbolic statement includes open and closed statements as well as tf-statements.

The inference pattern for another example of the same type as Example 1 is given here. The argument is left as an exercise.

Example 2. (Lewis Carroll)

> Babies are illogical. Nobody is despised who can manage a crocodile. Illogical people are despised.
> _____
> Babies cannot manage crocodiles.

Let

> *Bx*: *x* is a baby,
> *Ix*: *x* is illogical.
> *Dx*: *x* is despised,
> *Cx*: *x* can manage a crocodile,

then the inference pattern is:

$$\forall x [Bx \to Ix]$$
$$\forall x [Cx \to \sim Dx]$$
$$\underline{\forall x [Ix \to Dx]}$$
$$\forall x [Bx \to \sim Cx].$$

Example 3.

> Every living thing is a plant or an animal. John's goldfish is alive and it is not a plant. All animals have hearts.
> _____
> John's goldfish has a heart.

Let the universe consist of all living things, and let

Px: x is a plant,
Ax: x is an animal,
Hx: x has a heart,
a: John's goldfish,

then the inference pattern is:

$$\forall x \, [Px \lor Ax]$$
$$\sim Pa$$
$$\underline{\forall x \, [Ax \to Hx]}$$
$$Ha.$$

(Observe that, when the universal quantifiers are dropped, statements concerning the specified object are used.)

Argument.

(1)	$\forall x \, [Px \lor Ax]$	P
(2)	$\sim Pa$	P
(3)	$Pa \lor Aa$	(1), Rule IV
(4)	Aa	(2), (3), T8
(5)	$\forall x \, [Ax \to Hx]$	P
(6)	$Aa \to Ha$	(5), Rule IV
(7)	Ha	(4), (6), T3

∎

Example **4.**

Lions are dangerous animals.
There are lions.
_____
There are dangerous animals.

Let Lx: x is a lion,
Dx: x is a dangerous animal,

then the inference pattern is:

$$\forall x \, [Lx \to Dx]$$
$$\underline{\exists x \, [Lx]}$$
$$\exists x \, [Dx].$$

An informal argument will be given first. The premise involving the existential quantifier states that there is an existential object. If we assume that we can designate this object by $\not a$ (read "a stroke") then we can obtain $L\phi$. By dropping the universal quantifier we obtain $L\phi \to D\phi$. Then by the Law of Detachment we can obtain $D\phi$. Since an object exists for which Dx is true, we can state that $\exists\, x\, [Dx]$. Observe that the existential statement is used first. Why?

Informally stated, the following rule about existential quantification says that if a statement is true of some object then we may refer to this object by assigning it a name.

Rule VI. Existential Specification.

If **E** $x\, [Rx]$ *is assumed to be true (where Rx may or may not contain other symbols in addition to x), then the existential object ϕ can be used to represent the object for which Rx is true, provided ϕ has not already been used to represent some object in the discussion or in Rx. Thus by dropping the existential quantifier and replacing x by ϕ we can obtain $R\phi$.*

Informally, the second rule concerning existential quantification says that if an object has a specific property then there exists an object with this property.

Rule VII. Existential Generalization.

Let c be an object having a given property and let Pc be a symbolic expression of this property possessed by c, which may or may not contain other symbols in addition to c. If x is not one of the symbols occurring in Pc, then the existence of x can be expressed by replacing c by x and prefixing the existential quantifier to obtain $\exists\, x\, [Px]$.

The formal argument for Example 4 is now given.

Statement.

$$\forall\, x\, [Lx \to Dx]$$
$$\underline{\exists\, x\, [Lx]}$$
$$\exists\, x\, [Dx]$$

Argument.		
(1) $\exists\, x\, [Lx]$	P	
(2) $L\phi$	(1), Rule VI	
(3) $\forall\, x\, [Lx \to Dx]$	P	
(4) $L\phi \to D\phi$	(3), Rule IV	
(5) $D\phi$	(2), (4), T3	
(6) $\exists\, x\, [Dx]$	(5), Rule VII	∎

Remarks: Caution should be exercised in using the rules of specification and generalization.

(a) Do not drop a quantifier unless it covers an entire statement.

(b) Given two existential statements $\exists x [Qx]$ and $\exists x [Rx]$ do not conclude that a single object satisfies both statements. If, by using Rule VI, we obtain $Q\phi$ then we must introduce a new existential object such as ψ to obtain $R\psi$.

(c) From the fact that each object of a universe has an existential relationship with some other object do not conclude that all objects have this relationship with the same object. For example, from the fact that each person has a mother we cannot conclude that all people have the same mother. Let Mxy: x is the mother of y, then "For each y, there is an x such that x is the mother of y", is a true statement. Written symbolically this is $\forall y \exists x [Mxy]$. If we drop the universal quantifier we have $\exists x [Mxy]$: There is a mother of y. If we drop the existential quantifier we have $M\phi y$: Let ϕ be the mother of y. Since the existential element ϕ depends on y and y is not covered by a quantifier we cannot prefix the universal quantifier to $M\phi y$. If the error of prefixing the universal quantifier is made to obtain $\forall y [M\phi y]$, the existential quantifier could then be prefixed to obtain $\exists z \forall y [Mzy]$. This would mean that everyone has the same mother. It is possible, of course, starting with $M\phi y$, to state that $\exists z [Mzy]$ and then obtain $\forall y \exists z [Mzy]$, a statement equivalent to the original statement.

(d) From the fact that each object of a universe has an existential relationship with some other object do not conclude that two specific objects have this relationship to the same object, or to each other.

The statement "Everyone is indebted to someone", can be written symbolically as $\forall x \exists y [Ixy]$, where Ixy: x is indebted to y. For a specific person such as Charles Knox there is someone to whom he is indebted. If we let c represent Charles Knox then there is someone, whom we shall denote by ϕ, such that $Ic\phi$. Since ϕ denotes a person, ϕ is also indebted to someone, whom we shall denote by ψ. Then ψ is indebted to someone whom we shall denote by ϕ. Therefore, we can obtain $I\phi\psi$ and $I\psi\phi$.

We must be careful, however, not to make the error of concluding that $I\phi c$, or $I\psi c$, or $I\psi\phi$ is a true statement. The information at hand does not warrant such conclusions. It merely states that each person is indebted to someone, but the person to whom he is indebted is not identified.

***Example* 5.** If one person is more successful than another, then he has worked harder to deserve success. Albert has not worked harder than Ben. Therefore, Albert is not more successful than Ben.

Let Sxy: x is more successful than y,
        Wxy: x has worked harder than y to deserve success,
        a: Albert,
        b: Ben;

then the inference pattern is:

$$\forall x \, \forall y \, [Sxy \rightarrow Wxy]$$
$$\underline{\sim Wab }$$
$$\sim Sab$$

$Argument.$

(1)	$\forall x \, \forall y \, [Sxy \rightarrow Wxy]$	P
(2)	$\forall y \, [Say \rightarrow Way]$	(1), Rule IV
(3)	$Sab \rightarrow Wab$	(2), Rule IV
(4)	$\sim Wab$	P
(5)	$\sim Wab \rightarrow \sim Sab$	(3), T6
(6)	$\sim Sab$	(4), (5), T3

***Example* 6.** If all court decisions are correct then some students should study law. However, there are no students who should study law. Therefore, there are some court decisions which are incorrect.

Let Dx: x is a court decision,
           Cx: x is correct,
           Sy: y is a student,
           Ly: y should study law;

then the inference pattern is:

$$\forall x \, [Dx \rightarrow Cx] \rightarrow \exists y \, [Sy \wedge Ly]$$
$$\underline{\sim\exists y \, [Sy \wedge Ly] }$$
$$\exists x \, [Dx \wedge \sim Cx]$$

Argument.

(1) $\forall x [Dx \rightarrow Cx] \rightarrow \exists y [Sy \wedge Ly]$	P
(2) $\sim\exists y [Sy \wedge Ly] \rightarrow$ $\sim\forall x [Dx \rightarrow Cx]$	(1), ST6
(3) $\sim\exists y [Sy \wedge Ly]$	P
(4) $\sim\forall x [Dx \rightarrow Cx]$	(2), (3), ST3
(5) $\exists x [\sim(Dx \rightarrow Cx)]$	(4), $LV1^*$
(6) $\exists x [Dx \wedge \sim Cx]$	(5), ST19 ∎

Example 7. If there is a party then all of Jane's friends like all of Diana's friends. There is a party. Joe is Jane's friend. A non-Zymo must dislike one of Diana's friends. Therefore, there is a Zymo.

Let

Pz: z is a party,
Jx: x is a friend of Jane,
Dy: y is a friend of Diana
Lxy: x likes y,
b: Joe,
Zx: x is a Zymo;

then the inference pattern is:

$$\exists z [Pz] \rightarrow \forall x \forall y [(Jx \wedge Dy) \rightarrow Lxy]$$
$$\exists z [Pz]$$
$$Jb$$
$$\underline{\forall x [\sim Zx \rightarrow \exists y [Dy \wedge \sim Lxy]]}$$
$$\exists x [Zx]$$

Argument.

(1) $\exists z [Pz] \rightarrow \forall x \forall y [(Jx \wedge Dy) \rightarrow Lxy]$	P
(2) $\exists z [Pz]$	P
(3) $\forall x \forall y [(Jx \wedge Dy) \rightarrow Lxy]$	(1), (2), ST3
(4) Jb	P
(5) $\forall y [(Jb \wedge Dy) \rightarrow Lby]$	(3), Rule IV
(6) $\forall y [Jb \rightarrow (Dy \rightarrow Lby)]$	(5), ST14
(7) $Jb \rightarrow \forall y [Dy \rightarrow Lby]$	Jb is not covered by $\forall y$
(8) $\forall y [Dy \rightarrow Lby]$	(4), (7), ST3
(9) $\forall x [\sim Zx \rightarrow \exists y [Dy \wedge \sim Lxy]]$	P
(10) $\sim Zb \rightarrow \exists y [Dy \wedge \sim Lby]$	(9), Rule IV

* See page 316 for LV1.

(11) $\sim\!\exists\, y\, [Dy \wedge \sim\!Lby] \to Zb$	(10), ST6
(12) $\forall\, y\, [\sim\!(Dy \wedge \sim\!Lby)] \to Zb$	(11), LV2
(13) $\forall\, y\, [\sim\!Dy \vee Lby] \to Zb$	(12), ST17
(14) $\forall\, y\, [Dy \to Lby] \to Zb$	(13), Theorem IV
(15) Zb	(8), (14), ST3
(16) $\exists\, x\, [Zx]$	(15), Rule VII ■

EXERCISES

1. Give the argument for Example 2.*

2. Using the methods of this section, give an argument for the following statement:

$$\forall\, x\, [Px \to Qx] \to (\forall\, x\, [Px] \to \forall\, x\, [Qx]).$$

3. If each of the following inferences is valid give an argument which will establish its validity. If it is invalid, give a counter-example.

(a) Students of average intelligence can do arithmetic. A student without average intelligence is not a college capable student. Your students cannot do arithmetic. Therefore, your students are not college capable. (Let Ix, Ax, Cx, and Yx represent the statements involving the key words intelligence, arithmetic, college, and yours, respectively.)

(b) All integers are rational numbers. Some integers are powers of 2. Therefore, some rational numbers are powers of 2.

(c) Some rational numbers are powers of 5. All integers are rational numbers. Therefore, some integers are powers of 5.

(d) Charity helps everyone. Someone wants security. Therefore, there is someone who is helped by charity and who wants security.

(e) If there is a mathematician who has proved the theorem, then all of your statements are correct. However, one of your statements is incorrect. Therefore, there is no mathematician who has proved the theorem.

---

* For other Lewis Carroll examples see Robert R. Christian, *Introduction to Logic and Sets* (New York, Ginn, 1958), pp. 67–70.

(*f*) Chickens are quadrupeds. Quadrupeds eat grain. Therefore, chickens eat grain.

(*g*) Elephants are quadrupeds. Chickens are quadrupeds. Therefore, some chickens are elephants.

(*h*) If an integer is divisible by 10 then it is divisible by 2. If an integer is divisible by 2 then it is divisible by 3. Therefore, an integer divisible by 10 is divisible by 3.

(*i*) Everyone chooses between good and evil. James has chosen not to do evil. If anyone chooses to do good or if he is forced to obey the laws then he has an excellent chance for happiness. Therefore, James' chances for happiness are excellent.

(*j*) All required courses meet on Friday. There are courses that do not meet on Friday. Therefore, there are courses that are not required.

(*k*) There is no required course that I can take this semester. The courses that I cannot take this semester or next summer will be taken at another university when I am employed. I cannot take science next summer and it is a required course. I cannot pass science if I am employed. Therefore, I shall fail science.

(*l*) No trustworthy person who is in business is untruthful. Some people are untruthful. Therefore, no trustworthy people are in business.

(*m*) Some mathematicians are applied scientists. Some mathematicians like all applied scientists. Therefore, some mathematicians are not disliked by all mathematicians and some applied scientists are liked by some mathematicians.

(*n*) No friend of John's is a friend of Paul's. One cannot influence everyone without being a friend of Paul's. There is no one whom Dale cannot influence. Therefore, Dale is not a friend of John's.

Answers to Selected Exercises

Page 237
1. (*a*), (*c*), (*e*), (*h*), (*i*), (*k*), (*l*), (*n*), (*o*), (*q*), (*s*), (*t*), (*v*).

Page 244
The classifications listed will be indicated by tf, cj, d, cd, b, and n, respectively. Classifications other than the ones given may be possible.

1. (*a*) d.   (*g*) tf or n.   (*m*) tf or d.   (*s*) tf.
   (*b*) cj.   (*h*) cj.   (*n*) cd.   (*t*) d.
   (*c*) b.   (*i*) tf.   (*o*) tf.   (*v*) cj of two cd.
   (*d*) tf or n. (*j*) tf or n.   (*p*) tf or n.   (*v*) tf.
   (*e*) cd.   (*k*) tf.   (*q*) b.
   (*f*) tf.   (*l*) cd.   (*r*) tf or n.

3. (*a*) Forgiveness is not the best thing to give to your enemy.
   (*b*) California is not rich with the romance of the past.
   (*c*) County health officers do not try to combat dirt and infection.
   (*d*) The Arabian Nights atmosphere did not hold many terrors for Lotta.
   (*e*) In Bombay and Calcutta peddlers and tradesmen are not numerous.
   (*f*) It is not true that everyone can increase his creative abilities.
       There is a person who cannot increase his creative abilities.
       Not everyone can increase his creative abilities.

Page 252
2. (*a*) The diameter of the earth is 3,000 miles or three-eighths of sixteen is six. True.
   (*b*) If the diameter of the earth is 3,000 miles then $2 + 4 = 7$. True.

(c) The earth is a planet if and only if Jupiter revolves around the sun. True.

(d) If three-eighths of sixteen is six then $2 + 4 = 7$. False.

(e) If $2 + 4 = 7$, then the earth is a planet. True.

(f) The earth is a planet and the diameter of the earth is 3,000 miles. False.

(g) The diameter of the earth is not 3,000 miles and three-eighths of sixteen is not six. False.

(h) The diameter of the earth is not 3,000 miles. True.

(i) The earth is not a planet or .75 is a whole number. False.

(j) If three-eighths of sixteen is six, then the diameter of the earth is 3,000 miles. False.

(k) If the earth is a planet and Jupiter revolves about the sun then $2 + 4 = 7$. False.

(l) The earth is a planet and Jupiter revolves about the sun, or the earth is a planet and $2 + 4 = 7$. True.

3. (a) False.   (b) True.   (c) True.   (d) True.

Page 269

·**1.** (a) The search for truth is not an important branch of human endeavor or mathematics has not played a major role in it.

(b) You've become completely covered with dirt from the rodeo arena, and you're panting with joy and excitement, and (but) you have no symptoms of rodeo fever.

(c) You are properly trained and (but) you will not be able to earn money.

(d) A politician achieves success in our time and he does not become well known.

(e) Today's turnpikes carry only air-supported vehicles and (but) they may not last for generations without further maintenance.

(f) The sky does not turn from atmospheric blue to vacuum black, or the stars do not appear in the sky, or the sun is not a diamond glory, or the rocket thrust is not cut off, or there is no stark unbroken silence.

(g) A first class traveler does not receive an invitation to the captain's party during the voyage and (but) does not consider himself snubbed.

(h) We take a vacation, you do not worry about finances, and (but) you do not enjoy it.
We will take a vacation, you will not worry about finances, and (but) you will not enjoy it.

(i) We take a vacation, you do not worry about finances but you do not enjoy it; or we take a vacation, you worry about finances but you enjoy it.

(j) He receives a good commission, he invests wisely, but he will not make a profit; or he does not invest wisely and he will make a profit.

2. (a), (b), (d), (e), (g).

3. (a) If John is correct, then Frank is elected.
   (b) Jack will notify her or Jane will be in danger.
   (c) Jack is guilty or Frank did not lie.
   (d) It may be raining and our food may be lost, or it may be raining and our food may be stolen.
   (e) If Jack can win the prize then he has the correct number.
   (f) He is not the father of Paul and he is not the father of Frank.

4. (a) $\sim p \wedge q \wedge r$. (b) $p \wedge q$. (c) $p \vee \sim p$.
   (d) $p \vee p \to p$. (e) $q \wedge s$. (f) $w \wedge s$.

Page 285

1. (a) Valid.

(1)	$r \to s$	P
(2)	$\sim s \to \sim r$	(1), T6
(3)	$\sim s$	P
(4)	$\sim r$	(2), (3), T3.

(c) Invalid. Let r be false and s be true, then $r \to s$ is true and $\sim r$ is true, but $\sim s$ is false.

(e) Valid.

(1)	$\sim q$	P
(2)	$\sim p \vee \sim q$	(1), T21
(3)	$\sim(p \wedge q)$	(2), T17.

(g) Invalid. Let the statements involved have one of the following sets of truth-values. Then the premises are true but the conclusion is false.

p	q	w	r	t
T	F	T	F	T
F	T	F	T	T

(i) Valid.

(1)	$\sim r \vee w$	P
(2)	$\sim w$	P
(3)	$\sim r$	(1), (2), T8
(4)	$\sim r \to (s \to \sim t)$	P
(5)	$s \to \sim t$	(3), (4), T3
(6)	$\sim p \to s$	P
(7)	$\sim p \to \sim t$	(5), (6), T4
(8)	$t \to p$	(7), T6.

(k) Invalid.

p	q	r	s
F	F	F	F

(m) Invalid. p: The parakeet likes celery. $p \to q$

                q: Jim will buy celery. p.

Let p and q both be false.

(o) Valid. p: Los Angeles is in California. $\sim p \to \sim q$

           q: Golf balls are sold in Chicago. q

                                         p.

        (1) $\sim p \to \sim q$ P

        (2) $q \to$ p (1), T6

        (3) q P

        (4) p (2), (3), T3.

(q) Invalid. p: Wishes are horses. $p \to q$

            q: Beggars can ride. q

                                 p

p	q
F	T

(s) Invalid. w: Wages are raised. $w \to b$

            b: Buying increases. $d \to \sim w$

            d: There is a depression. $d \to \sim b$.

w	b	d
F	T	T

(u) Valid. w: The wire $\cdots$ clouds. $w \to p$

           p: It would pass $\cdots$ ribbon. $p \to f$

           f: Franklin was $\cdots$ shock. $w \to f$.

           (1) $w \to p$ P

           (2) $p \to f$ P

           (3) $w \to f$ (1), (2), T4.

(w) Valid. m: Marge needs a vacation. $(m \lor f) \to k$

           f: Frank needs a vacation. $f \to k$.

           k: Kate deserves an assistant.

           (1) $(w \lor f) \to k$ P

           (2) $(w \to k) \land (f \to k)$ (1), T12

           (3) $f \to k$ (2), T10.

Page 303

1. (a) 2, 4, 6.   (c) False, true, true.

2. (a) $Ex \lor Sx$.   (b) $Px \land Tx$.   (c) $Sx \to (Ex \land Tx)$.

    (d) $Px \leftrightarrow \sim Sx$.   (e) $\sim Qx \to \sim Sx$.   (f) $(Ex \land Rx) \to \sim Px$.

    (g) $Px \to Qx$.

    (h) If x is a prime greater than 2, then it is not even.

    (i) If whenever x is positive it is a perfect square, then x is not greater than 2.

    (j) x is not a prime, not greater than 2, and not a perfect square.

    (k) x is not a perfect square or not positive and 12 is less than 5.

3. (a) Cx: x is a cat. Tx: x has a tail. $\forall x [Cx \rightarrow Tx]$.

   (b) Mx: x is mine. $\sim\forall x [Mx]$, or $\exists x [\sim Mx]$.

   (c) Px: x is a person. Tx: x is teasing. $\exists x [Px \wedge Tx]$.

   (d) Px: x is a living person (in the stone $\cdots$ twenties).
Tx: x thought much about cooking in space (in the stone $\cdots$ twenties). $\forall x [Px \rightarrow \sim Tx]$.

   (e) Rx: x is a road. Lx: x leads to Rome. $\sim\forall x [Rx \rightarrow Lx]$, or $\exists x [Rx \wedge \sim Lx]$.

4. (a) There is a city which is a good starting point for a journey through Scotland's past.

   (b) Not all cities are a bad starting point for a journey through Scotland's past.

5. Ix: x is an Indian. Mx: x is a male. Hx: x wears a headdress.

   (a) $\forall x [Hx]$; $\exists x [Hx]$; $\forall x [\sim Hx]$; $\exists x [\sim Hx]$.

   (b) $\forall x [Mx \rightarrow Hx]$; $\exists x [Mx \wedge Hx]$; $\forall x [Mx \rightarrow \sim Hx]$; $\exists x [Mx \wedge \sim Hx]$.

   (d) $\forall x [(Ix \wedge Mx) \rightarrow Hx]$; $\exists x [Ix \wedge Mx \wedge Hx]$; $\forall x [(Ix \wedge Mx) \rightarrow \sim Hx]$; $\exists x [Ix \wedge Mx \wedge \sim Hx]$.

6. (a) Cx: x is correct. (i) $\forall x [\sim Cx]$, or $\sim\exists x [Cx]$.
(ii) $\sim\forall x [\sim Cx] \leftrightarrow \exists x [Cx]$. (iii) Something is correct.

   (b) Bx: x is bright. (i) $\forall x [Bx]$. (ii) $\sim\forall x [Bx] \leftrightarrow \exists x [\sim Bx]$. (iii) Something is not bright.

   (c) Mx: x is missing. (i) $\exists x [Mx]$. (ii) $\sim\exists x [Mx] \leftrightarrow \forall x [\sim Mx]$. (iii) Nothing is missing.

   (d) Wx: x is white. (i) $\exists x [\sim Wx]$. (ii) $\sim\exists x [\sim Wx] \leftrightarrow \forall x [Wx]$. (iii) Everything is white.

7. (a) Mx: x is a man. Nx: x is a miser.
(i) $\exists x [Mx \wedge Nx]$,
(ii) $\sim\exists x [Mx \wedge Nx]$. (iii) No man is a miser.

   (b) Dx: x is a dog. Ix: x is intelligent. (i) $\sim\exists x [Dx \wedge Ix]$, or $\forall x [Dx \rightarrow \sim Ix]$. (ii) $\exists x [Dx \wedge Ix]$. (iii) There exists an intelligent dog.

   (c) Bx: x is a bird. Fx: x can fly. (i) $\exists x [Bx \wedge \sim Fx]$.
(ii) $\forall x [\sim(Bx \wedge \sim Fx)] \leftrightarrow \forall x [\sim Bx \vee Fx] \leftrightarrow \forall x [Bx \rightarrow Fx]$.
(iii) All birds can fly.

   (d) Bx: x is a baby. Ix: x is illogical. (i) $\forall x [Bx \rightarrow Ix]$.
(ii) $\exists x [\sim(Bx \rightarrow Ix)] \leftrightarrow \exists x [\sim(\sim Bx \vee Ix)] \leftrightarrow \exists x [Bx \wedge \sim Ix]$.
(iii) There exists a baby which is not intelligent.

   (e) Gx: x is a guest. Ax: x has arrived. (i) $\forall x [Gx \rightarrow Ax]$.
(ii) $\sim\forall x [Gx \rightarrow Ax] \leftrightarrow \exists x [Gx \wedge \sim Ax]$.
(iii) There exists a guest who has not arrived.

8.   (a) $\exists\, x\,[Ax]$, $\exists\, x\,[\sim Ax]$, $\sim\forall\, x\,[\sim Ax]$, $\sim\forall\, x\,[Ax]$.
      (b) $\sim\exists\, x\,[Bx]$, $\forall\, x\,[\sim Bx]$, $\exists\, x\,[\sim Bx]$, $\sim\forall\, x\,[Bx]$.
      (c) $\forall\, x\,[Cx]$, $\exists\, x\,[Cx]$, $\sim\forall\, x\,[\sim Cx]$, $\sim\exists\, x\,[\sim Cx]$.
      (d) $\exists\, x\,[Dx]$, $\sim\forall\, x\,[Dx]$, $\exists\, x\,[\sim Dx]$, $\sim\forall\, x\,[\sim Dx]$.

9.   (a) $\exists\, x\,[\sim Px]$, $\exists\, x\,[Px]$, $\sim\forall\, x\,[Px]$, $\sim\forall\, x\,[\sim Px]$.
      (b) $\forall\, x\,[Px]$, $\exists\, x\,[Px]$, $\sim\exists\, x\,[\sim Px]$, $\sim\forall\, x\,[\sim Px]$.
      (c) $\forall\, x\,[\sim Px]$, $\exists\, x\,[\sim Px]$, $\sim\forall\, x\,[Px]$, $\sim\exists\, x\,[Px]$.

10. (a) In the universe of all snakes let Px: x is poisonous, and Ux: x is ugly. $\exists\, x\,[Px] \wedge \forall\, x\,[Ux]$. Closed.
     (b) Hx: x glitters. Gx: x is gold. s: The sun is gold. $\forall\, x\,[Hx \to Gx] \to s$. Closed.
     (c) Bx: x is bright. j: John is wrong. $Bx \vee j$. Open.
     (d) Px: x is a person. Gx: x grows old too soon. Sx: x becomes smart too late. $\forall\, x\,[Px \to (Gx \wedge Sx)]$. Closed.
     (e) Gx: Tom gave x to Mary. Vx: Mary gave x to Victor. $\exists\, x\,[Gx \wedge Vx]$. Closed.
     (f) In the universe of all living people let r: It rains, s: The sun shines, and Sx: x is not satisfied. $r \vee s \to \exists\, x\,[Sx]$. Closed.
     (g) Px: x is president. $Px \to \exists\, x\,[Px]$. Open.
     (h) Nx: x is an odd number. Px: x is a prime. $Nx \wedge Px$. Open.
     (i) $\exists\, x\,[Nx \wedge Px]$. Closed.
     (j) $\forall\, x\,[Nx \vee Px]$. Closed.
     (k) Rx: x is right. Wx: x is wrong. $\sim\exists\, x\,[Rx \wedge Wx]$. Closed.
     (l) Lx: Franklin does learn x. Rx: Franklin will remember x. $\forall\, x\,[Lx \to \sim Rx]$. Closed.
    (m) Sx: x is a senior. Px: x takes a sophomore to the prom. Jx: x is a junior. Tx: x will object. $\forall\, x\,[Sx \to Px] \to \forall\, y\,[Jy \to Tx]$. Closed.
     (n) Sx: x is a student. Mx: x likes mathematics. Hx: x does not like history. $\exists\, x\,[Sx \wedge Mx \wedge \sim Hx]$. Closed.
     (o) Px: x is a person. Gx: x will go. Tx: Enough people will be left to do x. $\exists\, x\,[Px \wedge Gx] \wedge \exists\, x\,[Px \wedge \sim Gx] \to \forall\, x\,[Hx]$. Closed.
     (p) Px: x is a person. Tx: x must be true to x. $Px \to Tx$. Open.
     (q) $\forall\, x\,[Px \to Tx]$. Closed.
     (r) In the universe of all living people let i: The investigator has the facts, and Hx: x is hiding information. $i \vee \exists\, x\,[Hx]$. Closed.

Page 316

1.   (a) This is of the form T18.
     (f) $(Px \wedge Qy) \to (Px \to Qy)$. Let $x = c$, then we have $(Pc \wedge Qc) \to (Pc \to Qc)$. If the antecedent is true then both Pc and Qc are true. Therefore $Pc \to Qc$ is true. Therefore, the statement is valid.

2. (a) $(Pb \wedge Qy) \rightarrow Pb$.

(b) $\sim(Qx \vee Px) \leftrightarrow \sim Qx \wedge \sim Px$.

(c) $[(Px \rightarrow Qx) \wedge (Qx \rightarrow Rx)] \rightarrow (Px \rightarrow Rx)$.

(d) $(\forall x [Sx] \rightarrow p) \rightarrow (\exists x [Sx] \rightarrow p)$.

(e) $\exists x [Px \wedge Qx] \rightarrow (\exists x [Qx] \wedge \exists x [Px])$.

(f) $(Qx \rightarrow Sx) \leftrightarrow (\sim Qx \vee Sx)$.

(g) $\forall x [Qx] \wedge \forall x [Sx] \leftrightarrow \forall x [Qx \wedge Sx]$.

(h) $\forall x [Qx] \leftrightarrow \sim \exists x [\sim Qx]$.

3. (a) It is not true that x is bad or x is green if and only if x is not bad and x is not green.

(c) x is green whenever x is bad if and only if x is not bad or x is green.

(e) If whenever x is bad then x is green and whenever x is green then x is cheap, then whenever x is bad then x is cheap.

(g) If a is bad and y is green then a is bad.

(i) For all x, if whenever x is bad then Tom is sad, then for each x, whenever x is sad then Tom is sad.

4. (b) This is of the form T15.   (d) This is of the form T9.

(f) This is of the form T4.   (h) This is of the form T14.

Page 329

2. Pxy: $3x - 2y = 7$.   (a) $\exists x \exists y [Pxy]$. True. $x = 3, y = 1$.

(c) $\exists y \forall x [Pxy]$. False. No fixed value of y can be used with all values of x.

(e) $\forall x \exists y [Pxy]$. False. If $x = 0$, then $y = -7/2$, which is not an integer.

4. (a) Ixy: x is indebted to y. $\forall x \exists y [Ixy]$.

(c) Hx: x is a healthy person. Wy: y is a kind of work. Dxy: x can do y. $\forall x \forall y [(Hx \wedge Wy) \rightarrow Dxy]$.

(e) Jx: x follows Jackson. Ix: x is an independent. Lxy: x likes y. $\forall x \forall y [(Jx \wedge Iy \rightarrow \sim Lxy]$.

(g) In the universe of people let Axy: x admires y. $\exists y \exists x [\sim Axy]$. In the universe consisting of everything let Px: x is a person, and Axy: x admires y. $\exists y \exists x [(Py \wedge Px) \rightarrow \sim Axy]$.

(i) In the universe of people let Nxy: x and y are neighbors, Hxy: x should help y, and Pxy: x will help y. $\forall x \forall y [(Nxy \rightarrow Hxy) \vee \sim Pyx]$.

(k) Gx: x is a person in this organization. Pxy: x protects y. $\exists x \forall y [Gy \rightarrow Pxy]$.

(m) Tx: x is a triangle. Sxy: x is similar to y. $\exists x \exists y [(Tx \wedge Ty) \wedge \sim Sxy]$.

5. (*a*) ∃ *x* ∀ *y* [∼*Ixy*]. There is someone who is not indebted to anyone.

(*c*) ∃ *x* ∃ *y* [*Hx* ∧ *Wy* ∧ ∼*Dxy*]. (There exists a healthy person and there exists a type of work which he cannot do.) There are healthy people who cannot do certain types of work.

(*e*) ∃ *x* ∃ *y* [*Jx* ∧ *Iy* ∧ *Lxy*]. There exists a follower of Jackson who likes an independent.

(*g*) ∀ *x* ∀ *y* [*Py* ∧ *Px* ∧ *Axy*]. Everybody is admired by everyone.

(*i*) ∃ *x* ∃ *y* [*Nxy* ∧ ∼*Hxy* ∧ *Pyx*]. There are people who should not help their neighbors but their neighbors will help them.

(*k*) ∀ *x* ∃ *y* [*Gy* ∧ ∼*Pxy*]. For every person there is someone in this organization whom he will not protect.

(*m*) ∀ *x* ∀ *y* [(*Tx* ∧ *Ty*) → *Sxy*]. Any two triangles are similar.

6. (*a*) There is someone whom everybody invites.

(*b*) If anyone has a friend then he has someone to share his leisure hours.

(*c*) Everyone agrees with someone and someone agrees with everyone.

(*d*) There are people who agree but are not friends.

(*e*) If two people share their leisure hours and they agree, then they may become friends.

(*f*) Given two distinct points there is a third point such that the second point is between the first and third points, and there is a fourth point such that the first is between the second and fourth points.

(*g*) Given two distinct points there is a third point between them.

(*h*) Given two points on the same circle there is a point equidistant from them.

(*i*) If a given line does not pass through a given point then there is exactly one line through the given point parallel to the given line.

(*j*) For each integer there is another integer which exceeds it by 3.

(*k*) If a first integer is not greater than a second integer, then it is less than the second integer or equal to it.

(*l*) There is a unique integer such that when it is added to a second integer the sum is the second integer, and there is a unique integer which when multiplied by a second integer the product is the second integer.

(*m*) Two integers have a greatest common divisor and a least common multiple.

Page 341

3. (*a*) *Ix*: *x* is a student of average intelligence. *Ax*: *x* can do arithmetic. *Cx*: *x* is a college capable student. *Yx*: *x* is your student.

$$\forall x\,[Ix \rightarrow Ax]$$
$$\forall x\,[\sim Ix \rightarrow \sim Cx]$$
$$\underline{\forall x\,[Yx \rightarrow \sim Ax]}$$
$$\forall x\,[Yx \rightarrow \sim Cx].$$

Argument.

(1)	$\forall x\,[Ix \rightarrow Ax]$	P
(2)	$Ix \rightarrow Ax$	(1), Rule IV
(3)	$\forall x\,[\sim Ix \rightarrow \sim Cx]$	P
(4)	$\sim Ix \rightarrow \sim Cx$	(3), Rule IV
(5)	$Cx \rightarrow Ix$	(4), ST6
(6)	$Cx \rightarrow Ax$	(2), (5), ST4
(7)	$\forall x\,[Yx \rightarrow \sim Ax]$	P
(8)	$Yx \rightarrow \sim Ax$	(7), Rule IV
(9)	$\sim Ax \rightarrow \sim Cx$	(6), ST6
(10)	$Yx \rightarrow \sim Cx$	(8), (9), ST4
(11)	$\forall x\,[Yx \rightarrow \sim Cx]$	(10), Rule V

(*i*) Gx: x chooses good. Ex: x chooses evil. j: James. Fx: x is forced to obey the laws. Hx: x has an excellent chance for happiness.

$$\forall x\,[Gx \vee Ex]$$
$$\sim Ej$$
$$\underline{\forall x\,[(Gx \vee Fx) \rightarrow Hx]}$$
$$Hj.$$

Argument.

(1)	$\forall x\,[Gx \vee Ex]$	P
(2)	$Gj \vee Ej$	(1), Rule IV
(3)	$\sim Ej$	P
(4)	Gj	(2), (3), ST8
(5)	$\forall x\,[(Gx \vee Fx) \rightarrow Hx]$	P
(6)	$(Gj \vee Fj) \rightarrow Hj$	(5), Rule IV
(7)	$Gj \vee Fj$	(4), ST21
(8)	Hj	(6), (7), ST3.

Frequently Used Statements

TAUTOLOGIES

T1. Law of Excluded Middle, $p \vee \sim p$.

T2. Law of Contradiction, $\sim(p \wedge \sim p)$.

T3. Law of Detachment, $[p \wedge (p \to q)] \to q$.

T4. Law of Syllogism, $[(p \to q) \wedge (q \to r)] \to (p \to r)$.

T5. Law of Double Negation, $\sim(\sim p) \leftrightarrow p$.

T6. Law of Contraposition, $(p \to q) \leftrightarrow (\sim q \to \sim p)$.

T7. $[(p \to q) \wedge \sim q] \to \sim p$.

T8. $[(p \vee q) \wedge \sim p] \to q$.

T9. $[(p \to r) \wedge (q \to s) \wedge (p \vee q)] \to (r \vee s)$.

T10. $(p \wedge q) \to p$.

T11. $[p \to (q \wedge r)] \leftrightarrow [(p \to q) \wedge (p \to r)]$.

T12. $[(p \vee q) \to r] \leftrightarrow [(p \to r) \wedge (q \to r)]$.

T13. $(p \leftrightarrow q) \leftrightarrow [(p \to q) \wedge (q \to p)]$.

T14. $[(p \wedge q) \to r] \leftrightarrow [p \to (q \to r)]$.

T15. $[p \wedge (q \vee r)] \leftrightarrow [(p \wedge q) \vee (p \wedge r)]$.

T16. $[p \vee (q \wedge r)] \leftrightarrow [(p \vee q) \wedge (p \vee r)]$.

T17. $\sim(p \wedge q) \leftrightarrow [\sim p \vee \sim q]$.

T18. $\sim(p \vee q) \leftrightarrow [\sim p \wedge \sim q]$.

T19. $\sim(p \to q) \leftrightarrow [p \wedge \sim q]$.

T20. $\sim(p \leftrightarrow q) \leftrightarrow [(p \wedge \sim q) \vee (\sim p \wedge q)] \leftrightarrow (p \leftrightarrow \sim q)$.

T21. $p \to (p \vee q)$.

NEGATIONS

Statement	Negation
$\sim p$	p
$p \wedge q$	$\sim p \vee \sim q$
$p \vee q$	$\sim p \wedge \sim q$
$p \rightarrow q$	$p \wedge \sim q$
$p \leftrightarrow q$	$(p \wedge \sim q) \vee (q \wedge \sim p)$

LOGICALLY VALID STATEMENTS

LV1. $\forall x [Px] \leftrightarrow \sim \exists x [\sim Px]$.

LV2. $\forall x [\sim Px] \leftrightarrow \sim \exists x [Px]$.

LV3. $\forall x [Px] \rightarrow \exists x [Px]$.

LV4. $\forall x [Px] \rightarrow Py$.

LV5. $Py \rightarrow \exists x [Px]$.

LV6. $\forall x [Px \wedge Qx] \leftrightarrow (\forall x [Px] \wedge \forall x [Qx])$.

LV7. $\exists x [Px \vee Qx] \leftrightarrow (\exists x [Px] \vee \exists x [Qx])$.

LV8. $(\forall x [Px] \vee \forall x [Qx]) \rightarrow \forall x [Px \vee Qx]$.

LV9. $\exists x [Px \wedge Qx] \rightarrow (\exists x [Px] \wedge \exists x [Qx])$.

LV10. $\forall x [Px \rightarrow Qx] \rightarrow (\forall x [Px] \rightarrow \forall x [Qx])$.

LV11. $\forall x [Px \rightarrow p] \rightarrow (\exists x [Px] \rightarrow p)$.

Part III

Abstract
Mathematical
Systems

Introduction to Groups

1. PRELIMINARY DEFINITIONS AND ASSUMPTIONS

Definition. *An **ordered pair** of objects is a set of two objects for which it has been decided which is to be considered first and which second.*

The reader has undoubtedly used ordered pairs of numbers in graphing. For example, a definite point on the graph is designated by the ordered pair $(5, -2)$, where 5 is the x-coordinate and -2 is the y-coordinate. Furthermore, he is aware of the fact that $(-2, 5)$ is a *different* ordered pair, for it represents a different point on the graph. We shall designate the ordered pair a and b by (a, b) and shall keep in mind that (b, a) is a different ordered pair.

The four fundamental operations of arithmetic are addition, subtraction, multiplication, and division. Mathematicians have found it very useful to consider operations of a more general type. For this reason we shall use the following definition.

Definition. *A **binary operation** is a correspondence which assigns exactly one element c to each ordered pair of elements (a, b).*

Example 1. Addition is a binary operation which assigns the number 5 to the ordered pair of numbers $(2, 3)$, since $2 + 3 = 5$.

Example 2. Subtraction is a binary operation which assigns the number -1 to the ordered pair $(2, 3)$, since $2 - 3 = -1$. but assigns the number 1 to the ordered pair $(3, 2)$, since $3 - 2 = 1$.

Here the importance of order shows up. We see that, in general, a binary operation applied to the pair (b, a) need not give the same result as when applied to (a, b).

We shall frequently denote a binary operation by $\circ$ (pronounced like the letter "o") and then the application of this operation $\circ$ to the elements a and b to produce c will be denoted by $a \circ b = c$ (read "a operating on b gives c," "a operation b is c," or simply "a, $\circ$, b equals c").

Example 3. Let $\circ$ mean to add the second number of an ordered pair to twice the first number. Then $a \circ b = 2a + b$ and $b \circ a = 2b + a$, and these results are not necessarily equal. When will $a \circ b = b \circ a$?

Assumptions Concerning the Special Sets. Many of the examples will involve special sets of numbers. For the sake of clarity we state specifically what is included in each set.

Definition. *The positive integers are the positive whole numbers:* 1, 2, 3, 4, 5, $\cdots$.

Definition. *The integers are the numbers* 0, 1, -1, 2, -2, 3, -3, $\cdots$. *We shall frequently denote the set of integers by* J.

Definition. *The even integers are the numbers of the form* $2n$, *where n is an integer; that is,* 0, 2, -2, 4, -4, 6, -6, $\cdots$.

Definition. *The odd integers are the numbers of the form* $2n + 1$ (or $2n - 1$) *where n is an integer; that is,* 1, -1, 3, -3, 5, -5, $\cdots$.

Definition. *The rational numbers are the numbers that can be expressed in the form* p/q, *where p and q are integers and* $q \neq 0$.
(Here we *assume* that these quotients are added and multiplied according to the rules for fractions, and that two such quotients p/q and c/d are equal if and only if $pd = cq$.)

We shall frequently denote the set of rational numbers by $\overline{R}$.

We shall *assume* that we know many of the properties of these special sets. In addition to assuming that we know how to add, subtract, multiply and divide these numbers we shall *assume* that the following conditions are satisfied.

(A1)   The sum, difference, or product of two integers is an integer.

If a, b, and c are rational numbers, distinct or identical, then

(A2) $(a + b) + c = a + (b + c)$,   (Associative Law of Addition)

(A3) $(ab)c = a(bc)$,   (Associative Law of Multiplication)

(A4) $a + b = b + a$,   (Commutative Law of Addition)

(A5) $ab = ba$,   (Commutative Law of Multiplication)

(A6) $a(b + c) = ab + ac$.   (Distributive Law of Multiplication with respect to Addition)

(A7)   The product of two nonzero rational numbers is a nonzero rational number.

(A8)   The sum and the product of two positive rational numbers are positive.

Assumption Concerning the Operations.   We shall also *assume* throughout this book that all operations are *well defined.*

Definition.   *A binary operation* $\circ$ *is* **well defined** *if replacing a and b in the equation a* $\circ$ *b = c by equal elements produces an element equal to c.*

This definition can be stated in symbols. If $a \circ b = c$, $a = a'$, $b = b'$, and $a' \circ b' = c'$, then $c = c'$. Expressed in nontechnical language it means that the operation working on equal elements produces equal results. It allows us to *substitute* equal quantities in a given statement involving the operation.

Definition.   (*The closure property*)   *A set H of elements a, b, c,* $\cdots$ *is* **closed with respect to an operation** $\circ$ *if for every ordered pair* (a, b) *such that a and b are in H, it is true that a* $\circ$ *b is in H.*

Example 1.   The set of positive integers is closed under addition, for the sum of two positive integers is a positive integer.

Example 2.   The set of odd integers is not closed with respect to division, for 3 divided by 5 gives 3/5 which is not an integer, hence not an odd integer.

Example **3.** The set of even integers is closed under addition. To show that the even integers are closed under addition let $2h$ and $2k$ represent two even integers. Their sum is $2h + 2k = 2(h + k)$. Since $h + k$ is the sum of two integers, and the sum of two integers is an integer, then $h + k$ is equal to some integer which we shall designate by t. Then $2(h + k) = 2t$ and is an even integer by definition.

EXERCISES

1. For each of the following statements which is a direct consequence of the assumptions of this section produce an argument which will show that the statement is true. For each statement which is not true give a counterexample. (A counterexample is an example which shows that the statement is not always true.)

(a)   The product of two even integers is always an even integer.

(b)   The difference between two even integers is always an even integer.

(c)   The quotient of two even integers is always an even integer.

(d)   The sum of two odd integers is always an odd integer.

(e)   The product of two odd integers is always an odd integer.

(f)   The sum of two rational numbers is always a rational number.

(g)   The product of two rational numbers is always a rational number.

(h)   The difference between two rational numbers is always a rational number.

(i)   The quotient of two rational numbers is always a rational number.

(j)   The quotient of two integers is always an integer.

(k)   The difference between two odd integers is always an even integer.

(l)   The product of an odd integer and an even integer is always an even integer.

(m) The sum of two nonzero rational numbers is always a nonzero rational number.

2. Test the following sets for closure with respect to the operation of (i) addition, (ii) subtraction, (iii) multiplication, (iv) division.

(a) The positive integers.   (b) The odd integers.

(*c*) the even integers.   (*d*) The integers.

(*e*) The integers from 1 to 36 inclusive.

3. Use assumption (A5) to show that if $a(b + c) = ab + ac$, then $(b + c)a = ba + ca$, where a, b, and c are rational numbers.

2. FIRST DEFINITION OF A GROUP

The word "group," like many other words such as "ring," "field," and "function," is a specifically defined term in mathematics, and the technical definition used by mathematicians is not the usual one to which most people are accustomed. (Read what Kasner and Newman have to say about this in *Mathematics and the Imagination* (New York, Simon and Schuster, 1940), pp. 4–5.) A group is a type of mathematical system.

Definition. *A **mathematical system** consists of a set of objects, one or more operations on these objects, and certain assumptions about the objects and the operations.*

Though the group is one of the simplest mathematical systems, the theory of groups is of fundamental importance to all of modern mathematics, and it has many useful applications to other branches of science.

The statements in the following definition are often referred to as the group axioms, or the group postulates.

Definition. *A **group** G is a nonempty set of elements and a binary operation* $\circ$ *for which the following conditions are satisfied.*

(*G*1) *G is closed with respect to* $\circ$.

(*G*2) *The associative law holds in G; that is,*
   $a \circ (b \circ c) = (a \circ b) \circ c$, *when a, b, and c are elements in G.*

(*G*3) *There is an identity element e in G such that*
   $e \circ a = a = a \circ e$, *for all elements a in G.*

(*G*4) *For each element a in G there is in G an inverse element of a denoted by* a^* *(read "a inverse") such that*
   $a \circ a^* = e = a^* \circ a.$

Definition. *A group G is a **finite group** if the number of elements in the set G is finite. Otherwise it is an **infinite group**.*

Before giving examples of groups we call the reader's attention to the following items.

An inverse element belongs to a *single* element and when operating on this element either on the right or on the left produces the identity element.

The identity element has the property of leaving *every* element unchanged when operating on it either on the right or on the left.

We shall usually say that "a set is a group with respect to an operation" rather than "a set and an operation form a group."

Other definitions of a group exist. We have chosen to consider this definition of a group first because it is easy to apply. The main objection to this definition is that the inverse is defined *in terms of* the identity. This presents difficulties in testing the independence of the group axioms.

Example **1.**   The integers J form a group under addition. To show that this is true we check each group axiom. Axiom $(G1)$ is satisfied, since the sum of two integers is an integer. Axiom $(G2)$ is satisfied by $(A2)$. Axiom $(G3)$ is satisfied by the number zero which serves as an identity element since $0 + a = a = a + 0$ for *every* integer a. For each integer a, the inverse is $-a$, since $a + (-a) = 0 = (-a) + a$, and thus $(G4)$ is satisfied. Since all of the group axioms are satisfied, the integers J form a group under addition. The integers are an infinite set; therefore, this is an infinite group.

Observe that 0 is the identity for *all* integers, while *each* integer has its own inverse. Thus -3 is the inverse of 3, and 3 is the inverse of -3, but 5 is the inverse of -5, and 0 is its own inverse.

Example **2.**   The nonzero rational numbers form a group under multiplication. The verification of $(G1)$ is one of the exercises on the closure property, and $(G2)$ follows from $(A3)$. Let p/q, where $q \neq 0$ and p are integers, represent a rational number. Then $(G3)$ is verified by observing that $e = 1$; for $(p/q) \cdot 1 = p/q = 1 \cdot (p/q)$, for every rational number p/q. If p/q is a nonzero rational number then $p \neq 0$ and the inverse is q/p since $(p/q) \cdot (q/p) = 1 = (q/p) \cdot (p/q)$; therefore $(G4)$ is verified. There is an infinite number of rational numbers; therefore, this is an infinite group.

***Example* 3.** The numbers 1 and -1 form a group under multiplication. In order to verify the first axiom we need only observe that the products involved are those obtained by multiplying 1 by 1, 1 by -1, and -1 by -1. Since each of these products yields 1 or -1, the set is closed with respect to multiplication. $(G2)$ follows from $(A3)$. As in the second example $e = 1$ and $(G3)$ is verified. We shall verify $(G4)$ by indicating the inverse of each element. Thus 1 is its own inverse, since $1 \cdot 1 = 1 = 1 \cdot 1$, and -1 is its own inverse since $(-1)(-1) = 1 = (-1)(-1)$. This is a finite group of two elements.

***Example* 4.** The objects 1, x, and x^2, where $x^3 = 1$ and these objects satisfy (A3), form a group under multiplication. In order to verify the first axiom we make the accompanying multiplication table. The fact that the interior of the table contains only the elements

	1	x	x^2
1	1	x	x^2
x	x	x^2	1
x^2	x^2	1	x

Multiplication Table

1, x, and x^2 indicates that this set is closed with respect to multiplication, hence $(G1)$ is verified; $(G2)$ is satisfied by the fact that it was given that the elements satisfy $(A3)$; and $(G3)$ is satisfied by the element 1. As in Example 3, we verify that inverses exist by indicating them. The element 1 is its own inverse; and each of the elements x and x^2 is the inverse of the other; therefore, $(G4)$ is satisfied. This is a finite group of three elements.

Definition. *The **order** of a finite group is the number of elements in the group. Infinite groups are of **infinite order**.*

Example 3 is a group of order 2, Example 4 is a group of order 3, and Examples 1 and 2 are groups of infinite order.

EXERCISES

1. When group axiom $(G2)$ is satisfied for a given set and a given operation we say that the operation is associative with respect to the set. Which of the four fundamental operations of arithmetic are associative when the elements operated on are the integers?

2. With respect to the operation of addition which of the following are groups? For each of these which is not a group indicate one axiom which is not satisfied.

(a) The even integers.

(b) The integral multiples of three; that is, $0, 3, -3, 6, -6, \cdots$.

(c) The set consisting of zero alone.

(d) The set consisting of the number 1 only.

(e) The odd integers.

(f) All numbers of the form $a + b \sqrt{2}$, where a and b are rational numbers.*

(g) All integral multiples of a fixed integer n.

(h) All numbers of the form $a + b \sqrt{2}$, where a and b are integers.*

(i) The rational numbers.

3. With respect to the operation of multiplication which of the following are groups? For each of these which is not a group indicate one axiom which is not satisfied.

(a) The positive integers.   (b) The even integers.

(c) The rational numbers.   (d) The odd integers.

(e) The set consisting of zero alone.

(f) The number 1 alone.

(g) All numbers of the form $a + b \sqrt{2}$, where a and b are rational numbers, with $0 + 0 \cdot \sqrt{2}$ omitted.

(h) All integral multiples of a fixed integer $n \neq 0$.

(i) All numbers of the form $a + b \sqrt{2}$, where a and b are integers, with $0 + 0 \cdot \sqrt{2}$ omitted.

(j) All integral powers of a fixed integer $n \neq 0$.

4. Show that each of these sets forms a group under the indicated operation.

(a) The rotations of the accompanying figure which leave the picture unchanged; that is, rotations through multiples of 60°, where the operation ○ acting on two rotations means that the first rotation is applied to the original figure and the second rotation is applied to the figure in the new position.

---

* Assume that the irrational numbers of the form $a + b \sqrt{2}$ are added, subtracted, multiplied, and divided according to the rules of high school algebra.

FIG. 1

(b) The numbers 1, −1, a, and −a, under multiplication, if these numbers and letters are multiplied as in high school algebra, except that $a^2 = -1$.

5. Do the integers form a group under the operation $\circ$, where $a \circ b = 2a + b$?

6. (a) Why must zero be omitted in Example 2?
(b) Why is $0 + 0 \cdot \sqrt{2}$ omitted in Exercises 3(g) and 3(i)?

7. (a) Give four examples of finite groups.
(b) Give four examples of infinite groups.

8. Summarize the information obtained thus far in this section by making two charts, the first indicating all groups under the headings "Set" and "Operation"; and the second indicating all sets which are not groups under the operations considered, along with the group axioms which are not satisfied. For the second chart use the headings "Set," "Operation," and "Axioms not satisfied."

3. COMMUTATIVE OR ABELIAN GROUPS

Definition.   *Two elements a and b are said to **commute** (or to be commutative) with respect to an operation $\circ$ if $a \circ b = b \circ a$.*

Definition.   *The **center** of a group is the set of all elements of the group which commute with **every** element of the group.*

Symbolically, the center of a group G is the set of all x in G such that $x \circ g = g \circ x$, for every element g of G.

Does every group have a center? By ($G3$) the identity element commutes with *every* element of the group, therefore it must be in the center. For some groups the center consists of just one element; namely, the identity. For others it contains more than just the identity, yet does not contain all elements, and is therefore a *proper subset* of the set of elements in the group. Sometimes it is the whole group. If the center is the whole group, the group is called a commutative or abelian group.

Definition. *A group G is* **commutative** *or* **abelian** *if* $a \circ b = b \circ a$ *for all elements a and b in G.*

If a group is not commutative, it is *noncommutative* or *nonabelian*. All of the group examples given in the preceding section are commutative.

4. AN EXAMPLE OF A NONCOMMUTATIVE GROUP

Let an equilateral triangle be placed with its centroid at the origin of a rectangular coordinate system in the xy-plane and let one of the vertices lie on the positive part of the x-axis. Number the vertices as indicated by the accompanying figure and consider some simple motions which, when applied to the triangle, bring it to rest in the same place. Even though the triangle moves, the lines OA, OB, and Ox remain fixed in their original positions.

If the triangle is given a turn of 180° about the line OA *as an axis*, vertex 3 will remain fixed and vertices 1 and 2 will be interchanged. Such a motion is a reflection about the line OA. It turns the triangle over in space. Then the triangle occupies the same space but the vertices are in different positions. Similarly, a reflection about the line OB will interchange the vertices 1 and 3 but leave vertex 2 fixed, and a reflection about the line Ox will interchange 2 and 3 but leave 1 fixed.

A 120° rotation of the triangle about the origin which keeps the triangle always in the plane, replaces 2 by 1; 3 by 2; and 1 by 3. A 240° rotation replaces 3 by 1; 2 by 3; and 1 by 2.

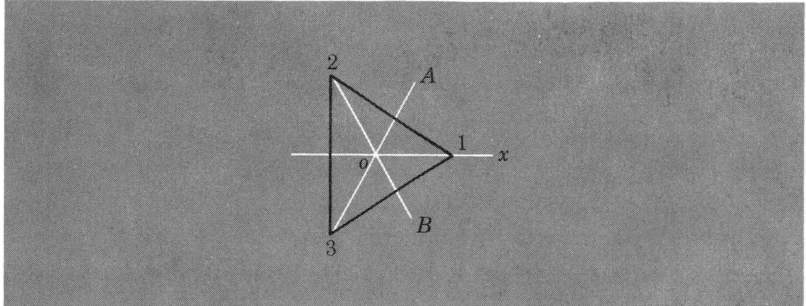

FIG. 2

We observe that leaving the triangle unmoved causes it to occupy the same position. It will prove convenient for us to include in the set of motions which we are considering that motion which results in no change of the vertices, just as it is convenient to have zero in the counting numbers.

We shall designate these six motions as follows:

I = the motion which causes no change of vertices,
T = a rotation through 120°,
T' = a rotation through 240°,
H = a reflection in the line OA,
K = a reflection in the line OB,
L = a reflection in the line Ox.

These six motions are usually referred to as the *symmetries of an equilateral triangle*.

Now we can consider the symmetries of an equilateral triangle as elements of a set and define on them an operation $\circ$ which will indicate that the first motion is to be followed by the second. Thus $T \circ K$ means that the triangle is first rotated through 120°, then reflected in the line OB. Since this gives the same result as the motion H, reflection in OA, applied to the original figure, we shall say that $T \circ K = H$. (Sketches or cardboard models may be helpful here.)

In order to systematize the work we make Table 1 for this operation. Let the horizontal spaces be called *rows* and the vertical spaces be called *columns*. To enter a result like $T \circ K = H$, we place H at the intersection of the row starting with T and the column headed by K.

$\circ$	I	T	T'	H	K	L
I	I	T	T'	H	K	L
T	T	T'	I	L	H	K
T'	T'	I	T	K	L	H
H	H	K	L	I	T	T'
K	K	L	H	T'	I	T
L	L	H	K	T	T'	I

Table 1

We then find $K \circ T$. This means that the figure is reflected in the line OB, then rotated through $120°$. The result is the same as the motion L applied to the original figure. Therefore, $K \circ T = L$, and we place this result at the intersection of the row starting with K and the column headed by T. Similarly, we find the result of applying the operation to every pair of elements and complete the table.

Observe that since $T \circ K \neq K \circ T$, the set contains noncommutative elements under this operation.

Does this set form a group under this operation?

Axion $(G1)$ is satisfied since the interior of the table contains only these six elements.

Axiom $(G3)$ is satisfied by I.

We exhibit the inverses to show that $(G4)$ is satisfied. T and T' are inverses, and each of the remaining elements is its own inverse. (To find the inverse of an element such as T, locate T on the left side of the table. Look for the identity I in the horizontal row starting with T. This procedure shows that $T \circ T' = I$. Next locate T' on the left of the table to see if $T' \circ T = I$. Since it does $(G4)$ is satisfied and T and T' are inverses.)

To show that $(G2)$ is satisfied we consider what happens to the vertices as the result of these motions.

For example, consider $(T \circ L) \circ T'$. The motion T, which is a rotation through $120°$, moves the vertex in position 1 into 2 position. Then the motion L, which is a reflection in Ox, sends the vertex in 2 position into 3 position. Therefore the motion $T \circ L$ sends the vertex in 1 position into 3 position.

T	L	$T \circ L$
1 into 2	2 into 3	1 into 3

The third motion T', which is a rotation through 240°, always sends the vertex in 3 position into 2 position.

$T \circ L$	T'	$(T \circ L) \circ T'$
1 into 3	3 into 2	1 into 2

Now consider $T \circ (L \circ T')$.

L	T'	$L \circ T'$
2 into 3	3 into 2	2 into 2
T	$L \circ T'$	$T \circ (L \circ T')$
1 into 2	2 into 2	1 into 2

Therefore in this specific case $(T \circ L) \circ T'$ and $T \circ (L \circ T')$ both send vertex 1 into vertex 2. Similar arguments will show that $(T \circ L) \circ T'$ and $T \circ (L \circ T')$ send vertex 2 into vertex 1, and vertex 3 into vertex 3. Therefore $(T \circ L) \circ T' = T \circ (L \circ T')$.

We want to know whether or not the associative law holds. This means that we want to know whether the result of the first two operations followed by the third is the same as the first operation followed by the result of the second and third. Unless there is some difference in what happens at some vertex then there is no difference in the entire motion, for every motion under consideration can be described in terms of its effect on the vertices.

Let us keep the argument absolutely general by using letters which may represent the same number, or distinct numbers. One motion sends the vertex in j position into k position, a second motion sends the vertex in k position into m position, and a third motion sends the vertex in m position into n position. Thus, when j, k, m, and n represent the vertex numbers, we shall represent the changes in vertices, j into k, k into m, m into n, by $j \to k$, $k \to m$, and $m \to n$, respectively. The symmetries of the equilateral triangle are associative if, for all choices of the vertices,

$$[(j \to k) \circ (k \to m)] \circ (m \to n) = (j \to k) \circ [(k \to m) \circ (m \to n)].$$

The result of $j \to k$ followed by $k \to m$ is $j \to m$, and the result of $k \to m$ followed by $m \to n$ is $k \to n$. After substituting these results we ask if

$$(j \to m) \circ (m \to n) = (j \to k) \circ (k \to n).$$

Each side of this expression represents $j \to n$, therefore these sides are equal. This shows that the same final result is obtained for a vertex by associating the elements differently. Since the position of the triangle is determined by the position of its vertices we conclude that associating the symmetries differently produces the same final result for the entire triangle; therefore, $(G2)$ is satisfied. Since all of the group axioms are satisfied, and certain elements do not commute, the set forms a noncommutative group under the given operation. It falls into a class of groups called *dihedral groups*.

One might ask whether a noncommutative group of fewer elements would be easier to understand. The answer is that it can be proved that all groups with fewer than six elements are commutative; hence a noncommutative group must contain *at least* six elements.

Remark.   Perhaps the reader may feel that it is easier to test associativity by checking *all* possible cases. From 6 objects we can obtain 20 distinct sets, each set consisting of 3 distinct objects. What is involved in testing *one* such set, say the set containing T, K, and L? We must consider all possible arrangements of these three objects and the two groupings of each arrangement. Thus we obtain

$$(T \circ K) \circ L \quad \text{and} \quad T \circ (K \circ L),$$
$$(T \circ L) \circ K \quad \text{and} \quad T \circ (L \circ K),$$
$$(K \circ L) \circ T \quad \text{and} \quad K \circ (L \circ T),$$
$$(K \circ T) \circ L \quad \text{and} \quad K \circ (T \circ L),$$
$$(L \circ T) \circ K \quad \text{and} \quad L \circ (T \circ K),$$
$$(L \circ K) \circ T \quad \text{and} \quad L \circ (K \circ T).$$

Then it is necessary to find the results of these operations from the table to see if the two expressions on each horizontal line are equal. For the first line $H \circ L = T'$ and $T \circ T = T'$; therefore the expressions on the first lines are equal. For the second line, $K \circ K = I$ and $T \circ T' = I$, therefore the expressions on the second line are equal. Thus each line must be checked and the table must be consulted many times to test this one set consisting of T, K, and L. Since there are twenty sets which contain distinct elements and twelve group arrangements of each set there are 240 grouped arrangements to consider. This does not include grouped arrangements involving elements that are not distinct, such as $(T \circ T) \circ K$ and $T \circ (T \circ K)$, or $(T \circ T) \circ T$ and $T \circ (T \circ T)$. These must also be considered in order to exhaust all possibilities.

5. FURTHER DISCUSSION OF THE NON-COMMUTATIVE GROUP

Let us describe the symmetries of an equilateral triangle in terms of their effect on the vertices. We shall denote H by (12) since it interchanges the vertices 1 and 2; K by (13) since it interchanges the vertices 1 and 3; and L by (23) since it interchanges the vertices 2 and 3.

We shall denote T by (123) since it sends 1 into 2, 2 into 3, and 3 into 1. This notation attaches a cyclic interpretation to a symbol like $(ijkm)$. Each object is changed into the one on the right if there is one on the right; and, if not, it is changed into the first object. Thus $(ijkm)$ means that i is changed to j, j to k, k to m, and m to i. Such a symbol is called a *permutation*. We shall also denote T' by (132) since it sends 1 into 3, 3 into 2, and 2 into 1. If now, we also denote I by the symbol (1), which shall mean that there is no change in the objects, we can make a new type of table for the example under consideration.

How does one then find the element equal to (23) ○ (132)? This is done by writing down the numbers in their regular order and then indicating under each number the number it has been changed to, and finally summing up the changes by reading the first and last lines. For example, to find the product (23) ○ (132) we write, in the first row, the numbers involved to obtain

$$1 \quad 2 \quad 3.$$

Since (23) instructs us to replace 2 by 3, we write 3 beneath 2. Similarly, (23) instructs us to replace 3 by 2, and to leave 1 unchanged. We therefore put 2 beneath 3 and 1 beneath 1, thus producing a second row. We now have

$$\begin{matrix} 1 & 2 & 3 \\ 1 & 3 & 2. \end{matrix}$$

Then (132) instructs us to replace 1 by 3, 3 by 2, and 2 by 1. This is applied to the second row to produce a third row. Under the 1 in the second row, we put 3, under the 3 in the second row, we put 2, and under 2 we put 1. We then have

$$1 \quad 2 \quad 3$$
$$1 \quad 3 \quad 2$$
$$3 \quad 2 \quad 1.$$

For the sake of clarity the explanation is repeated here followed by the instruction as to how to obtain the final result. The second line indicates that 1 was replaced by 1, 2 by 3, and 3 by 2, as instructed by (23). The third line indicates that 1 was replaced by 3, 3 by 2, and 2 by 1, as indicated by (132). The net result is found by reading only the first and last lines, disregarding the middle line. These lines indicate that 1 was replaced by 3, and 3 by 1, and that 2 remained unchanged. Thus (23) o (132) = (13).

This new type of notation makes it possible to find the result of one element operating on another without referring to a figure or to the type of motion. All entries for Table 2 can readily be computed by the procedure described in this section.

o	(1)	(123)	(132)	(12)	(13)	(23)
(1)						
(123)						
(132)						
(12)						
(13)						
(23)			(13)			

Table 2

As further examples of the result of combining two permutations we have that if $p = (13465)$ and $q = (563)$, then $p \circ q = (15)(34)$ as follows:

$$1 \quad 2 \quad 3 \quad 4 \quad 5 \quad 6$$
$$3 \quad 2 \quad 4 \quad 6 \quad 1 \quad 5$$
$$5 \quad 2 \quad 4 \quad 3 \quad 1 \quad 6.$$

Also $q \circ p = (13)(46)$, and $p \circ p = (14536)$.

In exercises involving permutations no operation will be indicated since it will be understood that permutations are to be combined according to the instructions given here.*

---

* Some authors reverse the order of the elements in defining the binary operation on permutations.

Suggestion for Finding the Center. If a group table is available, it is easy to find the elements which are in the center. To test a given element A consider the corresponding entries in the column headed by A and the row beginning with A. If the first entries are the same, consider the second. If the second entries are the same, consider the third. If, by proceeding in this manner, two corresponding elements are found which are unequal, then A is not in the center. If all corresponding elements are equal then $A \circ B = B \circ A$ for all B in the group and A is in the center. This checking can be done very easily by simultaneously moving the right hand from left to right along the row and the left hand down the column.

The reader may be encouraged to redouble his efforts to learn something about groups when he reads the following quotation from an address delivered by Richard V. Andree. His audience consisted of high school and college teachers of mathematics who were attending a National Science Foundation Summer Institute.

Group theory is very much in demand. I just this year found out about one of the uses of group theory, so it is fascinating to me. The physics department asked me some questions about group theory last fall, which I answered. Later I asked them why they were interested in group theory. They told me! When they got done, I found myself attending an hour seminar every Wednesday learning why physicists like group theory. One use is in the study of the structure of molecules. Consider a molecule—say methane, CH_4. The chemist tells us that it has one carbon atom and four hydrogen atoms. Now, the question is, "Just how are these atoms arranged?" They might be arranged with the four hydrogen atoms at the vertices of a square and the carbon at its center, or they might be arranged with the four hydrogens at the vertices of a tetrahedron and the carbon at the center. Other arrangements are also conceivable. With any of these arrangements, the hydrogen atoms have several possible motions. They are in constant vibration. In the tetrahedron arrangement, for example, they may have a motion where all four hydrogens go in together, and then go out together. They may have a sort of breather motion in which two atoms go in as the other two go out. In investigating this problem, the so-called space groups are set up and the space groups predict that if a certain structure were present then infra-red rays would excite a certain type of motion. In a similar fashion it is possible to predict that x-rays or beta rays, or Raman spectroscopy would have certain effects on the vibration pattern. Laboratory tests are conducted to see whether or not these effects are observed. Prediction and observation are then combined to determine the molecular structure and vibration pattern.

EXERCISES

The operation ○ used in the following exercises means the first motion followed by the second motion.

1. Make a table like Table 2 and fill in the proper elements. Then check with Table 1.

2. Show that the symmetries of a square form a noncommutative group under ○. This is called the octic group. It is one of the dihedral groups. (Make a table. It will be needed for other exercises.)

3. How many symmetries will a regular polygon of n sides have?

4. Do the symmetries of a regular polygon of n sides form a group under ○?

5. What is the center of the group of symmetries of a square?

6. What is the center of the group of symmetries of an equilateral triangle?

7. Do the symmetries of a rectangle form a group under ○?

8. Which of the elements in Exercise 7 commute with all elements in the set?

9. Give an argument similar to the one used for the symmetries of the equilateral triangle to show that permutations obey the associative law with respect to the operation defined on them.

10. Do the following eight permutations form a group?
(1), (13), (24), (1234), (12)(34), (13)(24), (14)(23), (1432)

11. A two-by-three matrix is a rectangular array having two rows and three columns, which can be denoted by $\begin{pmatrix} a & b & c \\ d & f & g \end{pmatrix}$.

The entries $a, b, c, d, f,$ and g are the elements of the matrix, and two matrices are equal if and only if the corresponding elements are equal.

(a) If the elements of a set of two-by-three matrices are integers and if the matrices are "added" by adding corresponding elements; that is, if

$$\begin{pmatrix} a & b & c \\ d & f & g \end{pmatrix} \oplus \begin{pmatrix} r & s & t \\ u & v & w \end{pmatrix} = \begin{pmatrix} a+r & b+s & c+t \\ d+u & f+v & g+w \end{pmatrix},$$

does this set of matrices form a group under $\oplus$?

(b) If the elements are rational numbers does the set form a group under this operation of matrix addition?

(c) Do these matrices commute under this operation?

6. SUBGROUPS

Definition. *A nonempty subset H of a group G is a* **subgroup** *of G if H is a group with respect to the operation of G.*

Every group has at least two subgroups; namely, the whole group and the group consisting of the identity alone. These two subgroups are called *improper* subgroups, and all other subgroups are called *proper* subgroups.

Example 1. The set of all even integers is a subgroup of the set of all integers under addition. In fact, the set of all integral multiples of a fixed integer k is a subgroup of the integers under addition. (Show that the group axioms are satisfied.)

Example 2. The set consisting of the numbers 1 and -1 is a subgroup of the non-zero rational numbers under multiplication. So also is the set of numbers of the form 2^n where n is an integer. (Verify the group axioms.)

Example 3. The set of symmetries of an equilateral triangle has the following six subgroups: The whole group; I, T, T'; I, H; I, K; I, L; and I. Which of these subgroups are abelian?

7. GROUP GENERATORS

One of the best ways to find subgroups of a given group is to assume that one or more group elements are in a certain subgroup and then determine what other elements this subgroup must contain. For example, if a subgroup of the group of symmetries of an equilateral triangle contains the element T' what else must it contain? Since it is closed, it must contain $T' \circ T' = T$, and since it contains T' and T it must contain $T' \circ T = I$. If the group is finite, perhaps the easiest way to determine all elements in the subgroup is to make a table.

First enter T' at the top and side of the table, then enter $T' \circ T' = T$ at the proper place. Since a new element T has been obtained, T is then entered at the top and side of the table and we have the partial Table 3. If now we enter $T' \circ T = I$, $T \circ T' = I$, and $T \circ T = T'$

	T'	T
T'	T	
T		

	T'	T
T'	T	I
T	I	T'

	T'	T	I
T'	T	I	
T	I	T'	
I			

| *Table 3* | *Table 4* | *Table 5* |

we obtain Table 4 and the new element I must be entered at the top and side of the table. This produces Table 5. Since $I \circ A = A$ for every element A of a group, no new elements are needed to complete Table 5. Does this show that I, T, and T' form a subgroup? This set is closed. It has an identity element, and an inverse for each element. The associative law must hold for the subgroup, otherwise there would be elements in the group which would not obey the associative law. Therefore the elements I, T, and T' form a subgroup of order three. Since $T' = T'$, $T = T' \circ T'$, and $I = T' \circ T' \circ T'$, it is possible to express the elements of this subgroup in terms of T'; therefore T' is the *generator* of this subgroup. It is often convenient to use the following notation: $A^2 = A \circ A$, $A^3 = A \circ A \circ A$, etc., and to speak of A^2, A^3 etc., as *positive powers* of the group element A. Thus the positive powers of T' form a subgroup of order three. The reader should ask whether the subgroup generated by T' can be generated by some other element. If so, there is another element such that its powers are equal to I, T, and T'.

As a second example let us consider the group generated by the element $B = (1234)$. We find that $B^2 = (13)(24)$, $B^3 = (1432)$, and $B^4 = (1)$; therefore B generates a group of order 4.

Groups can be generated by more than one element. What group is generated by the elements (12) and (132)? If the reader would set up a table, enter the given elements and find what other elements can be obtained from them he would find that $(12) \circ (12) = (1)$, $(12) \circ (132) = (23)$, $(132) \circ (12) = (13)$, $(132) \circ (132) = (123)$, and that the two given elements generate the symmetric group of six elements.

Definition. *A finite group is* **generated** *by the elements* a_1, a_2, a_3, $\cdots$, a_k *if every element of the group can be expressed in terms of these elements and the group operation.*

When the preceding definition is satisfied the elements a_1, a_2, a_3, $\cdots$, a_k are the *group generators* of the finite group.

To find the subgroups of a given finite group systematically, first find the subgroups generated by each of the elements, then find those generated by two of the elements, then those generated by three elements. Continue this procedure until it is no longer possible to increase the number of group generators.

If a group is infinite the positive powers of an element may not form a subgroup. For example, the integers form a group under addition, but the positive powers of 1 are 1, $1 + 1 = 2$, $1 + 1 + 1 = 3$, etc. The set of positive powers of 1 is the set of positive integers, which is not a group under addition. If both 1 and its additive inverse -1 are used as generators, a subgroup is obtained. Thus to generate an infinite group we use a given set of elements and their inverses.

Definition. *An infinite group is* **generated** *by the elements* a_1, a_2, a_3, $\cdots$, *if every element of the group can be expressed in terms of these elements, their inverses, and the group operation.*

When the preceding definition is satisfied the elements a_1, a_2, a_3, $\cdots$ are the *group generators* of the infinite group.

8. CYCLIC GROUPS

Let e represent the identity element of a group G, and for each element h in G let h^* represent its inverse. If $h^0 = e$, $h^1 = h$, $h^2 = h \circ h$, $h^3 = h \circ h \circ h$, etc., and $h^{-1} = h^*$, $h^{-2} = h^* \circ h^*$, $h^{-3} = h^* \circ h^* \circ h^*$, etc., then h^0, h^1, h^{-1}, h^2, h^{-2}, h^3, h^{-3}, $\cdots$ are *the integral powers* of h (or, for brevity, *the powers* of h). It can be shown that these powers obey the following laws of exponents.

If m and n are integers, then

$$(1)\ \ h^m \circ h^n = h^{m+n} \qquad\qquad (2)\ \ \left(h^m\right)^n = h^{mn}$$

The verification of these laws is left as an exercise.*

It is not necessarily true that $(h \circ r)^t$ is equal to $h^t \circ r^t$, where r is also in G. Why?

The powers of a given element h of a group G form a subgroup S of G.

To show closure in S we observe that $h^m \circ h^n = h^{m+n}$, where $m + n$ is an integer, and h^{m+n} is therefore an integral power of h, hence h^{m+n} is in S. The associative law holds in S, for if $(h^m \circ h^n) \circ h^t \neq h^m \circ (h^n \circ h^t)$, then since h^m, h^n, and h^t are elements of G, the associative law would not hold in G. In S there is $h^0 = e$, and therefore S contains an identity element. Also for each h^m in S there is h^{-m} in S and since $h^m \circ h^{-m} = e = h^{-m} \circ h^m$, then h^{-m} is the inverse of h^m; that is, $h^{-m} = (h^m)^*$.

Definition. *A group G is a* **cyclic group** *if there is an element h in G such that every element of G is an integral power of h.*

The element h is a *generator* of the group G.

We have just shown that the integral powers of a group element form a cyclic subgroup of the original group.

Definition. *The* **order** *of a group element is the order of the cyclic subgroup which it generates.*

Example 1. The permutation group (1), (123), (132) is a cyclic group of order three. Either of the elements (123) or (132) can generate the group. Therefore (123) and (132) are elements of order three.

Example 2. The integers form an infinite cyclic group under addition. The number 1 is the group generator.

Example 3. The numbers 1, -1, a, and $-a$, under multiplication, where these numbers and letters are multiplied as in high school algebra, except that $a^2 = -1$, form a cyclic group of order four. The element a generates the group since $a^1 = a$, $a^2 = -1$, $a^3 = -a$, and $a^4 = 1$. The element $-a$ is also a group generator. The element -1 generates a cyclic subgroup of order two.

---

* See Garrett Birkhoff and Saunders MacLane, *A Survey of Modern Algebra* (New York, Macmillan, 1953), pp. 133–134.

EXERCISES

1. List at least two proper subgroups of the following groups and tell which of the subgroups are abelian.

(a) The even integers under addition.

(b) The nonzero rational numbers under multiplication.

2. The group of symmetries of the square has ten subgroups. Five of them contain two elements, and three of them contain four elements.

(a) List all of the subgroups.

(b) Tell which subgroups are abelian.

3. (a) Show that the following twelve permutations form a group.

(1), (123), (132), (124), (142), (134), (143), (234), (243), (12)(34), (13)(24), (14)(32).

(b) Find the center of this group.

(c) Find all subgroups.

4. Make a chart in which you list all finite groups known to you along with their subgroups and the order of all groups involved. Use the headings "Finite Group," "Order of Group," "Subgroup," and "Order of Subgroup."

5. If m and n are integers and h and r are elements of a group G, show that

(a) $h^m \circ h^n = h^{m+n}$;   (b) $(h^m)^n = h^{mn}$;

(c) $(h \circ r)^t$ is not necessarily equal to $h^t \circ r^t$.

6. Find the permutation group generated by (13524). Give the order of the group and find all of the group generators.

7. Let x represent an element of a group G such that $x^6 = e$, where e is the identity element in G. For the cyclic subgroup generated by x find

(a) the order of the subgroup,

(b) the inverse of each group element,

(c) the order of each element,

(d) all subgroups.

8. If we assume that the elements 1, x, y, and xy are multiplied like numbers and letters in algebra and if $x^2 = 1$, $y^2 = 1$, and $xy = yx$, then these four elements form a group under multiplication, known as the *fours group*.

(a) Make a chart which will show that this set is closed under multiplication.

(b) Find the inverse of each group element.

(c) Find the order of each group element.

(d) Find all subgroups of this group.

9. REMARKS ON THE ORIGIN OF GROUPS

The student who delves into the origin of group theory uncovers many interesting facts about mathematics and mathematicians.

The group concept grew out of attempts to solve algebraic or polynomial equations.* We shall give the general form of this type of equation for the first five degrees along with some historical information. The following chart indicates who produced, for each general equation, an *algebraic solution* or a *solution by radicals*. By an *algebraic solution*, or a *solution by radicals*, we mean a *solution which can be obtained from the coefficients by a finite number of additions, subtractions, multiplications, divisions, and root extractions.* For example, $x^4 - 27x^2 + 48x - 48 = 0$ can be solved algebraically and its roots are $\dfrac{-\sqrt{3} \pm \sqrt{51 + 32\sqrt{3}}}{2}, \dfrac{\sqrt{3} \pm \sqrt{51 - 32\sqrt{3}}}{2}$.

The algebraic expression for the solution of the first degree equation $ax + b = 0$ is $x = -b/a$. A specific example of this type of problem is solved in the Ahmes papyrus, an Egyptian manuscript found in Egypt about one hundred years ago.† This papyrus, now in the British Museum, gets its name from the Egyptian scribe Ahamesu, though it

---

* An *algebraic* or *polynomial equation* is an equation obtained by setting a polynomial equal to zero. A polynomial in x of degree n is an expression which can be put into the form

$$a_0x^n + a_1x^{n-1} + a_2x^{n-2} + \cdots + a_n, \quad \text{where} \quad a_0, a_1, a_2, \cdots, a_n$$

are real or complex constants, $a_0 \neq 0$, and n is a nonnegative integer. (If the set of polynomials, rather than the set of polynomial equations, is under consideration it may be convenient to let n be zero. Then the polynomial is of degree zero and is a nonzero constant. The zero polynomial is the number 0. It does not have any degree.)

† This papyrus is a copy of an older one written about 2200 B.C.

Kind	Equation $(a \neq 0)$	Solved first by	Date
First degree or Linear	$ax + b = 0$	Egyptians	4,000 years ago
Second degree or Quadratic	$ax^2 + bx + c = 0$	Hindus and Arabs*	
Third degree or Cubic	$ax^3 + bx^2 + cx + d = 0$	Tartaglia (Italian)	1540
Fourth degree or Quartic	$ax^4 + bx^3 + cx^2 + dx + e = 0$	Ferrari (Italian)	Before 1550
Fifth degree or Quintic	$ax^5 + bx^4 + cx^3 + dx^2 + ex + f = 0$		

is also referred to as the Rhind papyrus, in honor of the first English-man who owned it. One of the problems stated there as "Hau, its whole, its seventh, it makes nineteen" would be stated today as "There is a number which when added to one-seventh of itself will produce nineteen." (The word "hau" is the Egyptian word for "unknown.") By present day methods we would write

$$x + \frac{x}{7} = 19,$$
$$7x + x = 133,$$
$$8x = 133,$$
$$x = 16\tfrac{5}{8}.$$

One author says that this procedure takes about one-tenth the time that it would take to read the complicated steps in the translation of the Egyptian solution.†

Our speed in dealing with this problem is due to our modern nota-tion. In fact, the progress of algebra was long hampered by cumber-some notation. At one time mathematicians used R to represent a number, Z to represent its square, and C to represent its cube. The letters p and m stood for plus and minus signs, which were not intro-duced until 1489 by the German Widmann. Thus the expression which we now write as $x^2 + 5x - 4$ would have been written as

$$1 \quad Z \quad p. \quad 5 \quad R \quad m. \quad 4$$

in a textbook written at that time. In 1572, Bombelli published an

* See Edward Kasner and James Newman, *Mathematics and the Imagina-tion* (New York, Simon and Schuster, 1940), p. 17.

† See D. E. Smith, *History of Mathematics* (New York, Ginn, 1925).

algebra in which he used 1 for the unknown quantity, 2 for its square, and 3 for its cube. Thus he wrote this expression as

$$1 \quad 2 \quad p. \quad 5 \quad 1 \quad m. \quad 4,$$

and Stevinus employed ①, ②, ③ in a similar way to write

$$1 \quad ② + 5 \quad ① - 4 \quad ⓪.$$

Vieta (1540–1603) used "A quadratus" and "A cubus" to represent the square and the cube of the unknown. It is a tribute to his skill that, in spite of cumbersome notation, he was able to find 23 roots of a certain algebraic equation of degree 45 when King Henry VI asked him to solve it. Had he known about negative numbers he could have found all 45 roots.* Descartes devised the present day notation x, x^2, x^3, $\cdots$ for powers, and this apparently simple contribution was a great step forward.

The solution of the general quadratic equation $ax^2 + bx + c = 0$ is

$$x = \frac{-b \pm \sqrt{b^2 - 4ac}}{2a}.$$

History does not credit any one person with this algebraic solution. E. T. Bell in his *Development of Mathematics* indicates that the Babylonians, about 2000 B.C., had verbal instructions for normalizing the equation and completing the square.

Though geometric solutions of quadratics were given in Book VI of Euclid's *Elements*, about 300 B.C., perhaps the first attempts at algebraic solutions are due to Diophantus, who lived about six centuries later. He gave rules for solving a simple equation of the first degree and a binomial quadratic, but rejected negative and imaginary roots.

Competent scholars disagree on many of the details concerning Arab and Hindu advances in algebra, yet most of them believe that both the Arabs and the Hindus could solve second degree equations. The Arab Al-Khowarizmi (about 825) and the Hindu Bhaskara (about 1150) wrote algebras and were able to solve quadratic equations geometrically and algebraically. Al-Khowarizmi considered only real and positive roots, but he recognized the existence of two roots. If

---

* See G. A. Miller, *Historical Introduction to Mathematical Literature* (New York, Macmillan, 1916), p. 227, and E. T. Bell, *Development of Mathematics*, 2nd ed. (New York, McGraw-Hill, 1945), pp. 217–219.

both roots were positive he frequently accepted only the root derived from the negative radical.

In 1540, Tartaglia solved the general cubic. This solution is frequently referred to as Cardan's solution since he was the first to publish it. It was the custom for a mathematician to withhold his discoveries until he had challenged other mathematicians to produce their own solutions. Tartaglia had given the solution to Cardan under a pledge of secrecy.*

Shortly after Tartaglia solved the general cubic, Ferrari, a pupil of Cardan's, found a solution for the general quartic and mathematicians set out in earnest to conquer the general fifth degree equation. During their search, which lasted about two hundred years, several mathematicians thought that they had solutions only to have someone find an error in each demonstration. A young Norwegian, Niels Henrick Abel (1802–1829), sent a supposed solution to a learned mathematician in Denmark but found the flaw in his reasoning even before the paper was returned to him. *He then set out to prove that such a solution for the general quintic is impossible.* The remarkable thing about this story is that he succeeded in doing this at the age of nineteen! This does not mean that a *special* fifth degree equation, such as $x^5 = 50$, has no algebraic expression which indicates its roots but it does mean that there is *no algebraic formula* which can be used for *all* fifth degree equations in the same way that the quadratic formula can be used for *all* quadratics. There is a formula involving the more complicated concept of elliptic functions, but no formula exists which involves only *algebraic expressions*. Mathematicians have even solved the general algebraic equation of degree n, but its solution involves Fuchsian functions.

No one can read the life story of Abel without lamenting the fact that this exceedingly gifted mathematician died at the age of twenty-seven of tuberculosis. It is fitting that Charles Hermite (1822–1901), a leading French mathematician of the nineteenth century and the solver of the general quintic by *elliptic* functions, could say of him without exaggeration, "Abel has left mathematicians enough to keep them busy for five hundred years." When Abel was asked how he had

---

* For a very interesting account of how Tartaglia became famous by accepting the challenge of a fellow countryman to compete in an algebra contest, see W. W. Rouse Ball, *A Short Account of the History of Mathematics* (London, Macmillan, 1927).

done all of this in the six or seven years of his working life he responded, "By studying the masters, not their pupils."*

Evariste Galois (1811–1832), a French mathematician—who, like Abel, had only a few years to work but nevertheless made outstanding contributions to mathematics—was the first person to formulate a method of determining *which* equations, regardless of their degree, are solvable by radicals. His work was so far advanced and so sketchily recorded that it did not receive due credit until many years after his death. Now it is considered so important that Galois theory is one of the standard courses in graduate mathematics. Galois theory was based on permutation groups, though the more modern approach to Galois theory is based on automorphism groups.

In the period from 1850 to 1920, groups dominated a large portion of mathematics and many prominent mathematicians such as Hamilton, Jacobi, Cauchy, Cayley, Sylvester, Jordan, Hölder, Hermite, Lie, and Klein became well versed in group theory. In fact, during this period the group was sometimes designated as the key to *all* mathematics. Today it is recognized as one of the basic concepts which have many applications, and it has taken its place among other enduring additions to the field of mathematical thought.

The present type of abstract group was introduced by Cayley in 1854, but satisfactory group postulates were not stated until the first decade of the twentieth century.

This discussion should show that a mathematical concept, such as the group concept, frequently evolves over a period of years and receives contributions directly and indirectly from many mathematicians. In this case a specific type of group; namely, the permutation group, proved to be useful in answering a question foremost in the minds of mathematicians and its use lead to the consideration of a more general type, namely the abstract group, which has now become part of the foundation of many mathematical theories.

On the applied side, it should be mentioned that within the last one hundred years the theory of groups has proved to be important in mathematical physics. It is studied in connection with quantum mechanics, one of the basic theories of atomic structure.

---

* For an interesting account of Abel's life, see E. T. Bell, *Men of Mathematics* (New York, Simon and Schuster, 1937).

10. STATEMENTS ABOUT GROUPS

One of our objectives is to produce rigorous mathematical proofs; however, we first introduce concepts frequently found in modern mathematics, many of which are new to the reader, under the basic assumption that a wealth of examples facilitates understanding of more difficult procedures, and a knowledge of mathematical systems helps in the recognition of the properties of systems frequently used. For example, after seeing nonassociative or noncommutative operations the reader can better appreciate associative or commutative operations.

Since our first objective is to build up an abundance of examples of fundamental concepts by means of an intuitive approach, we have thus far often refrained from saying that we have *proved* a given statement, and have not labeled certain basic statements as theorems, though we shall see later that some of these statements *are* theorems and some of the discussions that accompany them can be considered proofs if they are preceded by the proper undefined notions and assumptions. These statements will help us understand the forcefulness of dealing with abstract operations as well as abstract objects.

If we think constructively about groups we might ask such questions as "How many elements of a group behave like an identity?" If an element x of a group leaves every element of the group unchanged when operating on it on the left, we call it a left identity. If an element leaves every group element unchanged when operating on it on the right, it is a right identity.

Definition.   *If x is an element of a group G, and $x \circ a = a$ for every a in G, then x is a **left identity** in G.*

Definition.   *If x is an element of a group G, and $a \circ x = a$ for every a in G, then x is a **right identity** in G.*

These definitions are frequently written in a different form by using more symbolism. When dealing with sets we often use "$x \in A$" to mean that x is an element of A. Using this notation we have the following form of the first definition.

Definition.   *If $x \in G$, where G is a group, and $x \circ a = a$ for every $a \in G$, then x is a **left identity** in G.*

We now consider the question: "If x behaves like a left identity for *one* group element does it have any relation to the identity of the group?"

Since x is a left identity for some element, we know that there is an element which we shall call a, such that $x \circ a = a$. What statements can we obtain from this given statement? How do we go about getting a relationship between x and the identity e? What ammunition do we have at hand? We know that x and a are group elements. What properties does this fact bestow upon them? Since we are seeking the relationship between x and the identity e it probably is wise to choose a group property which will introduce the identity into the statements if one is available. We observe that every group element has an inverse; therefore, for the element a there is an inverse a^*, such that $a \circ a^* = e = a^* \circ a$. This statement would introduce e. We, therefore, use part of this statement and assert that

$$(1) \qquad\qquad a \circ a^* = e.$$

We combine this with the given statement $x \circ a = a$ by substitution. Since we have assumed that all operations are well defined, we can substitute for a its equal $x \circ a$ in (1), and obtain

$$(x \circ a) \circ a^* = e.$$

By the associative law we can change this to

$$x \circ (a \circ a^*) = e.$$

This simplifies to $x \circ e = e$, but since the group identity leaves every element unchanged when operating on it, it will leave x unchanged and we obtain

$$x = e.$$

Therefore, if an element behaves like a left identity for even one element of the group it *is* the identity.

The following statement and discussion present concisely what we have just observed. We denote the group G under the operation $\circ$ by $G(\circ)$.

Statement 1. *In a group $G(\circ)$, if $x \circ a = a$, then $x = e$.*

Discussion	*Reason*
There is an a^* in G such that $a \circ a^* = e$	By (G4)
$x \circ a = a$	Given
$(x \circ a) \circ a^* = e$	Substitution
$x \circ (a \circ a^*) = e$	By (G2)
$x \circ e = e$	By (G4)
$x = e$	By (G3) ∎

A Special Case of Statement 1. In a group $G(\circ)$, if $x \circ x = x$, then $x = e$.

To familiarize himself with this result the reader should (a) show how this follows from Statement 1, and (b) for practice, establish the same conclusion by using the group axioms. Further practice will be afforded if the reader now investigates what happens if an element acts as a right identity for one element. He should be able to make a statement similar to Statement 1 and to produce the steps in the discussion.

We now reflect upon the results of Statement 1. This statement really shows that there is only one identity in a group. We should observe that we could have approached this problem in an entirely different fashion. We could have started our constructive thinking about groups by asserting that a group has only one identity and attempting to "prove" this assertion. Such a start could best be handled by an indirect approach. Let us assume that there are two identities e and f. Our question is "Can e and f be distinct, or are they the same element?" How shall we proceed? We are not interested in other elements, since our question involves only e and f; therefore, it might be wise to work only with e and f. What can we do with them? There isn't much that we can do but let one of them operate on the other. We therefore consider $e \circ f$. We observe that since e is an identity, it must leave f unchanged when operating on it either on the right or on the left; therefore, $e \circ f = f$. Since we have assumed that f is also an identity, it must leave every group element unchanged when operating on it on the right or on the left; therefore, it must leave e unchanged, and $e \circ f = e$. Combining these two statements we have $e = f$. Therefore, the identities are not distinct but are equal, and there is only *one* identity in each group. We now write this statement and the discussion in concise form. Can you write down an acceptable discussion before consulting the one presented here?

Statement 2. *In a group $G(\circ)$ the identity is unique.*

Discussion.	*Reason*
Assume that there are two identities; namely, e and f.	Indirect argument
Then $\quad\quad e \circ f = f$.	By $(G3)$, since e is an identity.
Also $\quad\quad e \circ f = e$.	By $(G3)$, since f is an identity.
Therefore $\quad e = e \circ f = f$	The operation is well defined.
or $\quad\quad\quad e = f$	
and there is only one identity.	∎

We repeat our previous remark that Statements 1 and 2 are independent approaches. Actually Statement 1 is a stronger result since it says that an object which behaves like a left identity for *one* object is the two-sided identity. (Roughly speaking, we might say that any element which shows any sign of being an identity can quickly be proved to be the identity.) Whenever we assume less our conclusions are stronger in the sense that they apply to more situations. The special case of Statement 1 also says that the identity is the only element which when operating on itself leaves itself unchanged.

The next logical question would be, "How many inverses does an element of a group have?" Can you answer this question? Let us assume that an element of a group, denoted by a, has its usual inverse a^* and another inverse which we shall denote by y. Since a^* and y both satisfy $(G4)$ we have

$$a \circ a^* = e = a^* \circ a$$
and
$$a \circ y = e = y \circ a.$$
Therefore
$$a \circ a^* = a \circ y.$$

Let a^* operate on the left of each side of this equality. This produces $a^* \circ (a \circ a^*) = a^* \circ (a \circ y)$. By applying the associative law we have $(a^* \circ a) \circ a^* = (a^* \circ a) \circ y$. By using $(G4)$ again we have $e \circ a^* = e \circ y$. Using $(G3)$ we have $a^* = y$. Therefore, every element that acts like an inverse (or even like a right inverse, or a left inverse, as the reader can easily show) is a^*, and a has only one inverse.

Statement 3. *In a group $G(\circ)$ each element has a unique inverse.*

The formal discussion of this is left to the reader. Can you supply it?

Let us consider another type of discussion that can be applied to Statement 3. We start with the statement that $a^* = a^* \circ e$, and since $a \circ y = e = y \circ a$, we substitute $a \circ y$ for e, to obtain

$$a^* = a^* \circ (a \circ y). \text{ Then}$$
$$a^* = (a^* \circ a) \circ y, \text{ and}$$
$$a^* = e \circ y$$
$$a^* = y, \text{ as before.}$$

We frequently combine all of these steps into a concise presentation as follows:

Let a^* and y be any two inverses of a. Then $a \circ y = e = y \circ a$, and $a^* = a^* \circ e = a^* \circ (a \circ y) = (a^* \circ a) \circ y = e \circ y = y$.

The reader should separate this last line of equalities into its separate parts and give reasons for each part.

Remark. Observe the power of the abstract mathematical thinking involved in these statements. By Statement 2 we have reason to believe that *every* group has only one identity, regardless of the kind of objects, the number of objects, or the type of operation involved. Notice that we used only the group axioms to verify our statements rather than special properties of specific groups, therefore our arguments are perfectly general and all-inclusive as far as groups are concerned. Notice that our discussion required only a few steps to convince us that all groups have only one identity. If we had attempted to examine each group that we have encountered to discover the number of its identities, this method would be time consuming and could, at most, produce results *only for the groups considered* and not for *all* groups. It is the fact that our arguments hold for *all sets which satisfy the hypotheses* that makes them so powerful.

We now state the cancellation laws and discuss a statement about them.

Definition. *A mathematical system satisfies the **right cancellation law** for an operation $\circ$, if whenever $a \circ c = b \circ c$ then $a = b$.*

Definition. *A mathematical system satisfies the **left cancellation law** for an operation $\circ$, if whenever $c \circ a = c \circ b$ then $a = b$.*

Statement 4. *In a group the right and the left cancellation laws hold.*

Can you produce the discussion for the left cancellation law before consulting the one presented here?

Discussion for the left cancellation law. We have given that $c \circ a = c \circ b$. If we operate on the left of each side of the equality with c^* we obtain $c^* \circ (c \circ a) = c^* \circ (c \circ b)$. Then by $(G2)$ we have

$$(c^* \circ c) \circ a = (c^* \circ c) \circ b,$$

and by $(G4)$ we have $e \circ a = e \circ b,$

and finally by $(G3)$ we have $a = b.$ ∎

The discussion for the right cancellation law is left as an exercise for the reader.

Remarks. The student may find that the abstract discussions are more easily remembered if he thinks of certain specific cases and tries to generalize these. In Statement 4, if the group consisted of numbers under addition, how could he change the statement $c + a = c + b$ into the statement $a = b$? It is fairly easy to see that all he needs to do is to add $-c$ to each side. Thus $-c + (c + a) = -c + (c + b)$, or $(-c + c) + a = (-c + c) + b$, and $0 + a = 0 + b$, or $a = b$. If the group consisted of numbers under multiplication, how could he change $ca = cb$ into $a = b$? Merely by multiplying each side by $1/c$ to obtain

$$\frac{1}{c}(ca) = \frac{1}{c}(cb), \qquad \text{or} \qquad \left(\frac{1}{c} \cdot c\right) a = \left(\frac{1}{c} \cdot c\right) b,$$

and $1 \cdot a = 1 \cdot b$, or $a = b$. After considering these two examples, he should be able to observe that in each case it was necessary to operate on the left of each side of the equality, using the inverse of c under the given operation. This should suggest the general abstract procedure used in the discussion.

11. THE THEOREM OF LAGRANGE

Let S be a subgroup of a finite group G. We can consider a certain set of group elements of the form $s \circ r$ where s is an arbitrary element in S and r is a specific element in G. This set is a right coset of S, denoted by S_r.

Definition. *The **right coset** S_r of a subgroup S of a group G is the set of all elements of the form $s \circ r$ where s is an arbitrary element in S and r is a specific element in G.*

Example **1.**   In the group of symmetries of the equilateral triangle let S be the subgroup I, T, T'. Then the right coset S_H is the set $I \circ H$, $T \circ H$, and $T' \circ H$ which simplifies to H, L, and K. The right coset S_K is $I \circ K$, $T \circ K$, and $T' \circ K$ which simplifies to K, H, and L. Since S_H and S_K contain the same elements, $S_H = S_K$. Also S_I is the set $I \circ I$, $T \circ I$, and $T' \circ I$ which simplifies to I, T, and T'; and S_T is the set $I \circ T$, $T \circ T$, and $T' \circ T$ which simplifies to T, T', and I. Therefore $S_I = S_T$. In fact, the reader can show that $S = S_I = S_T = S_{T'}$ and $S_H = S_K = S_L$.

Example **2.**   In the group of symmetries of the equilateral triangle let S be the subgroup consisting of the two elements I and H. Then, using set notation*, we find that $S = \{I, H\}$, $S_T = \{T, K\}$, $S_{T'} = \{T', L\}$; that $S = S_I = S_H$; that $S_T = S_K$ and that $S_{T'} = S_L$.

Now consider a finite group G and a subgroup S having elements e, a, b, and c, where e is the identity element. We can see that $S_r = S$ if r is in S, for the subgroup is closed with respect to the group operation, and $e \circ r$, $a \circ r$, $b \circ r$, and $c \circ r$ are merely the elements of S arranged so that r is the first element in the set. If h is an element of G which is not in S then $S_h = \{e \circ h, a \circ h, b \circ h, c \circ h\}$ and S_h contains at least one element not in S, namely h itself. Can $a \circ h = b \circ h$? If so, then $(a \circ h) \circ h^* = (b \circ h) \circ h^*$, $a \circ (h \circ h^*) = b \circ (h \circ h^*)$, $a \circ e = b \circ e$, and $a = b$. Therefore the elements of S_h are distinct if the elements of S are distinct and the number of elements in S_h is the same as the number of elements in S. If k is another element of G which is not in S and is distinct from h then $S_k = \{k, a \circ k, b \circ k, c \circ k\}$. How many elements can S_h and S_k have in common? One of the following discussions shows that the answer is *all* or *none*. That is, two right cosets of the same subgroup either have no elements in common or they are identical sets.

Statement 5.   *A right coset of a subgroup S of a finite group G has the same number of elements as S.*

Discussion.   Denote the right coset by S_r; then for each s in S there is a unique element $s \circ r$ in S_r. Therefore S_r does not have more

---

* $\{a, b\}$ denotes the set whose elements are a and b.

elements than S. If two elements $s_1 \circ r$ and $s_2 \circ r$ of S_r are equal, then $s_1 \circ r = s_2 \circ r$. Since r^* exists in G then $(s_1 \circ r) \circ r^* = (s_2 \circ r) \circ r^*$, $s_1 \circ (r \circ r^*) = s_2 \circ (r \circ r^*)$, $s_1 \circ e = s_2 \circ e$, and $s_1 = s_2$. Therefore distinct elements in S correspond to distinct elements in S_r, and S_r cannot have fewer elements than S. Therefore, S and S_r have the same number of elements.   ∎

Statement 6.   *If S_h and S_k are two right cosets of the same subgroup S of a group G then either $S_h = S_k$ or the two cosets have no elements in common.*

Discussion.   If there is an element of G in both S_h and S_k, then there are elements s_1 and s_2 in S such that $s_1 \circ h = s_2 \circ k$. Since S is a subgroup, s_2^* exists in S, and

$$s_2^* \circ (s_1 \circ h) = s_2^* \circ (s_2 \circ k).$$

Then
$$(s_2^* \circ s_1) \circ h = (s_2^* \circ s_2) \circ k$$
$$= e \circ k = k,$$

and for every s in S, $s \circ [(s_2^* \circ s_1) \circ h] = s \circ k,$
$$[s \circ (s_2^* \circ s_1)] \circ h = s \circ k.$$

Since $s \circ (s_2^* \circ s_1)$ is an element of S, and every element of S_k can be expressed in the form $s \circ k$, where s is in S, then every element in S_k is in S_h.

A similar argument shows that every element of S_h is in S_k and therefore $S_h = S_k$ if the cosets have even one element in common.

If the cosets do not have one element in common then they have no elements in common. This is the second possibility.   ∎

The preceding discussions will help us consider the following question: If a finite group has a subgroup of order four what is the order of the group? As before let the subgroup be denoted by $S = \{e, a, b, c\}$. Then if h is an element of G which is not in the subgroup, $S_h = \{h, a \circ h, b \circ h, c \circ h\}$ and since h is not in S, then S and S_h are not the same coset. Since the elements of S_h are distinct elements of the group there must be at least eight elements in G. If there are exactly eight elements in G then four of them are in S and four are in S_h. If, however, there is an element k in G which is in neither of the cosets S or S_h, then S_k must contain four additional elements, G must contain at least twelve elements. If G contains exactly twelve elements, then it can be separated into the distinct cosets S, S_h, and S_k. If not, there is an additional element t in G which is not in any one of the three cosets already considered. But S_t must contain four distinct elements, none of which is in one of the cosets S, S_h, or S_k, therefore G must contain at least sixteen elements. Proceeding in this fashion we see that the finite group G can be separated into cosets which have no elements in common and the order of G must be a multiple of four. Therefore, a group of order five, six, eleven or thirteen cannot have a subgroup of order four.

The general case is given in the following theorem.

Statement 7. *Theorem of Lagrange. The order of a finite group G is an integral multiple of the order of each of its subgroups.*

Discussion. Let S be a subgroup of G, then G can be divided into distinct right cosets each of which has the same order as S. Therefore the order of G is an integral multiple of the order of S. ∎

EXERCISES

1. For group elements a, b, c, d, and g, can we conclude from $a \circ b = c \circ d$ that $g \circ (a \circ b) = (c \circ d) \circ g$? Why?

2. (a) Show that in a group $G(\circ)$ if $a \circ x = a$, then $x = e$.
  (b) In two ways, show that the Special Case of Statement 1 is true as indicated in the text.
  (c) Give the discussion for Statement 3.
  (d) Give the discussion for the right cancellation law.

3. Show that the identity of a subgroup must be the identity of the group.

4. (a) Show that every group of two elements is commutative.
  (b) Do the same for a group of three elements.
      Hint: Call the elements e (the identity), a, and b. Then consider the cyclic subgroup generated by a or b.

5. For a group prove that $(a \circ b)^* = b^* \circ a^*$.
Hint: Show that $b^* \circ a^*$ is an inverse of $a \circ b$ by showing that it satisfies $(G3)$, and then use Statement 3.

6. If a and b are elements of a group $G(\circ)$, show that
(a) if $a \circ b^* = e$, then $a = b$;
(b) if $a = b$, then $a \circ b^* = e$;
(c) $(a^*)^* = a$.

7. Show that if S is a nonempty set of elements each of which is in a group G, S is closed with respect to the group operation in G, and every element in S has an inverse in S, then S is a subgroup of G.

8. If the order of a group is a prime number, does it have any proper subgroups? Is it cyclic? Why?

12. OTHER DEFINITIONS OF A GROUP

In this section we shall give two other definitions of a group and prove that these definitions are equivalent to the first definition of a group.

In order to show that two definitions are equivalent we must show that when one of the definitions is satisfied then the other is also satisfied.

The second definition of a group as given here differs from the first definition by requiring only a left identity and left inverses instead of a two-sided identity and two-sided inverses.

Definition. *(Second Definition of a Group)* *A nonempty set G forms a group under an operation $\circ$ if* (G1), (G2), *and the following two conditions are satisfied:*

(1) There is a left identity element $\bar{e}$ such that $\bar{e} \circ a = a$, for every a in G.

(2) For each a in G there is a left inverse $\bar{a}^*$ in G such that $\bar{a}^* \circ a = \bar{e}$.

Statement 8.   *The first and second definitions of a group are equivalent.*

Discussion. We first show that if the first definition is satisfied then the second one is also satisfied. The conditions $(G1)$ and $(G2)$ are the same in both definitions. If a two-sided identity exists then certainly a left identity exists. If each element has a two-sided inverse then it has a left inverse. Therefore when the first definition is satisfied then the second definition is satisfied.

In order to show that when the second definition is satisfied then the first one is satisfied, we break the discussion into parts called lemmas.

Lemma I. *If the second group definition is satisfied, $x \in G$, and $x \circ x = x$, then $x = \bar{e}$.*

Discussion of Lemma I.

$x \circ x = x$	Hypothesis
There is a left inverse $\bar{x}^*$ for x in G.	(2)
Therefore, $\bar{x}^* \circ (x \circ x) = \bar{x}^* \circ x$	Well-defined operation
$(\bar{x}^* \circ x) \circ x = \bar{x}^* \circ x$	($G2$)
$\bar{e} \circ x = \bar{e}$	(2)
$x = \bar{e}.$	(1)

We now show that $(a \circ \bar{a}^*) \circ (a \circ \bar{a}^*) = (a \circ \bar{a}^*)$, then using Lemma I with $x = a \circ \bar{a}^*$ we will have $a \circ \bar{a}^* = \bar{e}$.

Lemma II. *If the second group definition is satisfied, then $(a \circ \bar{a}^*) \circ (a \circ \bar{a}^*) = (a \circ \bar{a}^*)$, for each a in G.*

Discussion of Lemma II.

$(a \circ \bar{a}^*) \circ (a \circ \bar{a}^*) = [(a \circ \bar{a}^*) \circ a] \circ \bar{a}^*$	($G2$)
$= [a \circ (\bar{a}^* \circ a)] \circ \bar{a}^*$	($G2$)
$= (a \circ \bar{e}) \circ \bar{a}^*$	(2)
$= a \circ (\bar{e} \circ \bar{a}^*)$	($G2$)
$= a \circ \bar{a}^*.$	(1)

Therefore, by Lemma I, $a \circ \bar{a}^* = \bar{e}$, and combining this statement with (2) we have $\bar{a}^* \circ a = \bar{e} = a \circ \bar{a}^*$. Then group axiom ($G4$) will be satisfied if we can show that $\bar{e}$ is a two-sided identity.

We now show that $\bar{e}$ as given by (1) is also a right identity.

Lemma III. *If the second group definition is satisfied, then $a \circ \bar{e} = a$, for each a in G.*

Discussion of Lemma III.

$a \circ \bar{e} = a \circ (\bar{a}^* \circ a)$	(2)
$= (a \circ \bar{a}^*) \circ a$	($G2$)
$= \bar{e} \circ a$	Lemmas I and II
$= a.$	(1)

Therefore $\bar{e} \circ a = a = a \circ \bar{e}$, and $\bar{e}$ satisfies $(G3)$. Since $\bar{e}$ is a two-sided identity and $\bar{a}^* \circ a = \bar{e} = a \circ \bar{a}^*$ then $(G4)$ is satisfied. Therefore the first group definition is satisfied whenever the second definition is satisfied, and the two definitions of a group are equivalent. ∎

Definition. (*Third Definition of a Group*) *A non-empty set* G *forms a group under the operation* $\circ$ *if* $(G1)$, $(G2)$, *and the following two conditions are satisfied for every two elements* a *and* b *of* G:

(1) *There is an element* x *in* G *such that* $a \circ x = b$.

(2) *There is an element* y *in* G *such that* $y \circ a = b$.

We shall now show that the third definition of a group is equivalent to each of the other two definitions. In the proof we shall use a cyclic argument indicated by the following symbolism.

first def. $\Rightarrow$ third def. $\Rightarrow$ second def. $\Rightarrow$ first def.

This symbolism is read "the first definition implies the third definition, the third definition implies the second definition, and the second definition implies the first" or "if the first definition is satisfied then the third definition is satisfied; if the third definition is satisfied then the second definition is satisfied; and if the second definition is satisfied then the first definition is satisfied."

Statement 9. *The first and third definitions of a group are equivalent.*

Discussion. We first show that if the first definition is satisfied then the third definition is satisfied.

By substituting for x we can show that $x = a^* \circ b$ is a solution of $a \circ x = b$, for

$$a \circ (a^* \circ b) = (a \circ a^*) \circ b = e \circ b = b.$$

Since G is closed with respect to the group operation, $a^* \circ b \, \epsilon \, G$, and a solution $x \, \epsilon \, G$ exists for $a \circ x = b$.

Assume that there is a second solution z. Then z satisfies the equation and $a \circ z = b$. Therefore $a \circ x = a \circ z$, since both are equal to b, and by the left cancellation law, $x = z$. Therefore, there is one and only one solution; that is, the solution is unique.*

By substituting for y we can show that $y = b \circ a^*$ is a solution of $y \circ a = b$, for

$$(b \circ a^*) \circ a = b \circ (a^* \circ a) = b \circ e = b.$$

Since G is closed with respect to the group operation, $b \circ a^* \, \epsilon \, G$, and a solution $y \, \epsilon \, G$ exists for $y \circ a = b$.

Assume that there are two solutions y and w. Then $w \circ a = b$ and $y \circ a = b$. Therefore $w \circ a = y \circ a$, and by the right cancellation law $w = y$. Thus the solution is unique, and

first definition $\Rightarrow$ third definition.

We now show that when the third definition is satisfied, the second definition is satisfied. We must establish the existence of a left identity and left inverses.

Using statement (2) of the third definition with $a = b$ we know that there is an element y in G such that $y \circ a = a$; that is, y operating on the left of a leaves a unchanged. We must now show that this same y operating on the left of *every* element of G leaves the element unchanged. Let b be any other element of G. We need to know the result of $y \circ b$.

Using (1) of the third definition we know that for each pair of elements a and b there is an element x in G such that $a \circ x = b$. In the statement $y \circ b$ we replace b by $a \circ x$ to obtain

$$y \circ b = y \circ (a \circ x) = (y \circ a) \circ x.$$

Now using the fact that $y \circ a = a$, we have

$$(y \circ a) \circ x = a \circ x = b.$$

Therefore, $y \circ b = b$ for every $b \, \epsilon \, G$ and y is a left identity, which we shall denote by $\bar{e}$.

Every element b has a left inverse, for (2) of the third definition indicates that for the two elements b and $\bar{e}$ there is an element z such that $z \circ b = \bar{e}$. Therefore

third definition $\Rightarrow$ second definition.

---

* Observe that if the elements of the group are numbers and the operation is addition the proof indicates that if $a + x = b$, then $x = (-a) + b$. If the operation is multiplication it indicates that $ax = b$ has the solution $x = (1/a)b$. Why is it unnecessary to say that $a \neq 0$?

In Statement 8 we showed that

$$\text{second definition} \Rightarrow \text{first definition.}$$

Therefore

$$\text{third definition} \Rightarrow \text{first definition,}$$

and the first and third definitions are equivalent. The equivalence of these two definitions can be indicated by the symbolism

$$\text{third definition} \Leftrightarrow \text{first definition}$$

which is read "the third definition is equivalent to the first definition" or "the third definition is satisfied if and only if the first definition is satisfied".

EXERCISES

1. Which of the following sets are groups under the indicated operation?

  (a) The set of integers under the operation $\circ$, where $a \circ b = a + b + 1$ for each pair of integers a and b.

  (b) All numbers of the form 3^n, where n is an integer, under multiplication.

  (c) All numbers of the form k^n, where k is a fixed nonzero rational number and n is an integer, under multiplication.

  (d) All numbers of the form $3^n \cdot 5^m$, where n and m are integers, under multiplication.

  (e) All numbers of the form $\dfrac{1 + 2m}{1 + 2n}$, where n and m are integers, under multiplication.

2. If $(G3)$ and $(G4)$ are replaced by axioms for a right identity and right inverses, respectively, is the resulting mathematical system a group? If so, produce the discussion.

3. What bearing do Statements 8 and 9 have on the process of testing for groups?

4. Determine whether the set of all subsets of a set forms a group under each of the following operations:

  (a) set union,   (b) set intersection,   (c) symmetric difference.

13. ISOMORPHISM INVOLVING ONE OPERATION

Let us consider the following question: Does the set of letters A, B, C, D, E, and F, where the operation is given by the accompanying table, form a group?

$\ominus$	A	B	C	D	E	F
A	A	B	C	D	E	F
B	B	C	A	E	F	D
C	C	A	B	F	D	E
D	D	F	E	A	C	B
E	E	D	F	B	A	C
F	F	E	D	C	B	A

Let us denote the set by S and the operation by $\ominus$. We observe that S is closed with respect to $\ominus$, therefore $(G1)$ is satisfied. We seek an identity element. If X represents any one of the elements of S we observe that $X \ominus A = X = A \ominus X$. Therefore, A is an identity element. For each element we need an inverse. We find that A, D, E, and F are their own inverses, since the second power of each is A, and that B and C are inverses. All that remains is the associative law. Checking this law from the chart involves much work, therefore we shall try to find a better approach.

Let us observe some other things about this set. There are six letters in S and $D \ominus C = E$ while $C \ominus D = F$; therefore this operation is noncommutative. This suggests that this set and the group of symmetries of an equilateral triangle, which we shall denote by G, may have some common properties. In S, observe that $B^3 = (B \ominus B) \ominus B$ $= C \ominus B = A$, and A is the "identity" element. Therefore, if this set forms a group, then B is of order three. Similarly, $C^3 = C \ominus C \ominus C$ $= B \ominus C = A$, and $D^2 = A$, $E^2 = A$, and $F^2 = A$. The group G also has an identity, two elements of order three and three elements of order two. This suggests comparing the given table with the table for the symmetries of the equilateral triangle. To do this we pair the objects of the two sets as follows:

$$
\begin{array}{ccccccc}
\text{Set } S: & A & B & C & D & E & F \\
& \updownarrow & \updownarrow & \updownarrow & \updownarrow & \updownarrow & \updownarrow \\
\text{Group } G: & I & T & T' & H & K & L
\end{array}
$$

Such a pairing is called a one-to-one correspondence since an object in either one of the sets is paired with one and only one object in the other set. Observe that we have paired elements of the same "order."

We want to know whether these two sets behave exactly alike under their operations. One of the easiest ways to examine their behavior is to replace each letter in the given table by its corresponding element as indicated by the pairing. That is, we replace A, everywhere it occurs in the given table by I, B by T, etc. If the resulting table and the table for the symmetries of the equilateral triangle are exactly alike, then we will conclude that this set S under the given operation behaves like G, and therefore must be a group. However, by replacement we obtain a table which indicates that $T \circ H = K$, but the table for G given on page 12 indicates that $T \circ H = L$. This shows that the pairing does not preserve the operation on G. Therefore we try again, by setting up a new one-to-one correspondence.

$$\begin{array}{lcccccc} \text{Set } S: & A & B & C & D & E & F \\ & \updownarrow & \updownarrow & \updownarrow & \updownarrow & \updownarrow & \updownarrow \\ \text{Group } G: & I & T & T' & H & L & K \end{array}$$

After making these substitutions we find that all of the entries agree with those in the table for G. (The reader may find it convenient to place the E row at the bottom and the E column to the right before substituting; then the replacements will produce the table for G just as it is given in the text.)

We therefore conclude that there is a one-to-one correspondence between these two sets which preserves the group operation in G. By this we mean that the two sets behave exactly alike under this correspondence. By finding the results of operations in one set we can predict the results of operations in the other set. This says essentially that S is the group of symmetries of an equilateral triangle in disguise. Since G obeys the associative law, so will S, and therefore S is a group.

Correspondences Which Preserve Operations. This idea of a one-to-one correspondence which preserves the operations on the sets is a very important one in mathematics; therefore we will pursue it further.

If there is a correspondence between two sets, it is often convenient to refer to an element in one set as an "object" and the corresponding element in the second set as its "image." Thus under our second correspondence L is the image of E, T is the image of B, and H is the image of D. It is also convenient to call $A \ominus B$ the "product" of A and B under the operation $\ominus$ and $T \circ H$ the "product" of T and H under the operation $\circ$.

When we say that the operation of the second set is preserved under the one-to-one correspondence we mean that the result will be the same whether we

(1) take the product of two elements in the first set and find the image of the product, or

(2) find the images of the two objects and take the product of the images in the second set.

This concept is sometimes stated roughly as follows:

The operations of two sets, each closed with respect to an operation, are **preserved under a one-to-one correspondence** *between the two sets if the image of the product is equal to the product of the images.*

It should be observed that if the operations are preserved under a one-to-one correspondence either set may be the object set if the other set is the image set.

In the first correspondence which we set up, the image of B was T, the image of D was H, and the product $B \ominus D = E$ had K as an image. However $T \circ H = L$ and therefore the image of the product was not equal to the product of the images; therefore the operation $\circ$ was not preserved.

The inequality of the results of these two procedures is shown by the following diagram.

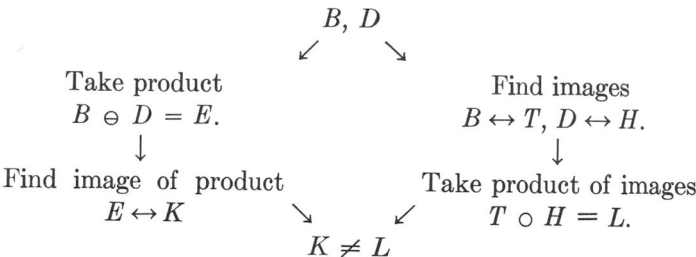

$$B, D$$

Take product
$B \ominus D = E$.

Find images
$B \leftrightarrow T, D \leftrightarrow H$.

Find image of product
$E \leftrightarrow K$

Take product of images
$T \circ H = L$.

$$K \neq L$$

In general, assume that there is a one-to-one correspondence between the sets R and W which makes an element a of R correspond to an element a' of W and that these sets are closed with respect to the operations $\ominus$ and $\circ$, respectively. Then this correspondence preserves the operation in W if and only if, whenever $y \leftrightarrow y'$, $z \leftrightarrow z'$ and $(y \ominus z) \leftrightarrow (y \ominus z)'$, then $(y \ominus z)' = y' \circ z'$. When this is true the sets R and W are isomorphic and the operation-preserving correspondence is called an isomorphism.

Definition. *Two sets R and W, closed with respect to the operations $\ominus$ and $\circ$, respectively, are* **isomorphic** *if there is a one-to-one correspondence $a \leftrightarrow a'$ between R and W such that whenever $y \leftrightarrow y'$, $z \leftrightarrow z'$ and $(y \ominus z) \leftrightarrow (y \ominus z)'$, then $(y \ominus z)' = y' \circ z'$.*

If R and W are isomorphic, then the correspondence between them is an *isomorphism.*

The following diagram indicates the basic idea of an isomorphism between two sets each having one operation defined on it.

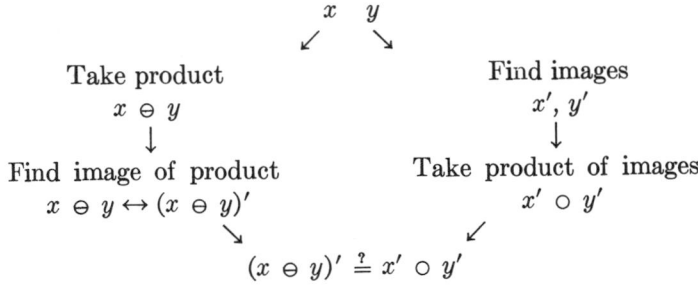

$$x \quad y$$

Take product $\quad\quad\quad\quad\quad$ Find images
$$x \ominus y \quad\quad\quad\quad\quad\quad x', y'$$
$$\downarrow \quad\quad\quad\quad\quad\quad\quad\quad \downarrow$$
Find image of product $\quad$ Take product of images
$$x \ominus y \leftrightarrow (x \ominus y)' \quad\quad\quad x' \circ y'$$

$$(x \ominus y)' \overset{?}{=} x' \circ y'$$

If, for each pair x and y, it is true that $(x \ominus y)' = x' \circ y'$ and the correspondence is one-to-one then the correspondence is an isomorphism.

When two sets, each having one operation defined on it, are isomorphic, then each statement of equality in the object set produces a statement of equality in the image set. For example, if $a \ominus b = c$, then $a' \circ b' = c'$ must be true for $(a \ominus b)' = c'$ and $(a \ominus b)' = a' \circ b'$; therefore $a' \circ b' = c'$. This is why we know that the set S, introduced at the beginning of this section, must obey the associative law. The associative law holds in G. If we consider G as the object set and S as the image set under the one-to-one correspondence which preserves products, then we know that $a \circ (b \circ c) = (a \circ b) \circ c$, for all elements of G. Therefore $(a' \ominus b') \ominus c' = a' \ominus (b' \ominus c')$, for all elements of S.

Types of groups. The concept of isomorphism allows us to classify groups according to types. Two groups are of the same type if and only if they are isomorphic.

Example 1.   The group S considered at the beginning of this section, the group G of the symmetries of the equilateral triangle, and the group consisting of the permutations (1), (123), (132), (12), (13), and (23) are all of the same type. This type is usually referred to as *the non-commutative group of order six.*

Example 2.   The permutation groups

$$R = \{(1), (1234), (13)(24), (1432)\} \quad \text{and}$$
$$W = \{(1), (13), (24), (13)(24)\}$$

are not isomorphic because R is a cyclic group of order four and W is a **fours group.** These are the only two types of groups of order four.*

Example 3.   The group J of integers $0, 1, -1, 2, -2, \cdots$ under addition is isomorphic to the group W consisting of the integral powers of 2 under multiplication. The correspondence is $n \leftrightarrow 2^n$, where n is an integer. Then $m \leftrightarrow 2^m$, and $n + m \leftrightarrow 2^n \cdot 2^m = 2^{n+m}$; therefore the image of the product is the product of the images.

Properties of an Isomorphism.

Statement 10.   *An isomorphism of two groups must*

(a) *make the identity elements correspond to each other,*
(b) *make inverses correspond, and*
(c) *make the nth power of an element correspond to the nth power of its image.*

Discussion.   Let the identity of the first group be denoted by e and its image by e', let c be another element of the first group and its image be c', and let the group operations be $\ominus$ and $\bigcirc$, respectively. Then $e \ominus c = c = c \ominus e$. Therefore $e' \bigcirc c' = c' = c' \bigcirc e'$. Thus e' behaves like an identity in the second group. By statement 2, e' is the identity of the second group, and the identity elements correspond.

---

* For additional information on the types of groups of orders one through eight, see W. Ledermann, *The Theory of Finite Groups* (New York, Inter-science Publishers, 1949), pp. 48–58.

If $c \ominus c^* = e = c^* \ominus c$, then $c' \circ (c^*)' = e' = (c^*)' \circ c'$. Since e' is the identity of the second group and inverses are unique in a group then $(c^*)'$ is the inverse of c'. That is, $(c^*)' = (c')^*$, which indicates that the image of the inverse is the inverse of its image, and inverses correspond.

Under the isomorphism $c \leftrightarrow c'$, therefore

$$(c^2)' = (c \ominus c)' = c' \circ c' = (c')^2;$$
$$(c^3)' = (c \ominus c \ominus c)' = c' \circ c' \circ c' = (c')^3, \text{ etc.}$$

Thus for every c of the first group

$$(c^k)' = (c')^k$$

if k is a positive integer. Does this equation hold if k is zero or negative? By Section 8, $c^0 = e$, $c^{-1} = c^*$ and $c^{-n} = (c^*)^n$. Similarly $(c')^0 = e'$, $(c')^{-1} = (c')^*$, and $(c')^{-n} = [(c')^*]^n$. If $k = 0$, the equation becomes $(c^0)' = (c')^0$. When this is simplified we have $(e)' = e'$, which is true since the identity elements correspond.

Since the equation holds for all group elements it is true when c is replaced by c^*. Thus

$$[(c^*)^k]' = [(c^*)']^k, \quad \text{where } k \text{ is a positive integer.}$$

Using $c^{-1} = c^*$, and $(c^*)' = (c')^* = (c')^{-1}$ we obtain

$$[(c^{-1})^k]' = [(c')^{-1}]^k,$$

which simplifies to $(c^{-k})' = (c')^{-k}$. Therefore the equation is true for negative integral powers, and we conclude that $(c^n)' = (c')^n$, for every integer n.

Statement 10 is frequently rephrased as follows: *An isomorphism preserves the identity element, inverses and powers.*

Can the image of an element of order n be an element of order m, where $m \neq n$, if the correspondence is an isomorphism?

Statement 11.   *If R and W, closed with respect to the operations $\ominus$ and $\circ$, respectively, are isomorphic, then W is a group if R is a group.*

Discussion.   Let a, b, and c be elements in R; then their images in W are a', b', and c', respectively; that is, $a \leftrightarrow a'$, $b \leftrightarrow b'$, and $c \leftrightarrow c'$.

We now check the group axioms for W. Axiom $(G1)$ is satisfied since W is closed with respect to $\circ$. For every triple of elements a, b, and c in R we have $(a \ominus b) \ominus c = a \ominus (b \ominus c)$ because R is a group.

The associative law holds in W, because the isomorphism produces the equality $(a' \circ b') \circ c' = a' \circ (b' \circ c')$. Let e represent the identity in R, then for every a in R, $a \ominus e = a = e \ominus a$ and therefore $a' \circ e' = a' = e' \circ a'$, for every a' of W. Therefore e' is an identity in W. For every a in R, a^* exists in R such that $a \ominus a^* = e = a^* \ominus a$; therefore $a' \circ (a^*)' = e' = (a^*)' \circ a'$ and the image of a^* is the inverse of a'; that is, $(a')^* = (a^*)'$. Thus every element in W has an inverse in W, and W is a group.

EXERCISES

1. (a) How many one-to-one correspondences are there between the groups S and G discussed at the beginning of this section?

   (b) Is it possible to find another one-to-one correspondence between S and G which is an isomorphism? If so, find one.

2. (a) There is only one type of group of order two. Why?

   (b) There is only one type of group of order three. Why?

   (c) How many types of groups are there of order five?

   (d) Generalize the concepts in the first three parts of this exercise.

3. Let G be the group having four elements 1, -1, a, and $-a$, where these numbers and letters are multiplied as in high school algebra except that $a^2 = -1$. Set up an isomorphism between G and one of the permutation groups given on page 47.

4. Find groups isomorphic to each of the following.

(a)

	I	A
I	I	A
A	A	I

(b)

	I	A	B	C
I	I	A	B	C
A	A	B	C	I
B	B	C	I	A
C	C	I	A	B

(c)

	I	A	B	C
I	I	A	B	C
A	A	I	C	B
B	B	C	I	A
C	C	B	A	I

5. In graphing, we use ordered pairs of numbers such as (a_1, a_2) and (b_1, b_2). We define the *scalar product* of these two ordered pairs to be $a_1 b_1 + a_2 b_2$, and denote it by $(a_1, a_2) \cdot (b_1, b_2)$. That is, we multiply the first elements, multiply the second elements, and add the results. This result can be described as the sum of the products of corresponding elements. If $p_1 = (a_1, a_2)$ and $p_2 = (b_1, b_2)$ then their scalar product can be indicated by $p_1 \cdot p_2$. Likewise, if ordered triples are given such as $v_1 = (a_1, a_2, a_3)$ and $v_2 = (b_1, b_2, b_3)$ we define the scalar product as $v_1 \cdot v_2 = (a_1, a_2, a_3) \cdot (b_1, b_2, b_3) = a_1 b_1 + a_2 b_2 + a_3 b_3$. Even if the second triple were written in vertical form we would still have

$$v_1 \cdot v_2 = (a_1, a_2, a_3) \cdot \begin{pmatrix} b_1 \\ b_2 \\ b_3 \end{pmatrix} = a_1 b_1 + a_2 b_2 + a_3 b_3.$$

(a) Compute the following scalar products:

$$(-3, 2) \cdot (1, -5); \qquad (-2, 5, -4) \cdot \begin{pmatrix} -1 \\ 0 \\ 2 \end{pmatrix};$$

$$(5, -2) \cdot \begin{pmatrix} -1 \\ -7 \end{pmatrix}; \qquad (1, 1, -1) \cdot (3, -1, 2).$$

(b) Does the set of all ordered triples of integers form a group with respect to the operation of taking the scalar product?

6. (a) A two-by-two matrix is a square array having two rows and two columns, which can be denoted by $\begin{pmatrix} a_{11} & a_{12} \\ a_{21} & a_{22} \end{pmatrix}$. The a's are the elements of the matrix. If matrix multiplication is defined by

$$\begin{pmatrix} a_{11} a_{12} \\ a_{21} a_{22} \end{pmatrix} \otimes \begin{pmatrix} b_{11} b_{12} \\ b_{21} b_{22} \end{pmatrix} = \begin{pmatrix} a_{11}b_{11} + a_{12}b_{21}, & a_{11}b_{12} + a_{12}b_{22} \\ a_{21}b_{11} + a_{22}b_{21}, & a_{21}b_{12} + a_{22}b_{22} \end{pmatrix},$$

replace the rows of the first matrix by v_1 and v_2, respectively, and the columns of the second matrix by w_1 and w_2, respectively, and write the matrix product* in terms of scalar products of the v's and w's.

---

* Let A represent the first matrix and B represent the second matrix. Let C represent the product matrix. Then we have $A \otimes B = C$. The *pattern* for finding the elements in C is as follows: To find the element in the ith row and the jth column of C, find the *scalar* product of the ith row of A and the jth column of B. (See Exercise 5 for the definition of the scalar product.) Thus, in the two-by-two case, element c_{21} in the second row and the first column of C is $v_2 \cdot w_1 = (a_{21}, a_{22}) \cdot \begin{pmatrix} b_{11} \\ b_{21} \end{pmatrix} = a_{21}b_{11} + a_{22}b_{21}$. In the three-by-three case (See Exercise 6b) it is $v_2 \cdot w_1 = (a_{21}, a_{22}, a_{23}) \cdot \begin{pmatrix} b_{11} \\ b_{21} \\ b_{31} \end{pmatrix} = a_{21}b_{11} + a_{22}b_{21} + a_{23}b_{31}$.

(b) If the three-by-three matrix $A = \begin{pmatrix} a_{11} & a_{12} & a_{13} \\ a_{21} & a_{22} & a_{23} \\ a_{31} & a_{32} & a_{33} \end{pmatrix}$

is written as $A = \begin{pmatrix} v_1 \\ v_2 \\ v_3 \end{pmatrix}$, where $v_1 = (a_{11}, a_{12}, a_{13})$,

$v_2 = (a_{21}, a_{22}, a_{23})$ and $v_3 = (a_{31}, a_{32}, a_{33})$; and the matrix

$B = \begin{pmatrix} b_{11} & b_{12} & b_{13} \\ b_{21} & b_{22} & b_{23} \\ b_{31} & b_{32} & b_{33} \end{pmatrix}$ is written as $B = (w_1, w_2, w_3)$, where

$w_1 = \begin{pmatrix} b_{11} \\ b_{21} \\ b_{31} \end{pmatrix}$, $w_2 = \begin{pmatrix} b_{12} \\ b_{22} \\ b_{32} \end{pmatrix}$, and $w_3 = \begin{pmatrix} b_{13} \\ b_{23} \\ b_{33} \end{pmatrix}$, then the

matrix product $C = A \otimes B = \begin{pmatrix} v_1 \cdot w_1 & .v_1 \cdot w_2 & v_1 \cdot w_3 \\ v_2 \cdot w_1 & v_2 \cdot w_2 & v_2 \cdot w_3 \\ v_3 \cdot w_1 & v_3 \cdot w_2 & v_3 \cdot w_3 \end{pmatrix}$.

Rewrite the product C in terms of the elements of A and B.

7. (a) Find the matrix products $A \otimes B$ for

$$A = \begin{pmatrix} 0 & -1 \\ 3 & 5 \end{pmatrix}, \qquad B = \begin{pmatrix} 4 & -2 \\ 1 & 0 \end{pmatrix};$$

$$A = \begin{pmatrix} -1 & 4 & 5 \\ 2 & -3 & 1 \\ 0 & 0 & -2 \end{pmatrix}, \quad B = \begin{pmatrix} 5 & -1 & 0 \\ 0 & 3 & -4 \\ 1 & 2 & -2 \end{pmatrix}.$$

(b) Use the matrices $\begin{pmatrix} 2 & -3 \\ 1 & 5 \end{pmatrix}$ and $\begin{pmatrix} 1 & 1 \\ -1 & 2 \end{pmatrix}$ to show that matrix multiplication is not commutative in general.

(c) Show that the matrices $\begin{pmatrix} -2 & 0 \\ 0 & -2 \end{pmatrix}$ and $\begin{pmatrix} 0 & 2 \\ -2 & 0 \end{pmatrix}$ commute under $\otimes$.

8. (a) Show that the following sets of matrices are groups under matrix multiplication. (If tables are used it may be convenient to let a capital letter represent each matrix.)

(b) Find a group isomorphic to each of these groups.

(c) Indicate all subgroups of each group.

(i) $\begin{pmatrix} 1 & 0 \\ 0 & 1 \end{pmatrix}, \begin{pmatrix} -1 & 0 \\ 0 & -1 \end{pmatrix};$

(ii) $\begin{pmatrix} 1 & 0 \\ 0 & 1 \end{pmatrix}, \begin{pmatrix} -1 & 0 \\ 0 & -1 \end{pmatrix}, \begin{pmatrix} 0 & 1 \\ -1 & 0 \end{pmatrix}, \begin{pmatrix} 0 & -1 \\ 1 & 0 \end{pmatrix};$

(iii) $\begin{pmatrix} 1 & 0 \\ 0 & 1 \end{pmatrix}, \begin{pmatrix} -1 & 0 \\ 0 & -1 \end{pmatrix}, \begin{pmatrix} 0 & 1 \\ -1 & 0 \end{pmatrix}, \begin{pmatrix} 0 & -1 \\ 1 & 0 \end{pmatrix},$

$\begin{pmatrix} 0 & 1 \\ 1 & 0 \end{pmatrix}, \begin{pmatrix} 0 & -1 \\ -1 & 0 \end{pmatrix}, \begin{pmatrix} 1 & 0 \\ 0 & -1 \end{pmatrix}, \begin{pmatrix} -1 & 0 \\ 0 & 1 \end{pmatrix};$

(iv) $\begin{pmatrix} 1 & 0 & 0 \\ 0 & 1 & 0 \\ 0 & 0 & 1 \end{pmatrix}, \begin{pmatrix} 0 & 1 & 0 \\ 0 & 0 & 1 \\ 1 & 0 & 0 \end{pmatrix}, \begin{pmatrix} 0 & 0 & 1 \\ 1 & 0 & 0 \\ 0 & 1 & 0 \end{pmatrix},$

$\begin{pmatrix} 0 & 1 & 0 \\ 1 & 0 & 0 \\ 0 & 0 & 1 \end{pmatrix}, \begin{pmatrix} 0 & 0 & 1 \\ 0 & 1 & 0 \\ 1 & 0 & 0 \end{pmatrix}, \begin{pmatrix} 1 & 0 & 0 \\ 0 & 0 & 1 \\ 0 & 1 & 0 \end{pmatrix}.$

14. THE GROUP AS AN AXIOMATIC SYSTEM

The group is one of the simplest examples of the axiomatic or postulational approach, which is the rigorous form of mathematical reasoning demanded by twentieth century mathematics.*

An axiomatic system has the following integral parts:

(1) undefined notions,　　　　(2) definitions,
(3) axioms,　　　　　　　　　(4) theorems.

On first thought one might see no need for undefined terms, but a bit of consideration will show that it is impractical, if not impossible, to define all terms. Just as a child must learn his first words by association and use them as building blocks for his vocabulary, the mathematician takes certain terms as undefined and uses these primitive terms, as they are often called, to state definitions, axioms and theorems.

* Present day terminology includes at least two other appropriate names for an axiomatic system. They are "deductive theory" and "postulate system".

Axioms are statements which are accepted without proof as a basis for argument, and theorems are statements which are logical consequences of the axioms and definitions. It should be observed in passing that some statements can be considered either as axioms or as definitions. For example, $(G1)$, $(G2)$, $(G3)$, $(G4)$, and the nonempty property can be considered as axioms that must be satisfied if G is a group and "group" is an undefined term, or they can be considered as part of the definition of a group.

We shall indicate briefly how to present the group as an axiomatic system. First we choose the following undefined terms:

"set,"   "is an element in,"   "operation."

Using these undefined terms and simple English, we then state some definitions.

Definition. *An **ordered pair** of elements is a set of two elements for which it has been decided which is to be considered first and which is to be considered second.*

The ordered pair consisting of a and b is denoted by (a, b).

Definition. *A **binary operation** is an operation which assigns a third element c to each ordered pair of elements (a, b).*

The operation is denoted by $\circ$ and the result of the operation is denoted by $a \circ b = c$.

Definition. *A binary operation $\circ$ is **well defined** if replacing a and b in the equation $a \circ b = c$ by equal elements produces an element equal to c.*

Definition. *A set H is **closed with respect to an operation** $\circ$ if for every ordered pair (a, b) such that a and b are in H, $a \circ b$ is in H.*

Definition. *A **group** G is a nonempty set of elements and a binary operation $\circ$ for which the following conditions are satisfied.*
$(G1)$ *G is closed with respect to $\circ$.*
$(G2)$ *The associative law holds in G; that is,*
        $a \circ (b \circ c) = (a \circ b) \circ c$, when a, b, and c are elements in G.

(G3) *There is an identity element e in G such that*
      $e \circ a = a = a \circ e$, *for all elements a in G.*

(G4) *For each element a in G there is in G an inverse element of a*
      denoted by a^* such that $a \circ a^* = e = a^* \circ a$.

Then Statements 1, 2, 3, 4, 8, and 9 are theorems and the discussions which follow them are proofs.

Let us add two definitions to those already given and prove a theorem as an example.

Definition. *The **center of a group** G is the set of all x in G such that $x \circ g = g \circ x$ for every element g of G.*

Definition. *A nonempty subset H of a group G is a **subgroup** of G if H is a group with respect to the operation of G.*

Theorem. *The center of a group is a subgroup of the group.*

Proof. Let C represent the center of the group G.

To prove that C is closed we must show that when x and y are in C then $x \circ y$ is in C. To show that $x \circ y$ is in C we must show that this element commutes with every element of G; that is, we must show that $(x \circ y) \circ g = g \circ (x \circ y)$ for every g in G.

$(x \circ y) \circ g = x \circ (y \circ g)$	Associative Law in G.
$= x \circ (g \circ y)$	Since y is in the center $y \circ g = g \circ y$.
$= (x \circ g) \circ y$	Associative Law in G.
$= (g \circ x) \circ y$	Since x is in the center $x \circ g = g \circ x$.
$= g \circ (x \circ y)$.	Associative Law in G.

Therefore $(x \circ y) \circ g = g \circ (x \circ y)$ for all g in G and $x \circ y$ is in the center. Thus C is closed.

The elements of C must obey the associative law since they are also elements of G and G is a group.

The identity of G commutes with all elements in G and is therefore in the center C. It is the identity for C also.

We must now show that if x is in C then its inverse, x^*, is also in C. That is, we must show that x^* commutes with all elements of G because x commutes with all elements of G.

$x \circ g = g \circ x.$	x is in the center.
$x^* \circ (x \circ g) = x^* \circ (g \circ x).$	Well-defined operation.
$(x^* \circ x) \circ g = (x^* \circ g) \circ x.$	Associative Law in G.
$e \circ g = (x^* \circ g) \circ x.$	$x^* \circ x = e$ in G.
$g = (x^* \circ g) \circ x.$	e is the identity in G.
$g \circ x^* = [(x^* \circ g) \circ x] \circ x^*$	Well-defined operation.
$= (x^* \circ g) \circ (x \circ x^*)$	Associative Law in G.
$= (x^* \circ g) \circ e.$	$x \circ x^* = e$ in G.
$g \circ x^* = x^* \circ g.$	e is the identity in G.

Therefore x^* commutes with every element g in G, and is in the center C. Thus every element in C has an inverse in C, and C is a subgroup of G.   ∎

Note: If the reasons for each step are omitted the existence of inverses can be shown more briefly as follows:

$$x \circ g = g \circ x$$
$$x^* \circ (x \circ g) \circ x^* = x^* \circ (g \circ x) \circ x^*$$
$$(x^* \circ x) \circ (g \circ x^*) = (x^* \circ g) \circ (x \circ x^*)$$
$$e \circ (g \circ x^*) = (x^* \circ g) \circ e$$
$$g \circ x^* = x^* \circ g$$

When additional definitions—such as the definitions of a commutative group, a cyclic group, a right coset, and a group isomorphism—are introduced, then additional theorems can be proved which involve these concepts. In proving a theorem care must be taken not to use anything which is not stated in the axioms or definitions, or not proved, in previous theorems. The reader might profit from trying to produce a rigorous sequence of definitions and theorems starting with the undefined terms suggested here.

Concluding Remarks.

1. Many abstract mathematical systems are groups with respect to one or more of their operations; therefore the group concept is often useful in defining such systems.

2. Our approach to group theory has been an intuitive one. Many examples, explanations, and motivating remarks were included in

order to facilitate the understanding of the abstract concepts. A rigorous theoretical treatment usually reduces the material presented to a bare minimum, and the reader is usually left to think up his own examples. In order to be rigorous, an approach should follow the postulational method; that is, it should proceed from undefined terms to definitions and axioms stated in terms of simple English and the undefined terms, then to theorems which can be proved from these definitions and assumptions by means of logic. After certain theorems are proved they become new tools for proof and may also be combined with definitions to prove other theorems.

At this point the reader would profit by scanning some books on group theory or abstract mathematical systems. Even though an author does not specifically state what undefined terms he is using, these can be detected because no definitions are given for them.

3. For an interesting statement as to the importance of group theory see Richard V. Andree, *Selections from Modern Abstract Algebra*, page 79. This reference indicates that the thermodynamics of heat transfer can be presented concisely by using group concepts.

Introduction to Rings and Fields

15. INTRODUCTORY REMARKS

Throughout the preceding sections we used the symbol " $\circ$ " to denote the group operation. This was done for two reasons: first, to impress the reader with the fact that in considering a general statement for groups one need not know what the operation is, nor even what the objects are, if he knows what axioms they satisfy; and second, to remind him that he must be sure not to assume that the operation has special properties of familiar operations such as addition or multiplication.

In working with groups we not only deal with the objects in abstract form but we also deal with the group operation in abstract form. The student has had some experience with abstraction of objects in high school algebra. When he let x represent a number, he was treating numbers in an abstract manner. He could not assume any special properties of the number, or numbers, represented by x unless they were possessed by all numbers in the set to which x was assumed to belong. In modern mathematics we do not restrict the objects to numbers, nor do we restrict the operations to the fundamental operations of arithmetic, which are addition, subtraction, multiplication, and division, but instead we consider many types of objects and many binary operations on them.

413

We shall now consider some systems which have two operations. In the beginning of this chapter we shall denote these operations by "$\circ$" and "$\ominus$".

16. DEFINITION OF A RING

Definition. *A **ring** R is a nonempty set of elements satisfying the following axioms under the operations $\circ$ and $\ominus$.*

(R1)   *R is an abelian group under $\circ$.*

(R2)   *R is closed with respect to a second binary operation $\circ$.*

(R3)   *The operation $\ominus$ is associative; that is,*

$$a \ominus (b \ominus c) = (a \ominus b) \ominus c \text{ when } a, b, \text{ and } c \text{ are in } R.$$

(R4)   *The distributive laws hold; that is,*

$$a \ominus (b \circ c) = (a \ominus b) \circ (a \ominus c); \text{ and}$$
$$(b \circ c) \ominus a = (b \ominus a) \circ (c \ominus a), \text{ when } a, b, \text{ and } c \text{ are in } R.$$

Definition. *A ring R is **commutative** if $a \ominus b = b \ominus a$ for all a and b in R.*

Observe that we know by (R1) that the first operation is commutative for *every* ring; that is, $a \circ b = b \circ a$, for all a and b in R. A commutative ring is one in which the *second* operation $\ominus$ is commutative. Since there are rings which are noncommutative, this is not a trivial requirement.

Definition. *A ring R has a **unit** (or **identity**) element if there is an element e' in R such that $e' \ominus a = a \ominus e' = a$, for every element a in R.*

Observe that by (R1) *every* ring has an identity with respect to the first operation $\circ$. A ring with unit must also have an identity for the second operation.

***Example* 1.**   The integers J form a ring under addition and multiplication. We have already shown they form an abelian group under addition, thus (*R*1) is satisfied. Since the product of two integers is an integer, (*R*2) is satisfied. Axiom (*R*3) follows from (*A*3); and (*R*4) follows from (*A*5) and (*A*6). Therefore, *J* is a ring. Actually it is a commutative ring with a unit element.

Example 2. The reader can now verify that the even integers form a ring under addition and multiplication. This is an example of a commutative ring *without* a unit element.

Example 3. A ring which contains only one element is the ring which contains only the number zero, under addition and multiplication.

It is instructive to observe that had we chosen the ring as the first mathematical system to study we would have defined it without using the group concept. The commutative group axioms would, of necessity, be included in the ring axioms, and these could be followed by axioms (*R*2), (*R*3), and (*R*4), as shown here.

Definition. (*Expanded form*) *A* **ring** *R is a nonempty set of elements satisfying the following axioms under the operations* $\bigcirc$ *and* $\ominus$.

(*P*1)   *R is closed under the binary operation* $\bigcirc$.

(*P*2)   *The associative law holds for* $\bigcirc$*; that is,*
   $a \bigcirc (b \bigcirc c) = (a \bigcirc b) \bigcirc c$*, when a, b, and c are in R.*

(*P*3)   *For the operation* $\bigcirc$ *there is an identity element e in R such that* $e \bigcirc a = a = a \bigcirc e$*, for all a in R.*

(*P*4)   *For each a in R there is in R an inverse of a under* $\bigcirc$*, denoted by* a^**, such that* $a \bigcirc a^* = e = a^* \bigcirc a$.

(*P*5)   *The commutative law holds for* $\bigcirc$ *in R; that is,*
   $a \bigcirc b = b \bigcirc a$*, for all a and b in R.*

(*P*6)   *R is closed with respect to a second binary operation* $\bigcirc$.

(*P*7)   *The associative law holds for* $\ominus$*; that is,*
   $a \ominus (b \ominus c) = (a \ominus b) \ominus c$*, when a, b, and c are in R.*

(*P*8)   *The distributive laws hold; that is,*
   $a \ominus (b \bigcirc c) = (a \ominus b) \bigcirc (a \ominus c)$*,   and*
   $(b \bigcirc c) \ominus a = (b \ominus a) \bigcirc (c \ominus a)$*, when a, b, and c are in R.*

Various arrangements of these axioms may be found in other books dealing with rings, or with modern higher algebra.

Observe that using the group concept allows us to present a more compact form of the definition, though a book dealing exclusively with rings would, in all probability, refrain from introducing the concepts of other mathematical systems.

We shall now assume that an axiomatic approach has been made to groups based on the undefined terms given in Section 14, and that all the theorems (formerly called statements) about groups have been proved rigorously. We shall build upon this foundation by adding new definitions, such as the definition of a ring, and proving new theorems. Therefore, where we formerly used the words "statement" and "discussion" we shall now use "theorem" and "proof," respectively.

Throughout the rest of the text it will be convenient for us to denote the two ring operations as addition and multiplication even though these operations may not be addition and multiplication. We shall also denote the identity under the first operation by 0 (zero). It is assumed that, at this point, the reader is well enough initiated into thinking of operations in an abstract manner for us to adopt this usual simplification of notation.

We shall now rewrite some of the definitions with the simplified notation in order to orient the reader.

Definition.   (Rewritten)   *A **ring** R is a nonempty set of elements satisfying the following axioms:*

(R1)   *R is an "additive" abelian group.*

(R2)   *R is closed with respect to a second binary operation called "multiplication."*

(R3)   *"Multiplication" is associative; that is,*

$$a(bc) = (ab)c, \text{ for all } a, b, \text{ and } c \text{ in } R.$$

(R4)   *The distributive laws hold; that is, $a(b + c) = ab + ac$ and $(b + c)a = ba + ca$, for all a, b, and c in R.*

We remind the reader that there are two abstract operations involved in this definition and that we merely call them addition and multiplication for convenience.

Definition.   (Rewritten)   *A ring R is **commutative** if $ab = ba$ for all a and b in R.*

Definition. (Rewritten)   *A ring R has a **unit** (or **identity**) element if there is an element e′ in R such that e′a = ae′ = a, for every a in R.*

Definition.   *If a ≠ 0 and b ≠ 0 are elements of a ring R, and if ab = 0, then a and b are **divisors of zero**.*

With this simpler notation we shall now give further examples of rings.

Example 4.   Let S be the set of all pairs of integers (a, b) where "addition" and "multiplication" of elements are defined as follows:

$$(a, b) + (c, d) = (a + c, b + d),$$
$$(a, b)(c, d) = (ac, bd).$$

We verify $(R1)$ as follows: S is closed with respect to "addition" since $(a + c, b + d)$ is a pair of integers; thus $(G1)$ is satisfied. Now

$$[(a, b) + (c, d)] + (f, g) = (a + c, b + d) + (f, g)$$
$$= (\{a + c\} + f, \{b + d\} + g) = (a + \{c + f\}, b + \{d + g\})$$
$$= (a, b) + (c + f, d + g) = (a, b) + [(c, d) + (f, g)],$$

and S satisfies $(G2)$. The identity under "addition" is $(0, 0)$, and the inverse of the element (a, b) under "addition" is $(-a, -b)$, thus $(G3)$ and $(G4)$ are verified; therefore S is an "additive" group. S is commutative under "addition" since

$$(a, b) + (c, d) = (a + c, b + d) = (c + a, d + b) = (c, d) + (a, b);$$

Thus $(R1)$ is satisfied.

S is closed with respect to "multiplication" since (ac, bd) is a pair of integers. To verify $(R3)$ we observe that

$$[(a, b)(c, d)](g, h) = (ac, bd)(g, h) = (\{ac\}g, \{bd\}h)$$
$$= (a\{cg\}, b\{dh\}) = (a, b)(cg, dh) = (a, b)[(c, d)(g, h)].$$

To verify $(R4)$ we observe that

$$(a, b)[(c, d) + (g, h)] = (a, b)(c + g, d + h) = (a\{c + g\}, b\{d + h\})$$
$$= (ac + ag, bd + bh) = (ac, bd) + (ag, bh)$$
$$= (a, b)(c, d) + (a, b)(g, h).$$

The other distributive law can be similarly proved. Thus S is a ring.

S is also commutative since $(a, b)(c, d) = (ac, bd) = (ca, db) = (c, d)(a, b)$. It has a unit for "multiplication"; namely, $(1, 1)$.

It should be obvious from these verifications that the associative, commutative, and distributive properties of S are consequences of these same properties of the integers.

S has divisors of zero. The "additive" identity, or "zero," is the element $(0, 0)$, and the product of the "nonzero" elements $(a, 0)$ and $(0, d)$ is the "zero" element $(0, 0)$; hence $(a, 0)$ and $(0, d)$ are divisors of zero.

***Example* 5.** Let A be any abelian group. On A define a second operation $\circ$ having the property that $a \circ b = 0$, for all a and b in A. Then A is a commutative ring. It is called a trivial ring since all "products" are zero. For most groups this will be a ring without a unit, but if the group A is the number 0 alone under addition then 0 is the unit element.

EXERCISES

1. Tell which of the following sets of numbers form rings under addition and multiplication.

(a) The rational numbers R'.

(b) All integral multiples of the integer 3.

(c) All integral multiples of a fixed integer k.

(d) All rational numbers of the form $n/2^k$, where n and k are integers.

(e) All numbers of the form $a + b\sqrt{2}$, where a and b are integers.

(f) All numbers of the form $a + b\sqrt{2}$, where a and b are rational numbers.

2. Which of the sets in Exercise 1 are commutative rings with units?

3. Show that the second distributive law holds for Example 4.

4. Let A and B be two rings. Let R consist of all pairs (a, b) where a is an element of A and b is an element of B. If "addition" and "multiplication" are defined as follows, is R a ring?

$$\text{"Addition":} \quad (a_1, b_1) + (a_2, b_2) = (a_1 + a_2, b_1 + b_2)$$
$$\text{"Multiplication":} \quad (a_1, b_1)(a_2, b_2) = (a_1 a_2, b_1 b_2)$$

5. Let R be a commutative ring with unit, and x be a symbol. Define a polynomial over R as an expression of the form

$$a_0 x^n + a_1 x^{n-1} + \cdots + a_{n-1} x + a_n$$

where $a_0, a_1, \cdots, a_n$ are in R and n is zero or a positive integer. Show that if these polynomials are added and multiplied as in ordinary algebra they form a commutative ring with unit. This ring is denoted by $R[x]$. Observe that a_0 can be 0.

6. Rewrite the expanded form of the definition of a ring using the operations $+$ and $\cdot$ instead of $\circ$ and $\ominus$.

7. (a) Let R be all two-by-two matrices whose elements are rational numbers. Does R form a ring under matrix addition and matrix multiplication? (See Exercise 11 of Section 5, and Exercises 5 and 6 of Section 13.)

　　(b) Is it a commutative ring with unit?

17. THEOREMS ABOUT RINGS

Remark on Notation. Since we are calling the operations "addition" and "multiplication," we shall henceforth:
  (*i*)　denote the "additive" inverse of a by $-a$, the "additive" identity by 0, and the "multiplicative" inverse of a, if it exists, by a^{-1} or $1/a$;
 (*ii*)　frequently indicate the second operation by means of a dot or by juxtaposition, writing either $a \cdot b$ or ab for the "product";
(*iii*)　denote $a + (-b)$ by $a - b$;
 (*iv*)　speak of a ring R with or without indicating the operations.

Notational remark (*iii*) indicates that subtraction is really the operation of "adding" a first element to the "additive" inverse of a second element. Similarly, $a \div b = a\left(\dfrac{1}{b}\right)$, and division is the operation of "multiplying" a first element by the "multiplicative" inverse of a second element.

The reader is advised to attempt the proof of each of the following theorems before reading the proof given. In this way he will discover his own ingenuity.

Theorem 1. *Let $R(+, \cdot)$ be a ring. Then for every a in R, $0 \cdot a = 0$; similarly, $a \cdot 0 = 0$.*

Proof. We consider the expression $(b + 0) \cdot a$. If we simplify inside the parentheses we obtain $(b + 0) \cdot a = b \cdot a$. If we apply the distributive law we obtain $(b + 0) \cdot a = b \cdot a + 0 \cdot a$. Therefore, $b \cdot a + 0 \cdot a = b \cdot a$. Since $0 \cdot a$ leaves $b \cdot a$ unchanged when "added" to it, then $0 \cdot a$ must be the "additive" identity. Therefore $0 \cdot a = 0$. Similarly prove that $a \cdot 0 = 0$. ∎

Theorem 2. *In a ring R the following statements hold:*

$$(i) \quad a(-b) = (-a)b = -(ab),$$
$$(ii) \quad (-a)(-b) = ab,$$
$$(iii) \quad a(b - c) = ab - ac.$$

Part (i) of this theorem indicates that the "product" of a and the "additive" inverse of b is equal to the "product" of the "additive" inverse of a and the element b and that each product is equal to the "additive" inverse of the "product" ab.

Proof of (i). Our plan here is to "add" $a(-b)$ to ab. If this produces 0, then $a(-b)$ is the "additive" inverse of ab which we write as $-(ab)$. By the distributive law, $(R4)$, and Theorem 1 we have $ab + a(-b) = a[b + (-b)] = a \cdot 0 = 0$. Therefore, $a(-b)$ is the additive inverse of ab. Since the inverse is unique and the inverse of ab is written $-(ab)$, then $a(-b) = -(ab)$.

Similarly, consider the expression $ab + (-a)b$. By the distributive law, $(R4)$, and Theorem 1 we have $ab + (-a)b = [a + (-a)]b = 0 \cdot b = 0$. Thus $(-a)b$ is an inverse of ab. Since the inverse is unique, we have that $(-a)b = -(ab)$. Therefore, $a(-b) = -(ab) = (-a)b$.

Proof of (ii). Observe that a *special case* of (ii) has long disturbed students of high school algebra. They are told that the product of two negative numbers is a positive number, and this seems hard to believe though they may be given some practical example in which this type of reasoning seems plausible. We shall present the discussion and then explain the situation further.

By the associative law for addition we have

$$[ab + a(-b)] + (-a)(-b) = ab + [a(-b) + (-a)(-b)].$$

We shall reduce each side of this equality separately, starting with the left side.

$$[ab + a(-b)] + (-a)(-b) = a[b + (-b)] + (-a)(-b) \qquad (R4)$$
$$= a \cdot 0 + (-a)(-b) \qquad (G4)$$
$$= 0 + (-a)(-b) \qquad \text{Theorem 1}$$
$$= (-a)(-b). \qquad (G3)$$

We now reduce the right side in an analogous manner.

$$ab + [a(-b) + (-a)(-b)] = ab + [a + (-a)](-b)$$
$$= ab + 0 \cdot (-b)$$
$$= ab + 0$$
$$= ab.$$

Therefore, $(-a)(-b) = ab.$

Part (ii) shows that in any ring the "product" of the "additive" inverses of two elements is equal to the "product" of the elements. This property is a consequence of the ring properties which were used in the proof; namely, $(R1)$, $(R2)$, and $(R4)$. The numbers which are used in high school algebra form a ring under addition and multiplication; therefore, the product of two negative numbers must be a positive number. In fact, any set of objects which is a group (not necessarily commutative) under a first operation, and which satisfies $(R2)$ and $(R4)$ must satisfy (ii).   ∎

The proof of (iii) is left as an exercise.

Definition. *A ring R satisfies the **right cancellation law** for "multiplication" if whenever a, b, and c are elements of R such that $c \neq 0$ and $ac = bc$, then $a = b$.*

Definition. *A ring R satisfies the **left cancellation law** for "multiplication" if whenever a, b, and c are elements of R such that $c \neq 0$ and $ca = cb$, then $a = b$.*

Theorem 3. *In a ring R the right cancellation law for "multiplication" is equivalent to the statement that there are no divisors of zero.*

Proof. We first show that the right cancellation law implies that there are no divisors of zero.

Let $ac = 0$, and assume that $c \neq 0$. Then since $0 \cdot c = 0$, $ac = 0 \cdot c$, and by the right cancellation law, which we are assuming is true, we have that $a = 0$. This proves that if the "product" of two elements is zero, and the one on the right is not zero then the one on the left must be zero; hence there are no divisors of zero.

We next prove that if there are no divisors of zero, then the right cancellation law is true.

If $ac = bc$, where $c \neq 0$, then $ac - bc = 0$, and $(a - b)c = 0$. But since we are assuming that there are no divisors of zero and $c \neq 0$, then $a - b = 0$. From this we obtain $a = b$. Therefore, when there are no divisors of zero, the right cancellation law holds.   ∎

Theorem 4. *In a ring R the left cancellation law for "multiplication" is equivalent to the statement that there are no divisors of zero.*

The proof is left as an exercise.

EXERCISES

1. Prove the second part of Theorem 1.

2. Prove part *(iii)* of Theorem 2.

3. Give all reasons omitted in the proof of Theorem 3.

4. Prove Theorem 4.

5. Show that the following are true in a ring:

(i) $(-a)(-b) = -[-(ab)]$

(ii) $-(-a) = a$

(iii) $-(a + b) = (-a) + (-b)$

(iv) $(a - b) - (c - d) = (a - c) - (b - d)$
        $= (a + d) - (b + c)$

(v) $(a - b)(c - d) = (ac + bd) - (bc + ad)$

(vi)   If $ab = ba$, then $a(-b) = (-b)a$ and if b^{-1} exists, then $ab^{-1} = b^{-1}a$.

6. Which of the four fundamental operations of arithmetic; namely, addition, subtraction, multiplication, and division is described by each of the following?

(a) Adding the additive inverse.

(b) Adding the additive inverse of the additive inverse.

(c) Multiplying by the multiplicative inverse.

(d) Multiplying by the multiplicative inverse of the multiplicative inverse.

18. THE INTEGERS MODULO N

In order to enhance our supply of examples of mathematical systems we introduce the integers modulo n, where n is a positive integer. Since we denote the set of integers by J, we shall denote the integers modulo n by J_n.

Definition. *An integer a is **divisible by** an integer b, if there is a unique integer c such that $cb = a$.*

Example. The integer 20 is divisible by the integer 5 since there is one and only one integer 4, such that $(4)(5) = 20$. When 20 is divided by 5 the *quotient* is 4. We also write $\frac{20}{5} = 4$.

Let us now separate the set of all integers into three subsets. In the first row we put all integral multiplies of 3.

$$\cdots, -12, -9, -6, -3, 0, 3, 6, 9, \cdots$$

(Three dots indicate the omission of terms; therefore, three dots on each side indicate that we include all positive multiples of 3 as well as all negative multiples of 3.)

We now obtain a different set by adding 1 to each number in the first set. Thus we obtain

$$\cdots, -11, -8, -5, -2, 1, 4, 7, 10, \cdots .$$

We obtain a third set by adding 2 to each of the multiples of three (or by adding 1 to each number in the second set, since that produces the same results). This third set is

$$\cdots, -10, -7, -4, -1, 2, 5, 8, 11, \cdots .$$

If we add 1 to each of the numbers in the third set we again obtain all multiples of 3. Observe that in these three sets we have all of the integers, for if we write the three sets together

$$\cdots, -12, -9, -6, -3, 0, 3, 6, 9, \cdots$$
$$\cdots, -11, -8, -5, -2, 1, 4, 7, 10, \cdots$$
$$\cdots, -10, -7, -4, -1, 2, 5, 8, 11, \cdots$$

and read down the columns we obtain

$$\cdots, -12, -11, -10, -9, -8, -7, -6, -5, -4,$$
$$-3, -2, -1, 0, 1, 2, 3, 4, 5, 6, 7, 8, 9, 10, \cdots.$$

Denote the first set by $\bar{0}$. Then

$$\bar{0} = \{\cdots, -12, -9, -6, -3, 0, 3, 6, 9, \cdots\} = \{3k\},$$

where k is an integer.

Denote the second set by $\bar{1}$. Then

$$\bar{1} = \{\cdots, -11, -8, -5, -2, 1, 4, 7, 10, \cdots\} = \{3k + 1\}.$$

Denote the third set by $\bar{2}$. Then

$$\bar{2} = \{\cdots, -10, -7, -4, -1, 2, 5, 8, 11, \cdots\} = \{3k + 2\}.$$

We then denote the set consisting of the three elements $\bar{0}$, $\bar{1}$, and $\bar{2}$ by J_3 (read "J sub-three") and call this set of three elements *the set of integers modulo 3*. Observe that each element of this set is itself a set; therefore, we have a set of sets.

If we define J_4, the set of integers modulo 4, in an analogous fashion, we obtain four elements which we can denote by $\bar{0}$, $\bar{1}$, $\bar{2}$, and $\bar{3}$ where

$$\bar{0} = \{\cdots, -12, -8, -4, 0, 4, 8, 12, 16, \cdots\} = \{4k\}, \; k \text{ an integer,}$$
$$\bar{1} = \{\cdots, -11, -7, -3, 1, 5, 9, 13, 17, \cdots\} = \{4k + 1\},$$
$$\bar{2} = \{\cdots, -10, -6, -2, 2, 6, 10, 14, 18, \cdots\} = \{4k + 2\},$$
$$\bar{3} = \{\cdots, -9, -5, -1, 3, 7, 11, 15, 19, \cdots\} = \{4k + 3\}.$$

Observe that $\bar{0}$ does not represent the same set in J_3 as it does in J_4. In J_3, it consists of all multiples of 3; in J_4 it consists of all multiples of 4. Also observe that $\bar{1}$ in J_3 consists of the set obtained by adding 1 to all multiples of 3, and that $\bar{1}$ in J_4 consists of the set obtained by adding 1 to all multiples of 4. Similar statements can be made about the other elements involved.

What, then, is meant by J_n, the set of integers modulo n, for a fixed integer n? It consists of the elements $\bar{0}, \bar{1}, \bar{2}, \bar{3}, \cdots, \overline{n-1}$,

$\bar{0}$ = all integral multiples of $n = \{kn\}$, and k is an integer,

$\bar{1}$ = $\{kn + 1\}$,

$\bar{2}$ = $\{kn + 2\}$,

.   .

.   .

.   .

$\overline{n-1} = \{kn + (n-1)\}$.

We now define two operations on J_3. By a *representative* of the element $\bar{0}$ we shall mean any integer in this set. For example, four representatives of $\bar{0}$ are 0, 3, -15, and 12. Three representatives of $\bar{2}$ are 2, 5, and 14. We shall call 0, 1, and 2 the *main representatives* of the elements $\bar{0}, \bar{1}$, and $\bar{2}$, respectively. To "add" two elements of J_3 we shall add the integers which are their main representatives. The sum of their main representatives will be a representative of some element of J_3 and this element will be the "sum" of the given elements. Some examples will make this clear. The accompanying table is an "addition" table for J_3.

$+$	$\bar{0}$	$\bar{1}$	$\bar{2}$
$\bar{0}$	$\bar{0}$	$\bar{1}$	$\bar{2}$
$\bar{1}$	$\bar{1}$	$\bar{2}$	$\bar{0}$
$\bar{2}$	$\bar{2}$	$\bar{0}$	$\bar{1}$

"Addition" for J_3

We have that $\bar{0} + \bar{1} = \bar{1}$, since $0 + 1 = 1$, and 1 is a representative of $\bar{1}$. Also $\bar{1} + \bar{2} = \bar{0}$, since $1 + 2 = 3$, and 3 is a representative of $\bar{0}$. Similarly, $\bar{2} + \bar{2} = \bar{1}$, since $2 + 2 = 4$, and 4 is a representative of $\bar{1}$. In the exercises which follow this section the reader is asked to show that the "sum" is independent of the choice of representatives.

To "multiply" two elements of J_3 we shall use a similar procedure. First we multiply the main representatives of the two elements. Their product is a representative of some element of J_3, and this element is the "product" of the given elements. We have the accompanying "multiplication" table. For example, $\bar{0} \times \bar{1} = \bar{0}$, since $0 \cdot 1 = 0$, and

$\times$	0	1	2
$\overline{0}$	$\overline{0}$	$\overline{0}$	$\overline{0}$
$\overline{1}.$	$\overline{0}$	$\overline{1}$	$\overline{2}$
$\overline{2}$	$\overline{0}$	$\overline{2}$	$\overline{1}$

"Multiplication" for J_3

0 is a representative of $\overline{0}$. Also, $\overline{2} \times \overline{1} = \overline{2}$, since $2 \cdot 1 = 2$, and 2 is a representative of $\overline{2}$. Similarly, $\overline{2} \times \overline{2} = \overline{1}$, since $2 \cdot 2 = 4$, and 4 is a representative of $\overline{1}$. In the exercises which follow the reader is asked to show that the "product" is independent of the choice of representatives.

The first chart for J_3 shows that this set is closed under "addition." It also shows that $\overline{0}$ satisfies $(G3)$, and that each element has an inverse, hence $(G4)$ is satisfied. (The fact that each element has an inverse can be read from the chart by observing that for each element there is an element which when "added" to it produces the identity element $\overline{0}$. Thus, $\overline{0}$ is its own inverse, and $\overline{1}$ and $\overline{2}$ are inverses of each other.) Axiom $(G2)$ is satisfied since the "sum" of elements depends upon the representatives, which are integers and are associative. Therefore, J_3 is a group under "addition"; in fact, it is a commutative group.

The "multiplication" chart for J_3 shows that $(R2)$ is satisfied, and since the associative and distributive properties of the elements follow from these properties of the integers, J_3 satisfies $(R3)$ and $(R4)$. Therefore, J_3 is a ring.

"Addition" and "multiplication" are defined in an analogous manner for J_n. The words *addition* and *multiplication* when used in connection with J_n will always mean "addition" and "multiplication" as defined in this section.

EXERCISES

1. (a) Is 0 divisible by 7? (b) Is 7 divisible by 0?
   (c) Is 0 divisible by 0?

2. (a) What integers are contained in the element $\overline{1}$ of J_5?
   (b) What integers are contained in the element $\overline{3}$ of J_7?

3. How many elements are there in (*a*) J_1? (*b*) In J_2?

(*c*) Are J_1 and J_2 rings?

(*d*) Do these two sets contain divisors of zero?

4. (*a*) Make addition and multiplication charts for J_4.

(*b*) Is J_4 a ring? (*c*) Does it contain divisors of zero?

5. Repeat Exercise 4 using (*a*) J_5. (*b*) J_6.

6. (*a*) Is J_n a ring? (*b*) For which integers *n* does J_n have divisors of zero?

7. For each of the following sets determine whether the nonzero elements form a group under multiplication.

(*a*) J_2; (*b*) J_3; (*c*) J_4; (*d*) J_5; (*e*) J_6; (*f*) J_7; (*g*) J_n.

8. (*a*) Show that "addition" and "multiplication" as defined for J_3 are independent of the choice of representatives of the elements.

(*b*) Generalize the answer for (*a*) to obtain corresponding results for J_n.

9. Two integers *r* and *s* are *congruent modulo n*, where *n* is an integer, if and only if there is an integer *k* such that $r - s = kn$. When this condition is satisfied we write $r \equiv s \pmod{n}$, which is read "*r* is congruent to *s* modulo *n*."

Show that the following statements are true.

(*a*) $r \equiv s \pmod{n}$, if *r* and *s* are two representatives of the same element in J_n.

(*b*) If $r \equiv s \pmod{n}$, and $s \equiv t \pmod{n}$, then $r \equiv t \pmod{n}$.

(*c*) If $r \equiv s \pmod{n}$, then $rt \equiv st \pmod{n}$.

(*d*) If $r \equiv s \pmod{n}$ and $t \equiv p \pmod{n}$, then $rt \equiv sp \pmod{n}$.

19. ASSUMPTIONS CONCERNING THE REAL AND COMPLEX NUMBERS

In the preceding sections we did not use the entire set of real numbers nor the set of complex numbers, though we did present some exercises involving real numbers of the form $a + b\sqrt{2}$, where *a* and *b* are rational numbers. The answers to exercises involving numbers such as $a + b \sqrt{2}$, where a and b are rational numbers, could be obtained from our knowledge of the rational numbers and operations with radicals. For this reason they were introduced before the real and complex numbers were discussed.

Through the ages man's desire to solve equations has caused him to use larger and larger sets of numbers. Since $x + 7 = 3$ has no solution in positive integers, he needed to introduce negative integers. Since $3x = 1$ has no solution in integers, he needed rational numbers. To solve $x^2 - 2 = 0$ he needed real numbers; and for $x^2 + 2 = 0$ he needed complex numbers. This last equation shows that even for simple polynomial equations the complex numbers are needed. Following this observation a logical question to ask is whether or not the complex numbers are enough to solve *all* polynomial equations. Mathematicians have proved that this set is sufficiently large for this purpose.

We shall now proceed to introduce the real and complex numbers. By an infinite decimal we shall mean any number written with a finite number of digits to the left of the decimal point and an infinite number of digits to the right of the decimal point.

Can every integer be written as an infinite decimal? It can. For example, $0 = 0.00000 \cdots$; $5 = 5.00000 \cdots$; and $-3 = -3.00000 \cdots$.

Can every rational number be written this way? It can. For example, $\frac{1}{3} = .33333 \cdots$; $\frac{28}{9} = 3.11111 \cdots$; $\frac{3503}{8} = 437.875000 \cdots$; $\frac{3}{7} = .428571428571428571 \cdots$; $\frac{125}{999} = .125125125 \cdots$; $\frac{31,416}{10,000} = 3.1416000 \cdots$; and $\frac{28}{99} = .28282828 \cdots$.

Definition. *An **infinite decimal** is a number written in the form* $\pm c_1 c_2 c_3 \cdots c_k . a_1 a_2 a_3 \cdots$, *where each c as well as each a is one of the digits* 0, 1, 2, 3, 4, 5, 6, 7, 8, *or* 9.

For an infinite decimal to exist, some rule must be stated or understood by means of which the digit a_j can be determined for each positive integer j.

Definition. *A decimal is a **repeating decimal** if there is a digit in the decimal such that the digits to the right of this certain digit are repetitions of a certain arrangement of a set of n digits where n is a fixed integer.*

Observe that these decimal equivalents of rational numbers are repeating decimals. For $\frac{1}{3}$, the decimal equivalent has a repeating 3, even from the beginning. For $\frac{28}{9}$, the digit 1 is repeated. For $\frac{3}{7}$, the decimal equivalent consists of a repetition of the digits 428571. For $\frac{3503}{8}$, the digit 0 is repeated. Can you tell what digits are repeated in the remaining examples?

Since all of the decimal equivalents of rational numbers that we have considered are repeating decimals this poses the question as to whether *every* rational number can be written as a repeating decimal. There is also the related question as to whether every repeating decimal is equivalent to a rational number. It can be proved that a number is a rational number *if and only if* it is a repeating decimal.*

Definition. *A decimal is a **terminating decimal** if there is a digit in the decimal such that all digits to the right of it are zero.*

As examples of terminating decimals we have $0.000 \cdots$; $5.000 \cdots$; $-3.000 \cdots$; $437.875000 \cdots$; $3.1416000 \cdots$; and $.125000 \cdots$.

There are many decimals which are not repeating decimals. For example,

$$\sqrt{2} = 1.414214 \cdots,$$
$$5 + \sqrt{3} = 6.732051 \cdots,$$
$$\pi = 3.1415926536 \cdots,$$
$$\sqrt[3]{35} = 3.271066 \cdots,$$
$$\sqrt{11} + \sqrt[3]{7} = 5.229556 \cdots.$$

The reason that we know that these decimals do not repeat is that mathematicians have proved that these numbers are *not* rational numbers; nevertheless, they are equal to infinite decimals.

The student should realize that the number $3.1 = \frac{31}{10}$ is a rational number. Similarly the numbers 3.14, 3.142, 3.1416, 3.141593, and 3.1415927 are all rational numbers, but the number which they approximate; namely, π, is *not* a rational number. This is not a fact that should be obvious to the student, since many years were spent

---

* See A. A. Albert, *College Algebra* (Chicago, University of Chicago Press, 1946), p. 71, or R. W. Brink, *College Algebra*, 2nd ed., (New York, Appleton-Century-Crofts, Inc., 1961), p. 23.

by mathematicians in trying to discover the true nature of π. Remarks on this number are given at the end of this section.

Definition. *A **real number** is a number that is equal to an infinite decimal.*

Observe that zero and all positive and negative infinite decimals are real numbers.

We shall frequently denote the set of real numbers by Q.

Definition. *A real number which is not a rational number is an **irrational** number.*

This definition indicates that the real numbers can be divided into two sets—the rational and the irrational numbers.

Definition. *The **complex numbers** are the numbers of the form $a + bi$, where a and b are real numbers and $i^2 = -1$.*

We shall frequently denote the set of complex numbers by C. Examples of complex numbers which are not real numbers are $3 - 4i$, $5 + 6i$, and $2i$. These numbers cannot be written as infinite decimals since no infinite decimal can represent i. Every real number a is a complex number since it can be written as $a + 0 \cdot i$.

On page 359, several assumptions concerning special sets were given. The following further ASSUMPTIONS are made at this time.

(A9) The sum, difference, product, and quotient of two real numbers is a real number, provided that division by zero is excluded.

(A10) If a, b, and c are complex numbers, distinct or identical, then $(a + b) + c = a + (b + c)$. (Associative Law of Addition)*

Since the complex numbers contain the real numbers (A10) holds for the real numbers. A similar remark is applicable to each of the following assumptions.

---

* For example,
$[(2 + 3i) + (4 + 6i)] + (1 + 2i) = (6 + 9i) + (1 + 2i) = 7 + 11i$, and
$(2 + 3i) + [(4 + 6i) + (1 + 2i)] = (2 + 3i) + (5 + 8i) = 7 + 11i$.
Therefore,
$[(2 + 3i) + (4 + 6i)] + (1 + 2i) = (2 + 3i) + [(4 + 6i) + (1 + 2i)]$.

If a, b, and c are complex numbers, distinct or identical, then:

(A 11) $(ab)c = a(bc)$ (Associative Law of Multiplication)

(A 12) $a + b = b + a$ (Commutative Law of Addition)

(A 13) $ab = ba$ (Commutative Law of Multiplication)

(A 14) $a(b + c) = ab + ac$ (Distributive Law of Multiplication with Respect to Addition)

(A 15)   The product of two nonzero complex numbers is a nonzero complex number.

(A 16)   The complex number $a + bi = 0$ if and only if $a = 0$ and $b = 0$.

(A 17)   The sum, or product, of two positive real numbers is positive.

Remarks on π. The number π is the ratio of the circumference of a circle to its diameter. The ancient Babylonians approximated π by the number 3. A little later, between 1850 and 1650 B.C., the Egyptians used the closer approximation $\frac{256}{81}$ which is approximately 3.16. Archimedes, one of the greatest mathematicians of all times, said that π is greater than $3\frac{10}{71}$ and less than $3\frac{1}{7}$. For many purposes mathematicians used $3\frac{1}{7} = \frac{22}{7}$ as a sufficiently accurate approximation. Starting with Van Rooman (1561–1615), who gave π to 17 decimal places, there was a growing interest among certain mathematicians to produce as many digits in the approximation as possible. Some of them thought that this number might be a repeating decimal, and therefore a rational number. Van Ceulen, at the end of the sixteenth century, gave 35 decimal places; Vega, at the end of the eighteenth century, gave 140 places (136 correct); Dase, at the middle of the nineteenth century, gave 200 places; Richter, 500 places; and William Shanks produced 707 places by 1853.

It was not uncommon for such a mathematician to spend ten years of his life in this type of computation. All such work was in vain, for, in 1882, Lindemann proved that π is a transcendental number, and no rational number is a transcendental number.

Modern high speed automatic digital computers can calculate π to 10,000 decimal places in a few days. Such computations show that Shanks made a mistake near the 250th decimal place.

The symbol "π" which we now use to denote the ratio of the circumference to the diameter was first introduced by an English writer, William Jones, in 1706. Euler adopted it, and it has been in use ever since.

Remark on $\sqrt{2}$. For the sake of discussion let us assume that $\sqrt{2}$ is a rational number. Then $\sqrt{2} = p/q$, where p and q are integers and the fraction on the right is reduced to lowest terms. Then by squaring and simplifying we obtain $2q^2 = p^2$. Since 2 divides the left side of this equation it must divide p^2. It can divide p^2 only if it divides p. Therefore p is an even integer which we shall denote by $2t$. Substituting for p we have $2q^2 = 4t^2$, or $q^2 = 2t^2$. By the same type of argument, q is an even integer. If p and q are both even, then p/q is not in reduced form. Therefore, the assumption that $\sqrt{2}$ is rational leads to a contradiction, and we conclude that $\sqrt{2}$ must be an irrational number. (In this discussion we have assumed certain properties of the integers; namely, (1) a quotient of two integers can be reduced to lowest terms, and (2) that 2 cannot divide p^2 without dividing p.)

EXERCISES

1. Show that each of the following numbers is an irrational number.
(a) $\sqrt{3}$; (b) $\sqrt[3]{2}$.

2. Which of the following are rational numbers? Give reasons for your answers. (a) $\sqrt{7}$; (b) 3.141593; (c) $\sqrt{25}$; (d) $\pi - 3$; (e) $\sqrt[3]{11}$; (f) $\sqrt[3]{1331}$; (g) $\sqrt{2} + 5$; (h) $2 + \sqrt[3]{2} + \sqrt[3]{4}$.

3. Let A = all terminating decimals and B = all repeating decimals. What is the relationship between these two sets?

4. (a) Is every terminating decimal equivalent to a rational number?
  (b) Is every rational number equivalent to a terminating decimal?

5. Use $(A\,16)$ to show that $a + bi = c + di$ if and only if $a = c$ and $b = d$.

20. DEFINITION OF A FIELD

The third type of mathematical system that we shall consider is the field. We first define a field as a special type of ring.

We shall continue to indicate the two operations involved as addition and multiplication though they are merely two abstract operations. We shall also denote the additive and multiplicative identities by 0 and 1, respectively.

Definition. *A field is a commutative ring of at least two elements, in which there is a unit and every nonzero element has a multiplicative inverse.*

A second definition of a field can be given in terms of the group concept.

Definition. *A field F is an additive abelian group which is closed under multiplication, and for which the nonzero elements form a multiplicative abelian group such that $a(b + c) = ab \mid ac$, for all a, b, and c in F.*

We shall establish the equivalence of these two definitions after giving some examples of fields.

Example **1.**   The rational numbers form a field under addition and multiplication. (This can be readily verified by using the second definition of a field and some information from previous examples and exercises.)

Example **2.**   The real numbers form a field under addition and multiplication. The verification is left for the student.

Example **3.**   The complex numbers form a field under addition and multiplication. The verification is left for the student.

Example **4.**   All numbers of the form $a + b\sqrt{3}$, where a and b are rational numbers, form a field under addition and multiplication.

In the verification we shall use the second definition of a field, shall denote the set of objects by F, and the set of nonzero elements of F by $\bar{F}$.

The group axioms are satisfied under addition as follows: The sum of two elements $a + b\sqrt{3}$ and $c + d\sqrt{3}$ of this form is $(a + c) + (b + d)\sqrt{3}$, which is an element of this form, since the sum of two rational numbers is a rational number. Thus $(a + c) + (b + d)\sqrt{3}$

can be written as $g + h \sqrt{3}$, where $g = a + c$ and $h = b + d$, and g and h are rational numbers. Therefore, $(G1)$ is satisfied. Axiom $(G2)$ is satisfied since F is a subset of C, the complex numbers, which are associative. The identity element is $0 + 0 \cdot \sqrt{3}$, and the additive inverse of $a + b \sqrt{3}$ is $-a - b \sqrt{3}$. Therefore $(G3)$ and $(G4)$ are satisfied, and F is a group. Since the complex numbers are commutative and F is a subset of C, then F is an abelian group under addition.

To show that F is closed under multiplication we must show that the product of two elements in F is in F. The product $(a + b \sqrt{3})(c + d \sqrt{3}) = (ac + 3bd) + (bc + ad) \sqrt{3}$, which can be written as $g + h \sqrt{3}$, where $g = ac + 3bd$ and $h = bc + ad$. Since g and h are numbers obtained from rational numbers by addition and multiplication, and the rational numbers are closed with respect to these two operations, g and h are rational numbers. Therefore, F is closed under multiplication.

We now show that $\bar{F}$ forms a multiplicative abelian group. The preceding paragraph shows that the product of two elements of the form $a + b \sqrt{3}$ is an element of this same form. To show that $\bar{F}$ is closed with respect to multiplication we must also show that the product of two nonzero elements is a nonzero element. This follows from $(A 15)$, therefore $\bar{F}$ is closed. Both the commutative property and the associative property for multiplication follow from these properties of C. The number $1 + 0 \cdot \sqrt{3}$ is the multiplicative identity. This number is merely the number 1 written in the required form. To show that $a + b \sqrt{3} \neq 0$ has an inverse we must show that $1/(a + b \sqrt{3})$ is of the form necessary to be in $\bar{F}$. To remove the radical from the denominator of this expression we multiply the numerator and the denominator each by $a - b \sqrt{3}$ to obtain

$$\frac{1}{a + b \sqrt{3}} = \frac{a - b \sqrt{3}}{a^2 - 3b^2} = \frac{a}{a^2 - 3b^2} - \frac{b}{a^2 - 3b^2} \sqrt{3} = g + h \sqrt{3},$$

where $g = \dfrac{a}{a^2 - 3b^2}$ and $h = - \dfrac{b}{a^2 - 3b^2}.$ To show that g and h are rational numbers we observe first that $a^2 - 3b^2 = 0$ if and only if $a = \pm \sqrt{3}b$, or $a/b = \pm \sqrt{3}$. This is impossible since the quotient of two rational numbers is a rational number and $\sqrt{3}$ is an irrational number. Since $j - k = j + (-k)$, where $-k$ is the additive inverse of k, and $j/k = j(1/k)$, where $1/k$ is the multiplicative inverse of k, the fact that g and h are rational numbers follows readily from the fact that the rational numbers form a field under addition and multiplication. Therefore the nonzero elements of F form a multiplicative abelian group.

The distributive law holds in F because it holds in C. Therefore F is a field.

Example **5.** The set J_3 is a field under "addition" and "multiplication."

Since we have already proved that J_3 is a ring and we have a multiplication table from which we can delete the row and column for $\bar{0}$ we can readily show that multiplication is commutative and that each non-zero element has a multiplicative inverse. Therefore, J_3 is a field of three elements.

Each of the first four examples contains an infinite number of elements and is therefore called an *infinite field*. The fifth example is a *finite field*.

EXERCISES

1. How does the second definition of a field insure the existence of at least two elements in a field?

2. Which of the following sets are fields under addition and multiplication?

(*a*) The positive real numbers.

(*b*) The set of all numbers $a + b \sqrt{2}$, where a and b are

        (*i*) rational numbers,   (*ii*) integers,

(*c*) The set of all numbers of the form $a + b \sqrt[3]{3} + c \sqrt[3]{9}$, where a, b, and c are (*i*) rational numbers,   (*ii*) integers,

(*d*) The set of all numbers of the form $a \sqrt{2}$, where a is a rational number.

(*e*) The set of all numbers of the form $a + b \sqrt[3]{25}$, where a and b are rational numbers.

(*f*) The set of all numbers of the form $a + bi$, where $i^2 = -1$, and a and b are rational numbers.

3. Which of the following sets are fields under "addition" and "multiplication" as defined for modular sets?

(*a*) J_2,   (*b*) J_4,   (*c*) J_5,   (*d*) J_6,   (*e*) J_n.

4. Define a field without using the concept of a group or a ring.

5. Does the set M of all two-by-two matrices whose elements are real numbers form a field under matrix addition and multiplication? (See Section 5, Ex. 11 and Section 13, Ex. 5, 6, 7.)

21. THEOREMS ABOUT FIELDS

Theorem 5. *A field has no divisors of zero.*

Proof. Let a and b be two elements of a field such that $ab = 0$, and $b \neq 0$. Then b^{-1} is in the field and

$$(ab)b^{-1} = 0(b^{-1}),$$
$$a(bb^{-1}) = 0,$$
$$a(1) = 0,$$
$$a = 0.$$

Therefore, if the product of two field elements is zero, one of them must be zero, and there are no divisors of zero. ∎

Remark. The reader should observe that in this discussion one of two things must be true. Either $b = 0$, or $b \neq 0$. (This is the logical concept of p or not p.) If $b = 0$, then there are no divisors of zero; and if $b \neq 0$, our argument shows that $a = 0$. Thus it is impossible for the product of two *nonzero* quantities to be zero. Therefore, there are no divisors of zero.

Theorem 6. *The two definitions of a field are equivalent.*

Proof. The first definition states that a field is a commutative ring of at least two elements, in which there is a unit and every nonzero element has a multiplicative inverse. Assuming that this definition holds for a set which we shall denote by H, we must show that the second definition also holds for H. To satisfy the second definition we must show that
(1) H is an additive abelian group,
(2) H is closed with respect to multiplication,
(3) the nonzero elements of H form a multiplicative abelian group, and
(4) the distributive law $a(b + c) = ab + ac$ holds in H.

Since it is assumed that H is a ring, conditions (1), (2), and (4) are true; therefore, only (3) remains to be investigated.

Since there are two elements in H, there must be at least one non-zero element. Let $\bar{H}$ denote the nonzero elements of H, and let ab represent the product of two elements in $\bar{H}$. If $ab = 0$, since $a \neq 0$, a^{-1} exists, $a^{-1}(ab) = a^{-1}(0)$, and $b = 0$. This contradicts the fact that b is a nonzero element. Therefore $ab \neq 0$ and the product of two nonzero elements is a nonzero element. Therefore $\bar{H}$ is closed and $(G1)$ is satisfied.

Axiom $(G2)$ is satisfied, because every ring obeys the associative law under multiplication.

Denote the unit element by e'. If $e' = 0$ and $c \neq 0$, then since $c \cdot e' = c = e' \cdot c$, we have $c \cdot 0 = c = 0 \cdot c$. However, in a ring $c \cdot 0 = 0$. Therefore, $c = 0$. Since this is a contradiction, $e' \neq 0$, and e' is in $\bar{H}$. Therefore $(G3)$ is satisfied.

For each $a \neq 0$, there is an inverse a^{-1} in H. If $a^{-1} = 0$, then $a \cdot a^{-1} = a \cdot 0 = 0$. But $a \cdot a^{-1} = e'$, and $e' \neq 0$. Therefore $a^{-1} \neq 0$, and a^{-1} is in $\bar{H}$. Thus $\bar{H}$ has an inverse for each element in it and $(G4)$ is satisfied.

Therefore $\bar{H}$ is a group. Since H is a commutative ring, $\bar{H}$ is a multiplicative abelian group and the second definition is satisfied.

Now we show that the second definition implies the first one. The second definition says that a field F is an additive abelian group which is closed under multiplication, and that the nonzero elements form a multiplicative abelian group such that $a(b + c) = ab + ac$, for all a, b, and c in F. We assume that this definition holds for a set F and show that the first definition must then hold for F. The first definition requires that F

(5) be a commutative ring,

(6) contain a unit and at least two elements, and

(7) contain a multiplicative inverse for every nonzero element.

Since the second definition is assumed, F is an additive abelian group and $(R1)$ is satisfied. Axiom $(R2)$ is satisfied since F is closed under multiplication. Since the nonzero elements form a multiplicative abelian group, the nonzero elements are associative with respect to multiplication. From the distributive law and the fact that F is an additive abelian group, we have $a \cdot b + a \cdot 0 = a \cdot b$ by evaluating $a(b + 0)$ in two ways. Therefore, $a \cdot 0 = 0$. Since products involving 0 are associative, $(R3)$ is satisfied. $(R4)$ follows from the distributive and abelian properties of multiplication given in the second definition, therefore (5) is satisfied. The multiplicative identity in F is a unit for *every* element since it is a unit for the nonzero elements and $a \cdot 0 = 0 = 0 \cdot a$ in a ring. F contains 0 and 1, which are distinct, and therefore contains at least two elements; therefore (6) is satisfied. Since the nonzero elements of F form a multiplicative group, (7) is satisfied.

Since each definition implies the other these definitions are equivalent. ∎

Theorem 7. *If K is a field, then* (1) *K must contain at least one nonzero element, and* (2) *for all a and b in K it is true that $a + b$, $a - b$, and ab are in K, and a/b is in K if $b \neq 0$.*

Proof. Since a field must contain at least two elements and the additive inverse zero is unique, then one of these two elements is not zero.

Since K is an additive group, then for all a and b in K, $a + b$ is in K. Also for every a in K, its inverse $-a$ is in K and the additive closure insures us that $a + (-b) = a - b$ is in K.

Since K is closed under multiplication, for all a and b in K, ab is also in K. Since the nonzero elements of K form a multiplicative group, if $b \neq 0$, then b has a multiplicative inverse b^{-1} and by the multiplicative closure of K, $a \cdot b^{-1} = a/b$ is in K. ∎

Theorem 8. *A subset K of a field F is a field under the same operations if K contains at least one nonzero element, and if for all a and b in K it is true that $a + b$, $a - b$, and ab are in K and that a/b is in K if $b \neq 0$.*

Proof. We observe first that K obeys the associative and commutative laws for addition and multiplication and also the distributive law, since it is a subset of F which obeys these laws. Since $0 \cdot a = 0$ in F, this equation holds in K.

We now verify the other axioms necessary to make K a field according to the second definition.

By hypothesis, K is closed with respect to addition. To produce an additive identity we observe that there is one element in K. Denote it by a, and let $b = a$ in the statement of the hypotheses which says that if a and b are in K, then $a - b$ is in K. Then $a - a = 0$ is in K. Since 0 and a are in K, then $0 - a = -a$ is in K. Therefore, K is an additive abelian group.

We now show that the nonzero elements of K, denoted by $\overline{K}$, form a multiplicative group. Axiom $(G1)$ is satisfied since F is a field and hence has no divisors of zero. Therefore, $\overline{K}$ can have no divisors of zero, and the product of two nonzero elements is a nonzero element. By hypothesis, there is at least one nonzero element, c, in $\overline{K}$. Then if c and b are in $\overline{K}$, c/b is in $\overline{K}$ if $b \neq 0$. Let $b = c$, then $c/c = 1$ is in $\overline{K}$. Now since 1 and $c \neq 0$ are in $\overline{K}$, $1/c$ is in $\overline{K}$, and c has a multiplicative inverse. Therefore, $\overline{K}$ is a multiplicative abelian group, and since it is closed under multiplication K is a field.   ∎

These theorems make it easy to determine whether or not certain sets are fields. For example, we can quickly show that the set K of all elements of the form $a + b\sqrt{5}$, where a and b are integers, is not a field, for 1 and $3 - \sqrt{5}$ are in K but their quotient is not in K. Observe that

$$\frac{1}{3 - \sqrt{5}} = \frac{3 + \sqrt{5}}{4} = \frac{3}{4} + \frac{\sqrt{5}}{4}$$

is not in K since $3/4$ and $1/4$ are not integers.

Using Theorem 8 we can conclude that a subset K of the complex numbers C is a field if it contains one nonzero element along with the sum, difference, and product of every two elements in K, and the quotient of these two elements when the divisor is not zero. Thus the set of all elements of the form $a + b\sqrt{7}$, where a and b are rational numbers, is a field since the sum, difference, product and quotient of two such elements is an element of this form.

A more difficult set to test is the set S consisting of elements of the form $a + b\sqrt[3]{2} + c\sqrt[3]{4}$, where a, b, and c are rational numbers. It is easy to see that the sum and the difference of two such numbers produces a number of the same form. Let us consider $\alpha = a + b\sqrt[3]{2} + c\sqrt[3]{4}$ and $\beta = d + e\sqrt[3]{2} + f\sqrt[3]{4}$. Then $\alpha\beta = (ad + 2bf + 2ce) + (ae + bd + 2cf)\sqrt[3]{2} + (af + be + cd)\sqrt[3]{4}$. Since the coefficients are produced by rational operations on rational numbers and the rational numbers form a field, the product is of the form $g + h\sqrt[3]{2} + k\sqrt[3]{4}$, where g, h, and k are rational numbers. We now show that if $\beta \neq 0$, then the quotient α/β is in S. To do this we look for an inverse for β. We seek the values of x, y, and z such that

$$(x + y\sqrt[3]{2} + z\sqrt[3]{4})(d + e\sqrt[3]{2} + f\sqrt[3]{4}) = 1.$$

Substituting x, y, and z for a, b, and c, respectively, in the product found above we obtain

$$(dx + 2fy + 2ez) + (ex + dy + 2fz) \sqrt[3]{2} + (fx + ey + dz) \sqrt[3]{4} = 1.$$

This will be true if and only if

$$\begin{cases} dx + 2fy + 2ez = 1, \\ ex + dy + 2fz = 0, \\ fx + ey + dz = 0. \end{cases}$$

This system of linear equations can be solved for x, y, and z to obtain

$$x = \frac{d^2 - 2ef}{w}, \quad y = \frac{2f^2 - de}{w}, \quad z = \frac{e^2 - fd}{w},$$

where $w = d^3 + 2e^3 + 4f^3 - 6def$. We observe that since $\beta \neq 0$, the numbers* d, e, and f are not all zero; hence $w \neq 0$. The inverse of β is $x + y \sqrt[3]{2} + z \sqrt[3]{4}$, where x, y, and z are rational numbers. Since $\alpha/\beta = \alpha(1/\beta) = \alpha\beta^{-1}$, and we have shown that the product of two numbers in S is in S, then the quotient is likewise in S. Therefore S is a field.

EXERCISES

1. Show that a subset K of a field F is a field under the same operations if the following three conditions are satisfied:

(i) K is closed with respect to addition and multiplication,

(ii) K contains 0 and 1, and

(iii)   for each $a \neq 0$ in K, the additive and multiplicative inverses of a are in K.

2. Which of the following sets are fields under addition and multiplication?

(a) The set of all numbers $a + b \sqrt{n}$, where n is an integer but not the square of an integer, and a and b are

(i) integers;   (ii) rational numbers.

(b) The set of all numbers of the form $a + b \sqrt[3]{m} + c \sqrt[3]{m^2}$, where m is an integer but not the cube of an integer, and a and b are

(i) integers;   (ii) rational numbers.

---

* See Albert, *op. cit.*, p. 84.

3. Show that the following definition is equivalent to one of the definitions of a field.

A field is a commutative ring of at least two elements in which the equation $ax = b$ has a solution for every pair of elements b and $a \neq 0$ in the ring.

4. Show that a commutative ring which has no divisors of zero and contains a unit distinct from the "additive" identity is a field if it contains only a finite number of elements.

5. If a field contains the rational numbers and the following number what is the form of its general element?

(a) $\sqrt{11}$;   (b) $3 + \sqrt{5}$;   (c) $\sqrt[3]{5} + \frac{3}{7}$;

(d) $\sqrt[4]{3}$;   (e) $\sqrt[5]{2}$;   (f) $\sqrt[5]{243}$.

6. Let S be a subset of the complex numbers which contains the number 5.

(a) If S is closed with respect to addition, subtraction, multiplication, and division, does it contain each of the following? Explain your answer.

(i) 0; (ii) 1; (iii) -1; (iv) all integers; (v) all rational numbers.

(b) Is S a field?

22. ISOMORPHISM INVOLVING TWO OPERATIONS

If two sets are given, each of which is closed with respect to two operations, then these sets are isomorphic if there is a one-to-one correspondence between the sets which preserves the operations.

Isomorphisms are useful in determining types of rings and fields just as they are in determining types of groups.

Definition. *Let H be a set closed with respect to two operations $\oplus$ and $\otimes$, and let K be a set which is closed with respect to two operations $\circ$ and $\ominus$. If there is a one-to-one correspondence $x \leftrightarrow x'$ between the sets H and K such that $(a \oplus b)' = a' \circ b'$ and $(a \otimes b)' = a' \ominus b'$, then this correspondence is an* **isomorphism** *between H and K.*

When two sets H and K satisfy the conditions of the preceding definitions they are *isomorphic*.

It is convenient to refer to sets which are closed with respect to two operations as *sets of double composition*.

Theorem 9. *If sets H and K are isomorphic sets of double composition, then* (a) *K is a ring if H is a ring, and* (b) *K is a field if H is a field.*

Proof of (a). If a, b, and c are elements of H then their images in K are a', b', and c', respectively; that is, $a \leftrightarrow a'$, $b \leftrightarrow b'$, and $c \leftrightarrow c'$.

Since H is a ring it is a group with respect to $\oplus$; therefore K is a group with respect to $\circ$, by Statement 11 of Section 13.

Since $a \oplus b = b \oplus a$, then $a' \circ b' = b' \circ a'$ and K is an abelian group under $\circ$.

K is closed with respect to $\ominus$. Since H is a ring $(a \otimes b) \otimes c = a \otimes (b \otimes c)$, therefore $(a' \ominus b') \ominus c' = a' \ominus (b' \ominus c')$ and K is associative under $\ominus$. Since H is a ring $a \otimes (b \oplus c) = (a \otimes b) \oplus (a \otimes c)$ and $(b \oplus c) \otimes a = (b \otimes a) \oplus (c \otimes a)$. Therefore $a' \ominus (b' \circ c') = (a' \ominus b') \otimes (a' \ominus c')$, and $(b' \circ c') \ominus a' = (b' \ominus a') \circ (c' \ominus a')$ and K is a ring.

Proof of (b). If H is a field, then H has all the properties of a ring and by part (a) K has all the properties of a ring. We need to show that K has a unit and that every nonzero element has an inverse under the second operation.

Since H is a field it has a unit element which we shall denote by u, such that for every a in H, $a \otimes u = a = u \otimes a$. Therefore $a' \ominus u' = a' = u' \ominus a'$, for every a', and u' is a unit in K. The "zero" element of H maps onto the "zero" element of K, and if a is a nonzero element of H, then there is in H an $\bar{a}$ such that $a \otimes \bar{a} = u = \bar{a} \otimes a$, and therefore $a' \ominus \bar{a}' = u' = \bar{a}' \ominus a'$. Thus $\bar{a}'$ is the inverse of a', and K is a field.   ∎

Example 1. Let (a, b) represent an ordered pair of positive integers. Define equality on these pairs as follows: $(a, b) = (c, d)$ if and only if $a - b = c - d$. Let $\{(a, b)\}$ denote the "equivalence class" consisting of all pairs equal to the pair (a, b). If "addition" and "multiplication" are defined on these equivalence classes as follows:

$$\{(a, b)\} \oplus \{(c, d)\} = \{(a + c, b + d)\},$$
$$\{(a, b)\} \otimes \{(c, d)\} = \{(ac + bd, ad + cb)\},$$

then the set T of all of these equivalence classes is isomorphic to the ring J of all integers under ordinary addition and multiplication.

This correspondence is one-to-one because an ordered pair of integers (a, b) has a unique difference $a - b$. Since all pairs in $\{(a, b)\}$ have the same difference, only one element of J corresponds to one element of T. Given an integer n in J, it determines a difference $c - d = n$. Then all ordered pairs (c, d) having the difference $c - d$ are in the element $\{(c, d)\}$ of T. Therefore one and only one element of T corresponds to each element of J.

Let $\{(a, b)\} \leftrightarrow a - b$. Then $[\{(a, b)\} \oplus \{(c, d)\}]' = \{(a + c, b + d)\}'$ $= a + c - (b + d) = a + c - b - d$; $\{(a, b)\}' = a - b$, $\{(c, d)\}'$ $= c - d$; and $\{(a, b)\}' + \{(c, d)\}' = a - b + c - d = a + c - b - d$. Therefore, the first operation is preserved. Also $[\{(a, b)\} \otimes \{(c, d)\}]'$ $= \{(ac + bd, ad + cb)\}' = ac + bd - (ad + cb) = ac + bd - ad$ $- cb$; $\{(a, b)\}' \cdot \{(c, d)\}' = (a - b)(c - d) = ac + bd - ad - cb$; and the second operation is preserved. Therefore T is a ring. This example looks less complicated when we see that every integer can be expressed as the difference between two positive integers. For example, $7 - 7 = 0$, $4 - 3 = 1$, and $2 - 3 = -1$. The sum and product defined are merely the pairs that correspond to the algebraic sum $(a - b) + (c - d)$ and the product $(a - b)(c - d)$.

Observe how much easier it is to prove that T is a ring by using an isomorphism than it is to verify all of the ring requirements.

***Example* 2.** The set M of matrices* of the form $\begin{pmatrix} a & b \\ -b & a \end{pmatrix}$, where a and b are real numbers, is isomorphic to the field C of complex numbers, under the one-to-one correspondence $a + bi \leftrightarrow \begin{pmatrix} a & b \\ -b & a \end{pmatrix}$.

If $(a + bi)' = \begin{pmatrix} a & b \\ -b & a \end{pmatrix}$ and $(c + di)' = \begin{pmatrix} c & d \\ -d & c \end{pmatrix}$, then

$$[(a + bi) + (c + di)]' = [(a + c) + (b + d)i]' = \begin{pmatrix} a + c & b + d \\ -(b + d) & a + c \end{pmatrix}.$$

Also

$$(a + bi)' + (c + di)' = \begin{pmatrix} a & b \\ -b & a \end{pmatrix} \oplus \begin{pmatrix} c & d \\ -d & c \end{pmatrix} = \begin{pmatrix} a + c & b + d \\ -(b + d) & a + c \end{pmatrix},$$

and matrix addition is preserved. For the second operation we have

* See Section 5, Ex. 11 and Section 13, Ex. 5, 6, 7.

$$[(a + bi)(c + di)]' = \begin{pmatrix} ac - bd & ad + bc \\ -(ad + bc) & ac - bd \end{pmatrix} \text{ and}$$

$$(a + bi)' \otimes (c + di)' = \begin{pmatrix} a & b \\ -b & a \end{pmatrix}\begin{pmatrix} c & d \\ -d & c \end{pmatrix} = \begin{pmatrix} ac - bd & ad + bc \\ -(ad + bc) & ac - bd \end{pmatrix};$$

and therefore matrix multiplication is preserved.

EXERCISES

1. Let S be the set of all ordered pairs (a, b) of integers subject to the following definitions of equality, "addition" and "multiplication."

Equality: $(a, b) = (c, d)$ if and only if $ad = bc$.
"Addition": $(a, b) \oplus (c, d) = (ad + bc, bd)$.
"Multiplication": $(a, b) \otimes (c, d) = (ac, bd)$.

Let $\{(a, b)\}$ represent the equivalence class consisting of all ordered pairs equal to the pair (a, b), where $b \neq 0$, and let T represent the set of all such equivalence classes. Prove that T is isomorphic to the field of rational numbers.

2. Show that the set of all matrices of the form $\begin{pmatrix} a & 0 \\ 0 & a \end{pmatrix}$, where a is a real number, is isomorphic to the field of real numbers.

3. Show that the set of all ordered pairs (a, b) of rational numbers subject to the following definitions is isomorphic to the field of numbers of the form $a + b \sqrt{2}$, where a and b are rational numbers.

Equality: $(a, b) = (c, d)$ if and only if $a = c$ and $b = d$.
"Addition": $(a, b) \oplus (c, d) = (a + c, b + d)$.
"Multiplication": $(a, b) \otimes (c, d) = (ac + 2bd, ad + bc)$.

4. Outline an axiomatic system for rings which does not use the group concept. Do the same for fields.

5. An *integral domain* is a commutative ring having a unit and no divisors of zero. Give an example of an integral domain which is not a field.

Answers to Selected

Exercises

The letters n, m, t, p, q, a, b, h, and k denote integers. When p/q or a/b represent rational numbers, then $q \neq 0$ and $b \neq 0$. (The reasons for the following arguments should be supplied by the reader.)

1. (a) $2n(2m) = 4nm = 2(2nm) = 2t$.

   (b) $2n - 2m = 2(n - m) = 2t$.

   (c) False. $4/6 = 2/3$.

   (d) False. $5 + 3 = 8 = 2t$.

   (e) $(2n + 1)(2m + 1) = 4nm + 2m + 2n + 1 = 2(2nm + m + n) + 1 = 2t + 1$.

   (f) $\dfrac{p}{q} + \dfrac{a}{b} = \dfrac{pb + qa}{qb} = \dfrac{h}{k}$, where $k \neq 0$.

   (g) $\left(\dfrac{p}{q}\right)\left(\dfrac{a}{b}\right) = \dfrac{pa}{qb} = \dfrac{h}{k}$, where $k \neq 0$.

   (h) $\dfrac{p}{q} - \dfrac{a}{b} = \dfrac{pb - qa}{qb} = \dfrac{h}{k}$, where $k \neq 0$.

   (i) Since the quotient exists we know that the divisor is not equal to zero. Therefore $p/q \div a/b$, where $a \neq 0$.

$$\frac{p}{q} \div \frac{a}{b} = \frac{p}{q} \cdot \frac{b}{a} = \frac{pb}{qa} = \frac{h}{k}, \text{ where } k \neq 0.$$

(j) False. 3/7.

(k) $(2n + 1) - (2m + 1) = 2n + 1 - 2m - 1 = 2n - 2m = 2(n - m) = 2t$.

(l) $2n(2m + 1) = 2(2nm + n) = 2t$.

(m) False. $(-3) + 3 = 0$.

2.

	(i)	(ii)	(iii)	(iv)
(a)	yes	no	yes	no
(b)	no	no	yes	no
(c)	yes	yes	yes	no
(d)	yes	yes	yes	no
(e)	no	no	no	no

Page 363

1. Addition and multiplication.

2. (a) group. (b) group. (c) group.
(d) G1, G3, or G4. (e) G1 or G3. (f) group.
(g) group. (h) group. (i) group.

3. (a) G4. (b) C3 or G4. (c) G4.
(d) G4. (e) group. (f) group.
(g) group. (h) G3 if $n \neq 1$, G4. (i) G4.
(j) group.

5. No.

6. (a) It has no inverse under multiplication.
(b) It has no inverse under multiplication.

Page 374

2. In exercises concerning the symmetries of a square we shall use the following notation:

I = No motion

R = Rotation through 90°

R' = Rotation through 180°

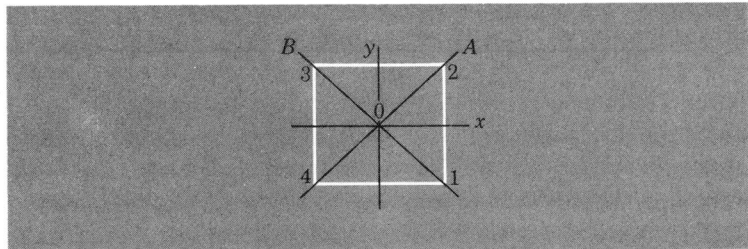

R'' = Rotation through 270°
H = Reflection in Ox
K = Reflection in Oy
L = Reflection in OA
M = Reflection in OB

3. $2n$.

4. Yes.

5. $\{I, R'\}$.

6. $\{I\}$.

7. Yes.

8. All.

10. Yes.

11. (a) Yes.　(b) Yes.　(c) Yes.

Page 379

1. (a) All integral multiples of 4; All integral multiples of 6. All of the subgroups are abelian.
　(b) $\{1, -1\}$; All integral powers of r, where r is a rational number which is not 0 nor 1. All of the subgroups are abelian.

2. (a) $\{I\}$; $\{I, R'\}$; $\{I, H\}$; $\{I, K\}$; $\{I, L\}$; $\{I, M\}$; $\{I, R, R', R''\}$; $\{I, H, K, R'\}$; $\{I, L, M, R'\}$; The whole group.
　(b) All are abelian except the whole group.

3. (b) $\{(1)\}$.　(c) $\{(1)\}$; $\{(1), (12)(34)\}$; $\{(1), (13)(24)\}$; $\{(1), (14)(23)\}$; $\{(1), (12)(34), (13)(24), (14)(23)\}$; $\{(1), (123), (132)\}$; $\{(1), (124), (142)\}$; $\{(1), (134), (143)\}$; $\{(1), (243), (234)\}$; The whole group.

6. Order 5; All elements except (1) are generators.

7. (a) 6.
　(b) x and x^5 are inverses; x^2 and x^4 are inverses; x^3 is its own inverse.
　(c) x is of order 6; x^2, order 3; x^3, order 2; x^4, order 3; x^5, order 6; x^6, order 1.
　(d) $\{x^6\}$; $\{x^2, x^4, x^6\}$; $\{x^3, x^6\}$; The whole group.

8. (b) Each element is its own inverse.
　(c) All elements are of order 2 except the identity which is of order 1.
　(d) $\{1\}$; $\{1, x\}$; $\{1, y\}$; $\{1, xy\}$; The whole group.

Page 393

1. No. The element g may not commute with the element $a \bigcirc b$.

4. The element a generates a cyclic subgroup. The order of this subgroup must be a divisor of 3. Therefore, it is either 1 or 3. If $a^1 = e$, then a and e are equal elements and the group contains only two distinct elements, instead of three. If $a^3 = e$, then a, a^2, and $a^3 = e$ are three distinct elements. Because the group is closed these three elements are in the group. Thus a is a group generator, the group is cyclic, and therefore, commutative. In fact, $a = a$, $a^3 = e$, and $a^2 = b$.

8. It has no proper subgroups because the order of each element must be a divisor of the order of the group, which is a prime p. Therefore each element is of order 1 or p. Only the identity is of order 1, therefore all other elements are group generators and the group is cyclic.

Page 398

1. All are groups.

2. Yes.

4. (a) No.   (b) No.   (c) Yes.

Page 405

1. (a) 720.   (b) Yes. Let A, B, C, D, E, and F correspond to I, T', T, H, K, and L, respectively. (There are others.)

2. (a) A group of order two is cyclic. The element of order two is the group generator. An isomorphism can be set up between two groups of order two by making the identity elements correspond to each other and the elements of order two correspond to each other.

(b) All groups of order three are cyclic. Such a group consists of an identity element and two generators. If R and W are groups of order three having generators r and w, respectively, then $r \leftrightarrow w$, $r^2 \leftrightarrow w^2$, $r^3 \leftrightarrow w^3$ is an isomorphism between them.

(c) One.

(d) If p is a prime integer, there is only one type of group of order p; namely, a cyclic group which has no proper subgroups. It consists of an identity element and p-1 generators.

3. The element a is a generator of the group. Let it correspond to (1234) or to (1432). If it corresponds to (1234) then, the isomorphism is produced in which a, -1, $-a$, and 1 correspond to (1234), (13)(24), (1432), and (1), respectively.

4. (a) $\{(1), (12)\}$.   (b) R of Example 2.   (c) W of Example 2.

5. (a) $-13; 9; -6; 0$.   (b) No.

6. (a) $\begin{pmatrix} v_1 \\ v_2 \end{pmatrix} \otimes (W_1, W_2) = \begin{pmatrix} v_1 \cdot w_1 & v_1 \cdot w_2 \\ v_2 \cdot w_1 & v_2 \cdot w_2 \end{pmatrix}$.

(b)

$$\begin{pmatrix} a_{11}b_{11} + a_{12}b_{21} + a_{13}b_{31}, & a_{11}b_{12} + a_{12}b_{22} + a_{13}b_{32}, & a_{11}b_{13} + a_{12}b_{23} + a_{13}b_{33} \\ a_{21}b_{11} + a_{22}b_{21} + a_{23}b_{31}, & a_{21}b_{12} + a_{22}b_{22} + a_{23}b_{32}, & a_{21}b_{13} + a_{22}b_{23} + a_{23}b_{33} \\ a_{31}b_{11} + a_{32}b_{21} + a_{33}b_{31}, & a_{31}b_{12} + a_{32}b_{22} + a_{33}b_{32}, & a_{31}b_{13} + a_{32}b_{23} + a_{33}b_{33} \end{pmatrix}.$$

7. (a) $\begin{pmatrix} -1 & 0 \\ 17 & -6 \end{pmatrix}; \begin{pmatrix} 0 & 23 & -26 \\ 11 & -9 & 10 \\ -2 & -4 & 4 \end{pmatrix}$.

(b) $\begin{pmatrix} 2 & -3 \\ 1 & 5 \end{pmatrix} \otimes \begin{pmatrix} 1 & 1 \\ -1 & 2 \end{pmatrix} = \begin{pmatrix} 5 & -4 \\ -4 & 11 \end{pmatrix}$;

$\begin{pmatrix} 1 & 1 \\ -1 & 2 \end{pmatrix} \otimes \begin{pmatrix} 2 & -3 \\ 1 & 5 \end{pmatrix} = \begin{pmatrix} 3 & 2 \\ 0 & 13 \end{pmatrix}$.

These products are not equal.

(c) $\begin{pmatrix} -2 & 0 \\ 0 & -2 \end{pmatrix} \otimes \begin{pmatrix} 0 & 2 \\ -2 & 0 \end{pmatrix} = \begin{pmatrix} 0 & -4 \\ 4 & 0 \end{pmatrix} = \begin{pmatrix} 0 & 2 \\ -2 & 0 \end{pmatrix} \otimes \begin{pmatrix} -2 & 0 \\ 0 & -2 \end{pmatrix}$.

8. (b) (i) $\{a, a^2 = 1\}$. (ii) $\{a, a^2, a^3, a^4 = 1\}$. (iii) The symmetries of the square. (iv) The symmetries of the equilateral triangle.

Page 426

1. (a) Ring.   (b) Ring.   (c) Ring.   (d) Ring.   (e) Ring.
(f) Ring.

2. (a) ;   (c) if $k = 1$;   (d) ;   (e) ;   (f).

4. Ring.

7. Non-commutative ring with unit.

Page 418

1. (a) Yes.   (b) No.   (c) No.

2. (a) $\cdots -19, -14, -9, -4, 1, 6, 11, 16, 21, \cdots$.
(b) $\cdots -25, -18, -11, -4, 3, 10, 17, 24, 31, \cdots$.

3. (a) One.   (b) Two.   (c) Yes.   (d) No.

4. (*b*) Yes. (*c*) Yes.

5. (*a*) J_5 is a ring without divisors of zero.
(*b*) J_6 is a ring with divisors of zero.

6. (*a*) Yes. (*b*) When n is not a prime integer.

7. (*a*) Yes. (*b*) Yes. (*c*) No. (*d*) Yes. (*e*) No. (*f*) Yes.
(*g*) Only if n is a prime integer.

Page 432

2. (*b*).

3. Each decimal in A is also in B; therefore, A is a subset of B.

4. (*a*) Yes. (*b*) No.

Page 435

2. (*a*) No. (*b*) Yes; No. (*c*) Yes; No. (*d*) No. (*e*) No.
(*f*) Yes.

3. J_2, J_5, and J_p, where p is a prime integer.

5. No.

Page 440

2. (*a*) (i) No. (ii) Yes. (*b*) (i) No. (ii) Yes.

5. Let a, b, c, d, and f represent rational numbers.
(*a*) $a + b \sqrt{11}$; (*b*) $a + b \sqrt{5}$; (*c*) $a + b \sqrt[3]{5} + c \sqrt[3]{25}$;
(*d*) $a + b \sqrt[4]{3} + c \sqrt[4]{9} + d \sqrt[4]{27}$;
(*e*) $a + b \sqrt[5]{2} + c \sqrt[5]{4} + d \sqrt[5]{8} + f \sqrt[5]{16}$; (f) a.

6. (*a*) (i) Yes; (ii) Yes; (iii) Yes; (iv) Yes; (v) Yes.
(*b*) Yes.

Page 444

5. The set of all integers is an integral domain with respect to ordinary addition and multiplication.

Index